KH Block MD

July 1969

THE ROLE OF LEARNING
IN PSYCHOTHERAPY

THE ROLE OF LEARNING IN PSYCHOTHERAPY

A Ciba Foundation Symposium

Edited by
RUTH PORTER

LITTLE, BROWN AND COMPANY

COMPANY

1968   BOSTON

First published 1968

Containing 30 illustrations

Standard Book Number 7000 1380 6

Contents

Prospects for the Future

Membership

Symposium on The Role of Learning in Psychotherapy held 31st
January–2nd February, 1968

N. E. Miller (Chairman)	Rockefeller University, New York
A. Bandura	Department of Psychology, Stanford University, California
G. M. Carstairs	Department of Psychiatry, University of Edinburgh
A. Dalla Volta	Institute of Psychology, Faculty of Medicine, University of Genoa
B. M. Foss	Department of Psychology, Institute of Education, University of London
J. D. Frank	Department of Psychiatry and Behavioral Sciences, Johns Hopkins University School of Medicine, Baltimore, Maryland
T. Freeman	Holywell Hospital, Antrim, Northern Ireland
M. G. Gelder	Institute of Psychiatry, The Maudsley Hospital, London
R. A. Hinde	Department of Zoology, University of Cambridge
H. F. Hunt	Department of Psychology, Columbia University, New York
B. Jansson	Psykiatriska Kliniken, Sahlgrenska Sjukhuset, University of Göteborg
I. C. Kaufman	Department of Psychiatry, State University of New York, Downstate Medical Center, Brooklyn, New York
C. C. Kiernan	Department of Psychology, Birkbeck College, University of London
L. Krasner	Department of Psychology, State University of New York, Stony Brook, New York
L. S. Kubie*	Department of Psychiatry, University of Maryland School of Medicine, Baltimore
A. A. Lazarus	Department of Behavioral Science, Temple University School of Medicine, Philadelphia, Pennsylvania
B. A. Lebedev	Mental Health Unit, World Health Organization, Geneva
S. Leder	Psychoneurological Institute, Warsaw
D. H. Malan	Tavistock Clinic, London

* Present address: Wheeler Lane, Sparks, Maryland

I. M. Marks   Institute of Psychiatry, The Maudsley Hospital, London

G. P. Sackett   Department of Psychology, Primate Laboratory, University
                         of Wisconsin, Madison

J. Sandler   Academic Department of Psychiatry, Middlesex Hospital
                         Medical School, and Index Project, Hampstead Child-
                         Therapy Clinic, London

P. E. Sifneos*   Department of Psychiatry, Massachusetts General Hospital,
                         and Department of Psychiatry, Harvard Medical School

* Present address: Department of Psychiatry, Harvard Medical School, Beth Israel Hospital, Boston, Massachusetts

The Ciba Foundation

The Ciba Foundation was opened in 1949 to promote international cooperation in medical and chemical research. It owes its existence to the generosity of CIBA Ltd., Basle, who, recognizing the obstacles to scientific communication created by war, man's natural secretiveness, disciplinary divisions, academic prejudices, and separation by distance and differences in language, decided to set up a philanthropic institution whose aim would be to overcome such barriers. London was chosen as its site for reasons dictated by the special advantages of English charitable trust law (ensuring the independence of its actions), as well as those of language and geography.

The Foundation's house at 41 Portland Place, London, has become well known to workers in many fields of science. Every year the Foundation organizes six to ten three-day symposia and three or four shorter study groups, all of which are published in book form. Many other scientific meetings are held, organized either by the Foundation or by other groups in need of a meeting place. Accommodation is also provided for scientists visiting London, whether or not they are attending a meeting in the house.

The Foundation's many activities are controlled by a small group of distinguished trustees. Within the general framework of biological science, interpreted in its broadest sense, these activities are well summed up by the motto of the Ciba Foundation: *Consocient Gentes*—let the peoples come together.

Preface

THIS symposium grew from discussions, in 1964, with Dr. Isaac Marks about the paucity of objective, and particularly of controlled, studies assessing the results of psychotherapy, and also about the lack of information about the factors that affect these results. The unlearning of maladaptive habits and the learning of new, more appropriate behaviours would seem to be two important factors that influence the outcome of psychotherapy. At that time it seemed that a meeting in which psychotherapists of different schools discussed their underlying theories, techniques and results was now possible and could be a useful approach to these problems.

Drs. Michael Gelder and David Malan were soon drawn into these discussions. Isaac Marks and Michael Gelder, using behavioural techniques, and David Malan, using brief dynamic psychotherapy, had already started some comparative studies on the results of their treatments of patients with phobias and other neuroses. With Professor Morris Carstairs' help we finally settled for a symposium whose subject would be the role of learning in psychotherapy. At this symposium ethologists, experimental psychologists and psychiatrists, and psychotherapists of all schools could meet.

Professor Neal Miller agreed to take the chair at this meeting and provided tremendously helpful advice about its form and membership, at first in letters from New York and later in personal talks with me, in Geneva, while he was there (very briefly), in connexion with his work for W.H.O. I would like to thank all these people, and also Dr. Joe Sandler, for their help in planning this symposium. I would also like to thank Dr. W. G. Joffe for his help in the editing of parts of this book.

In a meeting in which such varied and at times emotional and hotly disputed views might have inhibited constructive discussion, the open-mindedness of the participants and their capacity for accepting each other's points of view were noteworthy. The extent of agreement between the protagonists of the different schools was sometimes surprising. At one stage it even looked as if this might mask areas of disagreement, and thus useful material and constructive criticism be lost. Fortunately, Professor Neal Miller's chairmanship avoided this pitfall, and his sincere search for objective truth and acceptance of unorthodoxy were somehow transferred to all the participants.

The members of this symposium examined together their various techniques in a liberal way. They also looked, with scientific objectivity and with humanity, for new ways of assessing their results. It is hoped that this book may play some part in encouraging those who read it in the same sorts of ways.

RUTH PORTER

CHAIRMAN'S OPENING REMARKS

N. E. MILLER

I AM delighted to see you all here today. Some of you are old friends of mine. Others I know from the literature and am glad at last of the chance to meet you personally. We are all here with two main motives. As scientists we are dedicated to arriving at the truth; as clinicians we are interested in helping people—in trying to relieve the great tragedy and acute misery of mental illness.

As clinicians, we have all had the experience of success in the treatment of patients, and this can be enormously convincing. When one sees the inevitability of the way in which all the details about a case dovetail before one's eyes, one feels that this could not possibly be by chance. Sometimes, unfortunately, the direct observation of a case may be too convincing to the observer and not convincing enough to the person who reads the case history. But we have all also had the baffling experience of bitter failures which let us know in no uncertain terms that there is much about the treatment of patients that we do not yet understand. Let us hope that this conference can contribute in the long run to increasing our understanding of the many remaining mysteries of mental illness, and to helping us to relieve the misery of our patients.

We come from diverse backgrounds. In general, we represent two great traditions: that of Freud, a great scientist and a clinician with remarkable insight, and the tradition of another scientific giant, Pavlov, who worked in the laboratory but also, in his later years, became interested in the clinical applications of his discoveries. The purpose of bringing us from our diverse backgrounds to this symposium is to expose us all to new ideas and observations.

There are difficulties in communication for people from diverse backgrounds, but we have all been carefully selected as individuals who should be able to overcome these difficulties. We should be able to use our clinical skills to make others feel at ease, and to keep our own unconscious processes under control, so that we can operate at the very highest level of ego function and reality testing, engaging in sharp controversy without personal enmity.

Some of the differences that have arisen in connexion with psychotherapy may be like those of the proverbial blind men examining different parts of the elephant—the tusks, sides, legs or tail. So some differences may be due to the fact that we have dealt with dissimilar patients, in different ways, and have thus been observing and grouping together somewhat different phenomena. Other difficulties are connected with terminology; we should all be good enough teachers to define our terms and not use too much of our own specialized jargon. I find that when I have difficulty in expressing myself it makes it easier if, instead of trying to say the things that are on the very frontier of my thoughts, I concentrate on saying things I have thought about for some time until they have become quite clear. Because we come from such diverse backgrounds some of these simpler thoughts can make real contributions in the next three days. I do not mean to inhibit anyone from speculating on the frontiers of his thinking, but if (at least at first) we aim to present material that we are quite sure of, it will make communication easier.

The members of this group have in common their courage to be unorthodox. In this respect I remind you again of our patron saints: Pavlov, who certainly had a great deal of courage and proceeded against bitter opposition to develop his ideas; and of course Freud, who also possessed remarkable courage. I believe that if Freud, as a young man, were at this conference, he would be considered unorthodox, even by some of the psychoanalysts present. I remember that when he was a young man he tried to present to the Vienna Medical Society a case of hysteria in a male patient. One of the old greybeards said: "Obviously the young doctor doesn't know his Greek: 'hysteria' means 'womb sickness'." The other members of the society jeered and hooted Freud out of the room, thus preventing him from presenting his evidence. I trust that if Freud were here at this time, presenting ideas just as unorthodox now as when he started on his creative career, he would meet with a friendlier reception from all of us than he had from the Vienna Medical Society. In this spirit of unorthodox courage and tolerance, tempered with critical realism, let us begin our discussions.

THE PERSISTENCE OF ABNORMAL BEHAVIOUR IN MONKEYS FOLLOWING ISOLATION REARING

GENE P. SACKETT

Department of Psychology, Primate Laboratory, University of Wisconsin, Madison

EARLY life experiences in rhesus monkeys (*Macaca mulatta*) have produced persistent effects on behavioural development that invade every important response dimension. Animals reared without physical contact with age-mates and deprived of varied sensory experiences show abnormal levels of motor activity, exploratory behaviour, social reactivity, emotionality, and maternal and sexual responsiveness. Similarities in motor patterns between Abnormal Man and Abnormal Monkey suggest that the isolation-reared monkey can serve as a model for the development of abnormal behaviour in primates, although there is no clear evidence that the under-lying causes of abnormalities in the monkey reflect processes identical with the causes of abnormal behaviour in man. This paper describes some of the early effects of social deprivation, and the persistence of these effects to adulthood after various attempts at behavioural modification. Much of this work was conceived by Drs. Harry F. and Margaret K. Harlow, and the many students who have worked under Dr. Harlow at the Wisconsin Primate Laboratory. Parts of this paper thus summarize aspects of the contributions of all these workers to the understanding of primate behavioural development and insights into the genesis of abnormal behaviour.

THE REARING TREATMENTS

Control conditions

Animals reared with access to peers early in life are the control groups for much of the work discussed here. The three control situations include feral (*F*), mother–peer (*MP*), and together–together (*TT*) groups. Subjects in group *F* were born in south-east Asia, then captured and brought to the laboratory at various ages. Group *MP* consisted of monkeys reared by a real mother in a "playpen" apparatus (Harlow and Harlow, 1966). Each *MP* infant lived with its mother in a large cage and had daily access to age-mates in a play area adjacent to the cage. In the *TT* situation, neonates were taken from their mothers at birth and reared for 30 days in a nursery where they received hand-feeding from a human being (Blomquist and Harlow, 1961); they subsequently lived in wire cages, in groups of two to six animals, for the next 11 months.

Experimental conditions

Partial isolation. All the experimental treatments involved some degree of deprivation from peers during the first year of life. Partial isolation imposed a moderate degree of social and sensory restriction by rearing infants individually in bare wire cages (group *WC*). Although this condition has been used to generate baseline data for comparison with the effects of total isolation, the lack of physical peer contact for this group makes *WC* rearing an experimental treatment in the context of this paper. Following removal from the mother shortly after birth the *WC* neonates were hand-fed in the nursery for 30 days, receiving intimate physical contact with human beings. Subsequently, *WC* animals were housed singly, in a situation in which they could see and hear other monkeys and humans, but received no opportunities for physical contact with other animals (Fig. 1).

Early isolation. The primary experimental treatment concerned neonates reared in total isolation from birth. Fig. 2 illustrates the isolation unit employed in many studies (for example Rowland, 1964). Neonates were placed in the "mother-box" shortly after birth, and received hand-feeding, through portholes with minimal physical and no visual contact, for the first 30 days. The rest of the isolation period was spent in the living area where the animal could see itself and the bare metal walls, but was denied all visual, auditory and physical interaction with other monkeys. The sole source of varied stimulation occurred during learning tests presented in the Wisconsin General Test Apparatus (Harlow, 1949) built into the front section of the isolation unit.

Late isolation. Late isolates spent the first 30 days in the nursery receiving food by hand, then lived for some time in the *WC* condition or in an enclosed cage with a cloth surrogate mother and short daily periods of age-mate interaction. After this initial experience the subject was placed in total isolation.

Isolation with pictures. Neonates have also been reared in cages identical to those used in the *WC* conditions, but with metal and wooden partitions blocking visual access to the outside world, and with no opportunities for physical contact with peers. Varied visual input was provided by

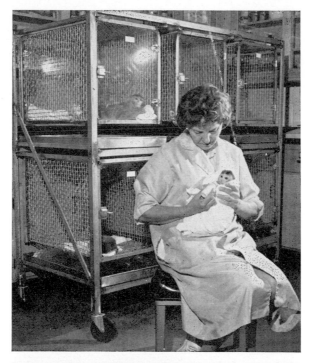

FIG. 1. Nursery rearing: hand-feeding with intimate human contact; and partial isolation cages allowing visual and auditory, but no physical, contact.

[*To face page* 4

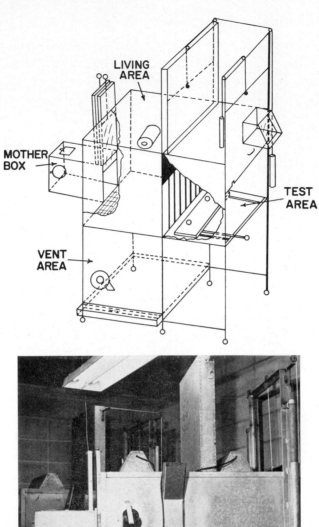

LIVING
AREA

MOTHER
BOX

TEST
AREA

VENT
AREA

FIG. 2. Total isolation: although constantly lighted, the enclosed walls and a "white noise" masking-sound precluded visual, auditory and physical contact with other animals during rearing.

photographic stimuli presented on a projection screen forming the back wall of the cage. The pictures presented to these isolates (group *PI*) in-included nine categories showing different types of monkeys and activities frequently seen in social interactions between laboratory monkeys: namely, (1) infants, (2) mothers and infants, (3–8) monkeys engaged in threat, withdrawal, fear, play, exploration, and sexual behaviours, and (9) monkeys doing nothing. A tenth category included control pictures of people, landscapes, building interiors, and geometric patterns. These stimuli were presented 5 days per week throughout the 9-month rearing period. In some trials the experimenter controlled the stimulus presentations and recorded the behaviour of the monkey while a given slide was on the screen, using a check-list procedure. In other trials the monkey itself could control the presentation of a picture by touching a lever.

EFFECTS OF ISOLATION ON EARLY BEHAVIOUR

Social behaviour after early isolation from birth to 6 (*6ME*) and 12 (*1YI*) months and late isolation from 7 to 12 (*6ML*) months was compared with social behaviour following equivalent periods of *WC* rearing (Rowland, 1964; Harlow, Dodsworth and Harlow, 1965). Testing was conducted in a playroom (Fig. 3) with two isolates and two *WC* animals in a group. The *1YI* group was characterized by inactivity, fear and withdrawal, almost complete absence of play and exploration, and inability to avoid aggression from the *WC* monkeys. The *6ME* group was also inadequate at the start of testing, but showed improvement in play and exploration during 32 weeks of social interaction, although the animals did not reach the levels of socialization displayed by the *WC* group. The *6ML* subjects displayed hyperactivity and hyperaggression which produced fear and withdrawal behaviour in their *WC* partners. The *6ML* animals also had higher levels of play and exploration than their disturbed *WC* partners. The general effects of these conditions can be seen in one measure—general disturbance involving fear and withdrawal responses—presented in Fig. 4. One full year of isolation thus completely destroyed the animal's ability to engage in social interaction. Six months of early isolation produced behavioural deficits that improved somewhat with experience. Late isolation also produced abnormal behaviour, but *6ML* animals were capable of engaging in some positive social behaviours.

Griffin and Harlow (1966) studied early isolation from birth to 3 months of age (*3ME*). This group of animals showed a severe post-isolation depression which lasted for one or two weeks. However, once they had recovered from this depression the *3ME* animals were indistinguishable from *WC* partners in all aspects of social behaviour. Thus, *3ME* isolation produced no detectable permanent abnormalities in infantile social adjustment.

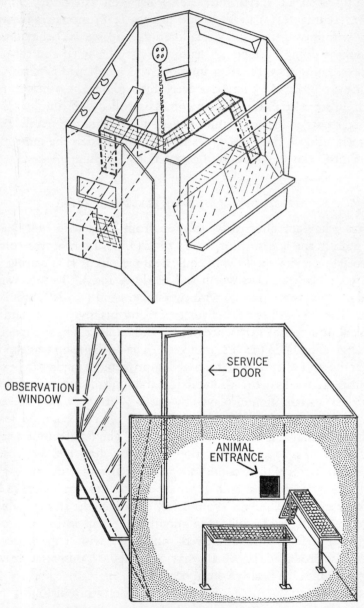

FIG. 3. Playrooms: situations used to study social development, containing toys, ladders and perches with clear-glass viewing windows.

These studies suggested that there was a critical age for exposure to social stimulation at which later qualitative changes in the characteristics of social behaviour can be produced in *WC* monkeys. This critical age seems to be between 3 and 6 months for quantitative deficits, and 6 to 12 months for producing complete destruction of social ability. However, a methodological difficulty raises the question of whether isolation effects in monkeys are

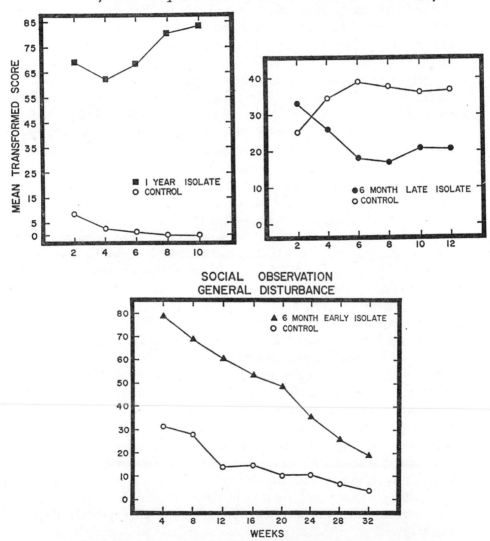

Fig. 4. General disturbance in *1YI*, *6ME* and *6ML* isolates compared with *WC* partial isolates in a playroom shortly after the end of the rearing experience. The measure is a composite of fear, withdrawal, rocking and huddling behaviours. (Taken from Rowland, 1964.)

due directly to the isolation treatment, or to the sudden influx in stimulation when the animal is removed from isolation (Sackett, 1965a). Thus, a major issue is this. Does isolation produce permanent anomalies within the animal, or are the abnormal behaviours of isolates environmentally produced by lack of adaptation to novel and complex inputs following isolation (Fuller, 1967)?

Clark (1967) attacked this issue. He raised animals adapted to a playroom with peer contact before putting them into late total isolation from 4 to 9 months (3ML). During the first 3 months these animals lived in enclosed cages with a surrogate mother while receiving daily age-mate experience in a playroom. During isolation they continued to receive *individual* adaptation to the playroom. A control group lived with the surrogate mother for 9 months and received the same total amount of individual and group adaptation as the 3ML group. In within-group playroom tests from months 10 to 15 the 3ML animals did not differ from controls in disturbance, motor activity and exploration, and scored higher in play and aggression. Thus, isolation *per se* did not produce abnormal behaviour. Clark is currently studying animals reared in total isolation for the first 6 months of life, which received individual playroom adaptation but no peer contact during isolation. Compared with non-isolated animals that received adaptation with peer experience, these 6ME animals are highly deficient in social behaviour. The behaviour of Clark's 3ML and 6ME groups suggests that the critical dimension underlying the effects of isolation is physical experience with age-mates between 3 and 9 months after birth, since individual adaptation was not sufficient to overcome isolation effects, while isolation preceded by both peer experience and individual playroom adaptation failed to produce marked abnormalities.

Two further methodological considerations in interpreting these data on isolation concern the composition of groups in post-rearing tests, and the behavioural adequacy of the control groups used to assess deficits. In between-group tests, such as those used by Rowland, early isolates were paired with WC animals who were more socially adequate, thereby maximizing the impact of the control animals on their isolate partners. In Clark's work, like-reared animals were tested together, so isolates were not directly compared with controls in the same groups. This within-group situation paired animals that were maximally similar in social ability, thereby lowering the chances that the isolate would be overwhelmed by more socially competent animals and minimizing differences in behaviour. Resolution of this issue probably demands either a combination of within-group and between-group comparisons, or tests of both experimental and control subjects with standard stimulus animals who differ in their social competence either naturally or by specific training. A second problem is that animals in the control groups in these studies were reared in partial isolation. The behaviour of partial isolates is known to be deficient (see, for example, Cross and Harlow, 1965; Sackett, 1967) compared with *MP* animals, so it is difficult to assess the true extent of social abnormality produced in these studies by the isolation.

In summary, isolation during the first year had the following effects on behavioural adequacy at 12 to 15 months. Early total isolation for 3 months did not produce behavioural deficits, for 6 months it produced quantitative deficits, while one full year of isolation completely destroyed social abilities. This suggests that certain critical experiences after the third month of life are necessary for normal social development. These critical experiences appear to involve direct physical contact with peers rather than simple adaptation to the post-rearing test situation. However, peer experience for isolates may be maximally beneficial only when animals of equal social competence are tested together. The exact locus of isolation effects is uncertain, because of (*a*) difficulties in comparing studies that differ in the amount of adaptation to post-rearing environments, (*b*) the specific composition of test groups, and (*c*) the use of controls whose behaviour is not normal.

LONG–TERM EFFECTS OF ISOLATION

Many studies have followed up the behaviour of isolates at various periods from juvenile (18 months–4 years) to adult (4·5 years) ages. Some of this work has employed a "stranger" technique in which experimental and control monkeys are paired in a small cage or a playroom with animals varying in age, sex and rearing conditions. Clark used an age-mate stranger test, finding that at 18 months of age monkeys in his *3ML* group were hyperaggressive, engaged in more infantile play, and were lower in sexual behaviours than *MP* animals. Even after extensive post-isolation testing between 15 months and 4 years of age, total and partial isolates were grossly abnormal compared with monkeys which had had early mother and peer experience (Mitchell *et al.*, 1966; Sackett, 1967). At 4 years of age *1YI* behaviour had not changed, still being characterized by inactivity, fear and disturbance, and almost no physical contact with other animals. Compared to *MP* controls, *6ME* and *6ML* isolates were also deficient in positive social behaviour, in sexual behaviour, and in non-social exploration. The behaviour of *WC* animals displayed many of the same abnormalities as the total isolates, except that 6-month isolates were extremely hyperaggressive, exhibiting inappropriate hostility toward age-mates, infants and adults. Thus early and late total isolation, as well as partial isolation, during the first year appears to produce permanent deficits in adult life in all major social activities.

Other follow-up work has suggested that total and partial isolation also produced deficits in non-social responding. Compared with *MP* subjects, *1YI*, *6ME* and *WC* subjects were unwilling to explore a novel environment, were low in gross motor activity, and either preferred low levels of complex visual input when allowed to explore differentially complex geometric patterns or were unwilling to explore these stimuli at all (Sackett, 1968). The *1YI* and *WC* animals also did not manipulate stimuli which involved complex proprioceptive input, spending almost no time swinging from a chain and showing interest only in a non-movable T-bar (Sackett, 1965b). Cross and Harlow (1965) have shown that even in the home cage, the environment to which the animal is certainly best adapted, rearing in partial isolation produces serious abnormalities. Animals between 1 and 7 years of age reared in wire cages showed more orality, self-aggression, fear, self-clutching and stereotyped movements in the home cage than did *MP* controls who were living in wire cages. Presentation of a fear stimulus produced fear and aggression in all subjects; but *MP* animals were more likely to direct aggression appropriately toward the experimenter, while *WC* animals more often arggessed themselves with vigorous self-biting.

The maternal behaviour of partial isolates has also received extensive study. Females reared in wire cages with or without surrogate mothers were generally inadequate primiparous mothers, spending less time cradling infants, being more abusive or indifferent, showing deficiencies in nursing, and rejecting their infants more often early in life than did feral-born mothers (Harlow *et al.*, 1966a). Tentative evidence from a current project (Harlow and Arling, 1968) suggests that experience with the first baby aids in maternal care of the second if the mother had received some peer experience during the first two years of life. But if peer contact is precluded until after the first two years it is likely that the mother will also be inadequate with her second infant.

The effects on adult heterosexual behaviours of being reared in partial isolation in wire cages or with surrogate mothers have been reported by Harlow and co-workers (1966b). Even after extensive social experience between 2 and 4 years of age, partial isolate males were totally inadequate in reproductive behaviour. Sequences of sexual behaviour, sexual unresponsiveness, threat and aggression were all abnormal in partial isolate males by comparison with feral control males. Female partial isolates were also deficient in sexual behaviour compared with feral controls, but peer experience during the second and third year of life did have some ameliorating effects on sexual behaviour in comparison with females deprived of peer contact for the first 4 years of life. It is interesting that partial isolate males became sexually aroused, as indicated by penile erection, during these tests; but they seemed incapable of directing their behaviour toward the appropriate anatomical parts of their sexually sophisticated partners, and of responding appropriately to "sexual invitation gestures" from these females.

In summary, the follow-up work indicated that total and partial isolation during the first year produced permanent deficits in many dimensions of behaviour. After extensive experience in social and non-social situations, as juveniles, pre-adults, and adults, isolates still showed bizarre personal behaviour, low motor activity, little or no non-social exploration or preference for complex stimulation, abnormal social interaction including hyperaggressiveness, and sexual and maternal inadequacies. This wide range of abnormality suggests that isolation may modify basic intellectual abilities, a hypothesis that has been tested in several studies.

Isolation and intellectual ability. The *1YI, 6ME, 6ML, 3ME,* and *WC* groups were tested for avoidance and discrimination learning ability after the rearing period. The total isolates did not differ from partial isolates in the acquisition of a shock-motivated avoidance response, in two-choice discrimination learning or in learning-set formation (Harlow and Griffin, 1965), and these groups did not differ from feral animals tested under similar conditions. A recent study compared 9-month isolates with *WC* controls in discrimination learning tests after extensive adaptation to the Wisconsin General Test Apparatus. Total isolates took more than twice as many days ($\overline{X}=107$) to reach various adaptation criteria in the novel test apparatus as did the controls ($\overline{X}=44$); but, once they had adapted, no differences appeared in their acquisition of a two-object learning set. Thus, the isolation procedures which produced devastating effects on social, emotional and curiosity behaviours failed to affect performance in standard laboratory tests of learning and "concept formation".

THE PICTURE-ISOLATE STUDY

The picture-isolate rearing condition was designed in part to avoid some of the methodological criticisms of previous work. The two major purposes of this work were to determine (*a*) whether visual social stimulation could offset the debilitating effects of isolation, and (*b*) whether a gradual

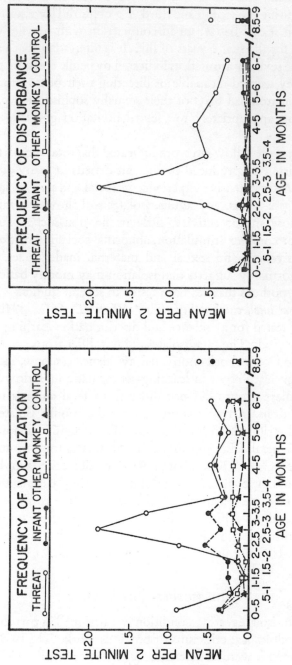

FIG. 5. For legend see facing page.

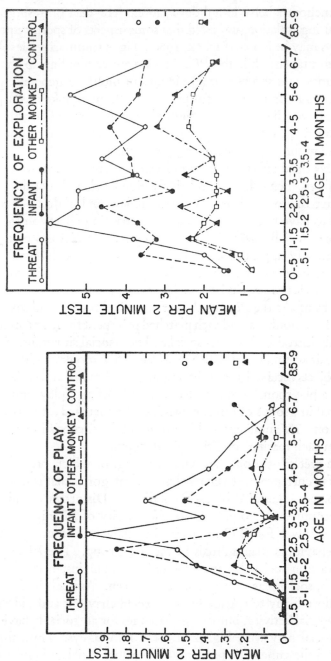

FIG. 5. Response to coloured slides by the picture isolates during nine months of experimenter-controlled tests. The "other monkey" category included all slides of monkeys other than those of infants and threat displays, as all seven categories except these two failed to elicit differential responses. The data are mean frequencies of vocalizing, disturbance and fear, play, and exploration during each 2-minute exposure of the slide.

introduction—or pacing—of post-rearing novelty and complexity would in any way ameliorate behavioural devastation. The data on response to the pictures during isolation suggested that some aspects of social responding in monkeys may be innate (Sackett, 1966). Fig. 5 summarizes developmental measures taken while the *PI* animals were responding to the ten picture categories, and shows that (*a*) pictures of monkeys generally produced more behaviour than control pictures without monkeys, (*b*) play exploration and vocalization were higher when pictures of infants and monkeys engaged in threat were on the screen, and (*c*) the only stimuli to release fear and withdrawal behaviours were pictures of monkeys displaying threat. This third effect was maturational, not appearing until 2·5 to 3·5 months of age, then rising to a relatively high level, and subsiding to a lower level after 100 to 120 days. Pictures of infants and of threat displays thus appeared to have non-learned prepotent activating effects on the behaviour of these socially naïve infant monkeys, while pictures of threat released the socially appropriate responses of fear and withdrawal at a critical age of 60–80 days after birth. This opportunity to practise socially appropriate behaviour may aid later social development.

At 10 months of age the *PI* animals were matched for age and sex with 9-month-old *WC* monkeys, and each matched pair spent the next 6 months being gradually introduced to new social and non-social situations. At 15 months each pair was matched with a peer-raised *TT* monkey of the same sex, and all subjects received 3 months of gradual individual and social-pair adaptation to a playroom. From 18 to 21 months of age, playroom tests were conducted in groups of three, consisting of a matched set of one *PI*, one *WC* and one *TT* monkey; and in groups of four, consisting of two monkeys from each rearing condition (Pratt, 1967).

Data for 12 weeks of testing are shown in Fig. 6, which presents the probability of occurrence for twelve behaviour categories that summarize the total response repertoire of each condition. Disturbance and fear behaviours accounted for 70 per cent of the activity of *PI* animals. The percentage was lower for *WC* monkeys, but they were more likely to show these behaviours than animals in the *TT* group. The *PI* subjects engaged in little non-social play and exploration, and no instances of active social approach, social play or aggression were seen. Animals in the *WC* group were more likely to engage in non-social behaviour and did show some positive social activity, but the probabilities for all social behaviours and for non-social play were higher in the *TT* monkeys. Thus, the *PI* group displayed the same basic patterns of abnormal social and non-social behaviour as had been seen in total isolates reared without pictures. Neither

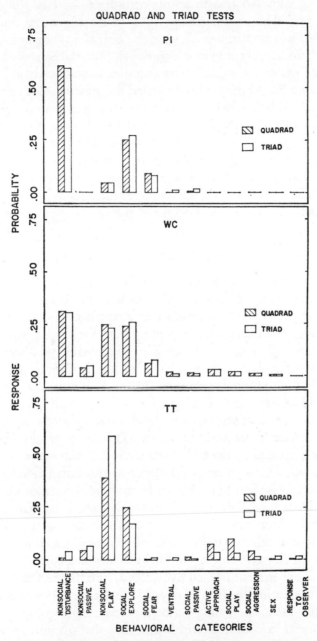

FIG. 6. Probabilities of occurrence for twelve behavioural categories representing the total response repertoire of *PI, WC* and
TT monkeys during social tests in three (triad) and four (quadrad)
animal groups.

visual social stimulation with an opportunity to practise some social behaviours, nor the gradual pacing of post-rearing novel and complex stimulation, was sufficient to alleviate the isolation syndrome. Also, *WC* partial isolation clearly produced large deficits in social behaviour compared with the effects seen in animals receiving peer contact early in life.

A major finding in this study concerned the presence of sex differences in the effects of isolation. Males were more damaged than females by total and partial isolation. The *PI* females had less fear and disturbance, and a higher incidence of non-social play and exploration, than *PI* males. Striking sex differences appeared in *WC* subjects, with disturbance and fear twice as likely for males while non-social play was 25 per cent more probable for females. In fact, the four *WC* females were the only total or partial isolates out of 16 animals to show any degree of positive social behaviour.

VERY EARLY EXPERIENCE AND LATER BEHAVIOUR

In addition to the picture-isolate experiment, other data suggest that although the effects of early experiences may be determined in part by post-rearing factors such as insufficient adaptation to test environments (Fuller, 1967), this explanation cannot account for some persistent rearing effects. Maternally inadequate, partial isolate females, who were generally indifferent or abusive to their babies, produced offspring that exhibited abnormally high physical aggression (Mitchell, Arling and Møller, 1967; Arling and Harlow, 1967). During infancy these offspring were frequently rejected during attempts to nurse, and some of them were violently physically attacked by their mothers. This type of abusive maternal behaviour decreased by the end of the second month as the infant learned to avoid attacks. Components of the hyperaggression in these inadequately mothered animals seem to have been learned from the mother during the first months of life. This suggests that early experience with a particular type of behaviour can affect later manifestations of that behavioural dimension—and this permanent learning of a basic social trait may occur as early as the first two months of life in rhesus monkeys.

A second experiment studied five groups, two that had received human hand-feeding during the first 30 days of life (Sackett, Porter and Holmes, 1965). After the hand-feeding period a partial isolate group spent the rest of the first year in individual wire cages; the other group was raised in the *TT* situation with other monkeys. A third group was reared with mothers and peers, thus receiving no early experience with humans. The remaining groups were *6ME* and *1YI* subjects, who had received neither human nor monkey contact early in life. All subjects had received extensive post-rearing social experience. At 3–4 years of age each subject was tested in a fear situation, and given a choice between standing near a human, an age-mate, or in a neutral area; the human was one of the ladies who performed hand-feeding in the nursery. The partial isolates, who had received intimate human contact, clearly preferred the human to the age-mate monkey

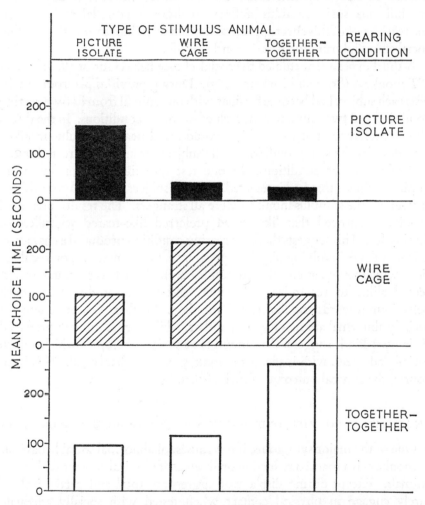

FIG. 7. Preference exhibited by *PI, WC* and *TT* animals for monkeys reared in like and different conditions. The data were taken during 10-minute trials in a three-choice situation involving strange and familiar stimulus animals; a fourth response of remaining in a neutral area was also allowed. Subtraction of the total choice times from 600 seconds (the total time of the test) gives the time an animal spent in this neutral area responding to none of the social stimuli.

3 years after termination of the hand-feeding experience. The *TT* and *MP* animals preferred the age-mate, showing that early peer experience can reverse preferences developed during neonatal feeding. The total isolates preferred the neutral area, indicating that lack of contact with human and monkey during the first 6 months of life produces an animal which does not approach any social stimulus in a fear situation. These data suggest that interaction with a specific social stimulus during the first 30 days of life can influence social stimulus preferences almost 4 years later. However, the persistence of this effect appears to depend on failure to experience other social stimuli during the first 6 months of life.

A third experiment studied the social-choice behaviour of *PI*, *WC*, and *TT* monkeys (Pratt and Sackett, 1967). During previous playroom social tests each subject had become familiar with one animal from its own rearing condition and two animals from each of the other conditions. In the three-choice preference test each subject could stand near a stimulus monkey reared under the same condition as the subject, or a monkey reared under one of the other conditions. In one test the stimulus monkeys were familiar animals that had interacted with the subject in the playroom; in a second test the stimulus monkeys were all strangers. The results, presented in Fig. 7, showed that like-reared preferred like-reared regardless of familiarity. This suggests that each rearing condition produced a character-istic set of cues involving physical appearance, motor patterns, or vocaliza-tions which served as effective stimuli for animals that were strangers, but reared alike, to recognize each other, and which produced approach behaviour towards the like-reared monkey. Further, this preference of socially abnormal animals for one another, while normal animals preferred their own kind, suggests that attempts at social "therapy" which match socially adequate with inadequate monkeys will probably fail. This is, of course, the general outcome of such efforts.

AN ATTEMPT TO COUNTERCONDITION AN ISOLATION-PRODUCED ABNORMALITY

One of the major symptoms, if not causes, of abnormal social behaviour in monkeys is a marked reduction or absence of physical contact with other animals. Except during displays of aggression, total and partial isolates rarely engage in physical contact when tested with socially adequate monkeys. The following study represents an attempt to apply "behaviour therapy" by conditioning the initiation and maintenance of physical contact (Sackett *et al.*, 1968). Three-year-old *PI*, *WC* and *TT* monkeys and 5-year-old *6ME* isolates, *WC* and *TT* animals were the subjects of this study. Pairing for sex as well as for rearing conditions and age was not possible because of the unavailability of suitable animals. The experimental design, sex distribution and testing schedules are presented in Table I.

TABLE I

EXPERIMENTAL DESIGN, SAMPLE COMPOSITION AND TESTING SCHEDULE EMPLOYED IN SHUTTLEBOX
CONDITIONING OF PHYSICAL CONTACT

EXPERIMENTAL DESIGN

	Age of subject	
Rearing condition	3 year	5 year
Total isolates	2 females	1 male 1 female
Wire cage	2 females	1 male 1 female
Together–together	1 male 1 female	1 male 1 female

TESTING SCHEDULE

	Baseline	*Shuttlebox conditioning*	Post-conditioning	
			Type I	*Type II*
Dual cage	4 trials with stimulus stranger	With shuttlebox stimulus monkey	3 trials with original stimulus monkey	3 trials with shuttlebox stimulus monkey
Playroom	6 trials in isolate, *WC, TT* triads	With shuttlebox stimulus monkey	3 trials in original triads	1 original-triad trial with shuttlebox monkey

Baseline social data were collected in two behavioural situations. In the dual-cage situation each subject was paired with an age-mate stranger of the same sex. The animals were placed in two cages separated by a guillotine door. The 10-minute trial began when this door was raised, allowing the subject and the stimulus stranger access to both cages. An observer recorded the total duration of seven measures of the subject's behaviour: (1) physical contact initiated by the subject; (2) locomotion, measured when the subject was moving; (3) proximity, measured when the subject and the stimulus monkey were in the same cage; (4) visual, tactual and oral environmental exploration; (5) socially elicited fear and disturbance; (6) aggression and threat; and (7) social exploration, measured when the subject oriented towards the stimulus animal. The second situation involved age-matched groups of three animals, an isolate, a *WC* and a *TT* subject, tested in a playroom. During a 30-minute trial the duration of (1) physical contact with other monkeys, (2) locomotion, (3) environmental exploration, (4) self-manipulation and stereotyped movements, (5) disturbance and fear, and (6) aggression was measured for each subject over a 5-minute period.

Physical-contact conditioning was performed in a shuttlebox avoidance apparatus containing a grid floor. Three- and 5-year-old stimulus animals, different from the animals used as stimuli in the dual-cage test, were trained to sit on a 1·5 × 1·5 ft. perch placed in the centre of the 5 ft. long, 3 ft. wide and 3 ft. high shuttlebox. After individual adaptation to the apparatus, each subject was given 25 trials per day with the trained stimulus monkey sitting on its perch under an avoidance conditioning paradigm. After a variable inter-trial interval (*ITI*), averaging 30 seconds, a flashing light, the conditioned stimulus (*CS*), was turned on for 10 seconds. At the end of the *CS* period the grid floor was electrified, (unconditioned stimulus—*UCS*), with a 0·3 mA current at 250 v for 30 seconds. The *CS* and *UCS* both terminated simultaneously at the end of the *UCS* period. Shock could be escaped if the subject maintained physical contact with the stimulus animal during the *UCS* period, and continued this contact during the *CS* period. If the subject broke physical contact during the *UCS* period it received shock until contact was remade or until the end of the *UCS* period. All animals received one full day of 25 trials. After the first day, training was ended when the subject fulfilled a learning requirement of 15 consecutive trials with continuous physical contact with the stimulus animal maintained during the total time of *ITI*, *CS* and *UCS*—a period of 1,050 seconds. After meeting this requirement each animal was given one more 25-trial "overtraining" session on the day before post-conditioning social tests began. Three transfer tests were given in the dual cage and playroom under the same conditions as the baseline tests (post-conditioning Type I), followed by three more dual-cage trials with the original stimulus animal replaced by the shuttlebox partner, and one playroom trial with the shuttlebox animal present with the original group members (post-conditioning Type II).

The results for avoidance conditioning of physical contact (Fig. 8) showed that all subjects met the required criterion by the sixth day, with isolates taking 2 to 4 more days to condition than the other groups. The young *WC* and *TT* animals conditioned most quickly, with adult subjects in these groups taking longer to meet the requirement. The adult *WC* male displayed hyperaggression toward the stimulus animal on days 1 and 2. Rather than discard this animal, he was given subconvulsive shock on "special treatment" trials at the end of the second day each time he attacked his partner. On day 3 this animal met the requirement of 15 trials during which continuous physical contact was maintained. On the "overlearning" trials all animals in each group spent the total 1,750 seconds in contact with

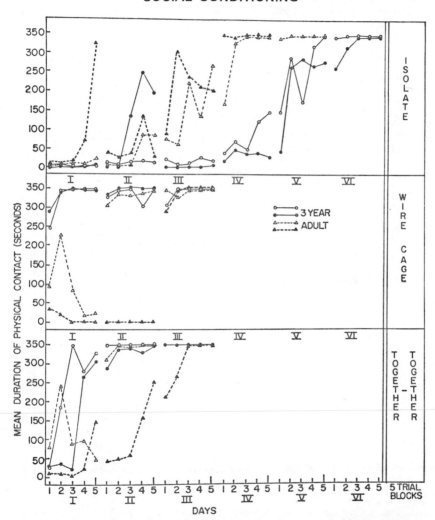

FIG. 8. Shuttlebox social conditioning of physical contact. The scores represent total time, in five trial blocks, on each of 6 test days during which the subject was in physical contact with the stimulus monkey. The maximum score of 350 sec. per block could be achieved by maintaining physical contact during all *ITI*, *CS* and *UCS* periods in that block. Testing ceased when the subject spent 15 consecutive trials (1,050 sec.) maintaining physical contact.

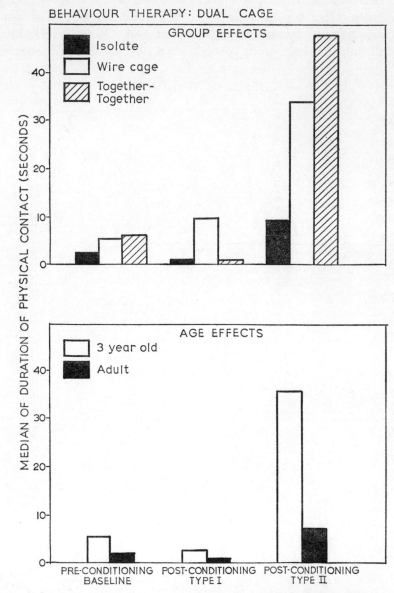

FIG. 9. Duration of physical contact initiated by the subject during baseline and post-conditioning trials in the dual-cage apparatus. Post-conditioning trials with the shuttlebox stimulus animal were the only trials producing significant changes from the baseline. Data are given for differences between groups and between ages.

the stimulus monkey, indicating that physical-contact conditioning had been complete.

In the Type I transfer tests in both the dual cage (Fig. 9) and the playpen (Fig. 10) the duration of physical contact did not change significantly from the baseline levels. Also in the dual cage no significant changes occurred in any of the other six behaviours after conditioning. In the playroom

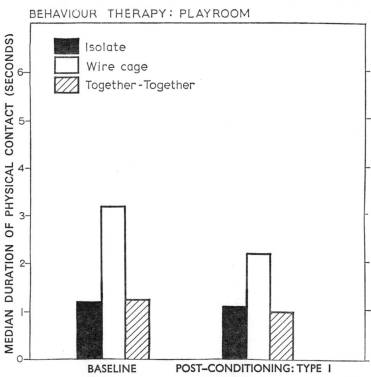

FIG. 10. Duration of total physical contact during playroom tests for the three groups. No significant changes occurred between baseline and post-conditioning trials.

situation results were also negative, except that the duration of locomotion decreased significantly in isolate and *WC* animals but increased in the *TT* monkeys.

In the Type II trials in the dual cage with the shuttlebox stimulus animal present (Fig. 9) all groups increased in physical contact, but *WC* and *TT* animals had significantly higher increases than the isolates. As shown in Fig. 9, this effect was due mainly to the young subjects, who had a median increase in physical contact of more than 30 seconds, compared with only 5 seconds for the adults. In the Type II playroom tests the isolate and *WC* monkeys showed a slight but not significant decrease in physical contact, while the *TT* animals exhibited a large relative increase. Social orientation also decreased for isolate and *WC* monkeys in the playroom when the shuttlebox stimulus animal was introduced, but this measure increased by over 30 seconds for *TT* subjects. This effect was also due primarily to changes in the younger animals.

In general, the results of this attempt at behaviour therapy were negative. No evidence of positive transfer of conditioning occurred unless a cue from the therapy situation, the shuttlebox stimulus animal, was present in the environment. Even then, positive transfer occurred primarily in the *TT* subjects, who were already socially adequate, and largely failed to occur in the socially abnormal isolate subjects. However, there was some evidence that what little transfer did occur in isolates, and the transfer shown in the *TT* animals, was greater in younger animals. This suggests that a behaviour therapy approach, conducted under more systematic conditions, might be beneficial with monkeys that have not yet reached adult levels of maturation.

SUMMARY AND CONCLUSIONS

We have seen that early rearing of rhesus monkeys without physical peer contacts produces persistent and damaging abnormalities in non-social, social, sexual and maternal behaviours. These abnormalities appear to be uncorrelated with intellectual deficits. Attempts to reverse these effects of early experience have been uniformly negative. After extensive post-rearing social experience, animals deprived of physical peer contact during the first 3 to 6 months of life failed to perform socially at levels comparable to those achieved by animals reared with peer experience. Monkeys receiving visual social experience from pictures, but otherwise isolated from social contact, showed appropriate social behaviour during rearing, but failed to develop normally after removal from isolation. Even when these monkeys were gradually paced in the introduction of novel and complex social and non-social stimulation, their behaviour was totally inadequate and failed to improve after repeated social experience. Thus, isolation *per se* from critical early social and non-social experiences appears to produce permanent anomalies within the animal which persist regardless of the degree of adaptation to post-rearing test situations. Evidence has also been presented to show that early learning, perhaps within the first month of life, can produce social traits, such as hyperaggression and preferences for specific social stimuli, that persist into adult life. Finally, although an attempt to condition increased physical contact in abnormal animals failed to transfer to a social situation that did not contain stimulus elements from the conditioning situation, some evidence for the value of such a "behaviour therapy" approach was obtained. This was particularly true for juvenile animals. Perhaps a more rigorous schedule of "therapy" sessions, with preliminary transfer tests in situations containing greater cue generalization from the conditioning situation, might produce more positive transfer effects.

ACKNOWLEDGEMENT

This research was supported by grant MH-11894 from the National Institute of Mental Health.

REFERENCES

ARLING, G. L., and HARLOW, H. F. (1967). *J. comp. physiol. Psychol.*, **64**, 371–377.
BLOMQUIST, A. J., and HARLOW, H. F. (1961). *Proc. Anim. Care Panel*, **11**, 57–64.
CLARK, D. L. (1967). Unpublished M.A. thesis, University of Wisconsin.
CROSS, H. A., and HARLOW, H. F. (1965). *J. exp. Res. Pers.*, **1**, 39–49.
FULLER, J. L. (1967). *Science*, **158**, 1645–1652.
GRIFFIN, G. A., and HARLOW, H. F. (1966). *Child Dev.*, **37**, 533–547.
HARLOW, H. F. (1949). *Psychol. Rev.*, **56**, 51–65.
HARLOW, H. F., and ARLING, G. L. (1968). Unpublished data.
HARLOW, H. F., DODSWORTH, R. O., and HARLOW, M. K. (1965). *Proc. natn. Acad. Sci. U.S.A.*, **54**, 90–97.
HARLOW, H. F., and GRIFFIN, G. A. (1965). In *The Biosocial Basis of Mental Retardation*, pp. 87–106, eds. Osler, S. F., and Cooke, R. E. Baltimore: Johns Hopkins Press.
HARLOW, H. F., and HARLOW, M. K. (1966). *Am. Scient.*, **54**, 234–272.
HARLOW, H. F., HARLOW, M. K., DODSWORTH, R. O., and ARLING, G. L. (1966a). *Proc. Am. phil. Soc.*, **110**, 58–66.
HARLOW, H. F., JOSLYN, W. D., SENKO, M. G., and DOPP, A. (1966b). *J. Anim. Sci.*, **25**, 49–65.
MITCHELL, G. D., ARLING, G. L., and MØLLER, G. W. (1967). *Psychonomic Sci.*, **8**, 209–210.
MITCHELL, G. D., RAYMOND, E. J., RUPPENTHAL, G. C., and HARLOW, H. F. (1966). *Psychol. Rep.*, **18**, 567–580.
PRATT, C. L. (1967). Unpublished M.A. thesis, University of Wisconsin.
PRATT, C. L., and SACKETT, G. P. (1967). *Science*, **155**, 1133–1135.
ROWLAND, G. L. (1964). Unpublished doctoral dissertation, University of Wisconsin.
SACKETT, G. P. (1965a). *Child Dev.*, **36**, 855–868.
SACKETT, G. P. (1965b). *Percept. Mot. Skills*, **20**, 985–988.
SACKETT, G. P. (1966). *Science*, **154**, 1468–1472.
SACKETT, G. P. (1967). *J. comp. physiol. Psychol.*, **64**, 363–365.
SACKETT, G. P. (1968). *Anim. Behav.*, in press.
SACKETT, G. P., PORTER, M., and HOLMES, H. (1965). *Science*, **147**, 304–306.
SACKETT, G. P., SINGH, S. D., GRADY, S. A., and TRIPP, R. L. (1968). Unpublished data.

DISCUSSION

Bandura: Did you conduct your behaviour therapy under varying environmental conditions? I am wondering if the failure in transfer of the new behaviours is due to factors within the monkeys or to the invariant conditions under which the treatment was conducted.

Sackett: This is certainly a problem. We purposely used a very conservative method in our post-conditioning tests, in that these transfer trials were done in the original situations with *no specific cues* available from the shuttlebox. When cues for generalization from the conditioning situation in the Type II transfer tests (this volume, p. 23) were made available, there was some transfer. If we had first provided cues through which the animal could generalize the experiences with the shuttlebox, we might have obtained more positive results. But I think that even if we had done this it would not have helped the total-isolate (*TI*) animals, although the wire-cage (*WC*) animals might have been aided by allowing generalization.

Kubie: I am interested in the influence of smell and taste on development. Purely visual isolation is one thing, visual and auditory isolation combined with isolation from physical contact is another. Much of the lore about smell and taste may be inaccurate; but the idea that an animal can smell fear in another animal or in a man may have an objective basis. And there may be other similar effects related to smell. What is the relationship of smell and taste to biting?

Sackett: I cannot throw much light on either of these problems. The literature suggests that smell is not a particularly salient modality for *Macaca mulatta*, except possibly in sexual behaviour, but these conclusions seem to be based more on hearsay than on scientific data. We are currently studying the preference of sophisticated male monkeys for the smell of females in different stages of oestrus but the results of this study are not available yet.

Hinde: Smell may be very important in sexual behaviour in rhesus monkeys and treatment of the females with steroids may influence sexual behaviour in the males through the change in smell of the female (Michael, R. P. [1968]. In *Endocrinology and Human Behaviour*, chap. 5, ed, Michael, R. P. London: Oxford University Press). The observation that the *TI* animals were sexually aroused but did not know how to orient their sexual behaviour (they either attacked the female, or themselves, while having an erection) suggests that they were responding to smell and that isolation, whatever else it did, did not destroy this response. The fact that visual stimuli are important in sexual arousal does not mean that olfactory stimuli are not.

Sackett: Experiments on the preferences of sophisticated males for females in different stages of oestrus are now being designed to study these problems.

Hinde: You describe the first 30 days of life in your animals as a "sensitive period" for the development of behaviour. But it seems to me that you are not using "sensitive period" in the rigid way in which J. P. Scott used the term "critical period" (1958. *Psychosom. Med.*, **20**, 42-54) when he described the development of social behaviour in puppies. Scott defined the critical period as a period in which *diverse* aspects of behaviour are particularly susceptible to modification. But you used the term more specifically, to mean a time when *particular* types of behaviour are liable to be affected. Have I understood you correctly?

Sackett: Yes. My meaning is that during this sensitive or critical period quantitative deficits in behaviour are laid down, and these decrease proficiency in many behaviours in the adult animal.

Hinde: I am still not clear about the monkeys that were looked after by a human handler for 30 days and were then divided into two groups, one having and the other not having peer experience for the next year. The behaviour of these animals was tested when they were 5 years old. Is that correct?

Sackett: Yes.

Hinde: The distinction that should be made about sensitive periods is whether the early experience influences subsequent behaviour in the test directly, or through some modification in the animal's responses to the experiences available to it in the period between rearing and testing. This is where all the misunderstandings have arisen.

Sackett: Although peer experience is given or withheld, for the first year of life only, in the two groups you have just described, all animals receive a great deal of varied social experience during the next 4 years, that is, before they are tested. On testing, the animals fall into two groups, consisting of animals that prefer a human being and those that prefer a monkey. I agree with your two possible interpretations of these findings. Experiences during the first year, or even in the whole period of 4-5 years after the first 30 days of life, may modify the early effects. Certainly the preference for humans in the first 30 days can be reversed through later experiences, or more of the animals would have preferred monkeys. But there could be a critical period during the first 6 months in which social attachments are formed. If the animal forms an attachment to a human being in the first 30 days, and is then exposed to a different social stimulus for 5 months or so, he may become "attached" to the latter stimulus. Or anything that happens at any time from 30 days to 5 years may be capable of reversing the early attachment. I doubt if this is the explanation, however, because in the period after the first year the experience of the two groups of animals was so similar. My impression is that a rigid critical period in which social attachments are formed exists in monkeys, but that this is a *long* period; at any time during, perhaps, the first year of life previous attachments can be broken and new ones made, but at the end of this period no more changes in social attachments will occur.

Hunt: If behaviour is different in the two groups because of different peer experiences in the first year of life, all later social experiences will be affected in consequence. Animals in the two groups may later have equivalent opportunities but be unable to utilize these equally effectively. And these effects of different conditions of early rearing will be cumulative.

Sackett: I agree. Another way of expressing this is to say that the interaction between rearing and testing conditions will be different in the two groups. What I have suggested is that the noxious effects of early rearing are permanent and produce an anomaly within the animal that cannot be reversed by the kinds of later experiences (for example, behaviour therapy) that we have given him. This is not to say that no later experiences can alter behaviour, but just that we have not found any.

Hinde: A very cautious statement!

Lebedev: Do monkeys have twins, in particular monozygotic twins? Have you reared two members of such a twinship in different conditions, and, if so, did the two members of a pair respond differently to behaviour therapy?

Sackett: The incidence of twinning in *M. mulatta* is about 1 per 10,000 births. In our laboratories only one mother has ever produced twins and both babies died. So study of the effects of different raising conditions on monozygotic twin monkeys is not feasible. *M. mulatta* is not fully mature until the age of 7 years, so it takes about 7 years to finish an experiment. It would take at least 100 years to collect a reasonable sample of twins. But a female monkey will readily adopt two babies—three if she is a good mother.

Miller: Early deprivation of peer experiences did not affect later learning in your monkeys, even when the animals were raised in the wire cage with complete visual deprivation. Is that right?

Sackett: Yes.

Miller: Then your monkeys must react differently from the way in which rats react.

Sackett: Yes. The explanation for these differences may be that isolation in rats gives rise to hyperactivity and a high level of exploratory behaviour; these interfere with the learning of adaptive responses (Woods, P. L., Fishe, A. S., and Ruckelshaus, S. I. [1963]. *J. comp. physiol. Psychol.*, **54**,

167-169). In our monkeys, on the other hand, isolation produces inactivity and diminished exploratory activities, which makes it difficult for the animal to respond *initially* to learning cues, although his response becomes normal later.

Lebedev: Have you used any specific neurophysiological techniques apart from conditioning and learning in your programmes?

Miller: Dr. Lebedev, you are following the Pavlovian practice of classifying learning and conditioning as neurophysiological measures. It is unusual for scientists in the West to think of conditioning in these terms.

Sackett: We have just started telemetry—monitoring the heart rate—but no results of these studies are available yet. We are also devising techniques for remote brain stimulation, and hope to study monkeys from birth to adulthood by these means.

Kubie: You have uncovered many interesting parallels, and some divergences, between the behaviour of monkeys and some of the observations by Spitz and Bowlby on the behaviour of human infants (Spitz, R. A. [1945]. *Psychoanal. Study Child*, 1, 53-74; Spitz, R. A. [1946]. *Psychoanal. Study Child*, 2, 313-342; Spitz, R. A. [1950]. *Int. J. Psycho-anal.*, 31, 131-143; Bowlby, J., Ainsworth, M., Boston, M., and Rosenblatt, D. [1956]. *J. med. Psychol.*, 29, 211-247). Can you give us a parallel time scale for the development of the human infant and the rhesus monkey?

Sackett: This question has to be asked but is impossible to answer. A very rough approximation is that *M. mulatta* in infancy develops about four times faster than the human neonate. This statement is almost meaningless because of within-species variations and the different rates of development of various sensory modalities and motor and reflex skills between species. Ideally, we should develop a theory that is age-independent and then look for age-independent situations in which to test it.

Kaufman: The rate of development of morphological, cognitive and perceptual processes varies widely in different species. We will never be able accurately to translate development from monkey to man. Some of the tests we use to assess the effect of a particular experience during rearing on the subsequent development of an animal may not be too relevant to what happens in other animals, including man. We should devise tests which have significance for the particular species we are testing in the real world in which it lives. I am concerned about using discrimination tests to assess development in monkeys. Of course any higher form needs to be able to discriminate, but it seems unlikely that the effect of being deprived of social experience on the development of the monkey will be best demonstrated by a discrimination test.

2*

Concerning the studies of behaviour therapy in monkeys, was your project to try and cure one symptom in an animal with a variety of abnormal behaviours?

Sackett: Yes.

Kaufman: What did you think would happen to the total behaviour of the animal if you were successful?

Sackett: I postulated that the aversion to physical contact shown by deprived monkeys is not only a symptom, but in part a cause, of their abnormal behaviour. If the monkey does not touch other monkeys he will not learn essential behaviour patterns. I hoped, therefore, that if we obtained transfer such that physical contact in a social situation increased, we might thereby induce transfer to other behaviours. Incidentally, we measured many other behaviours as well as physical contact but found only negative transfer effects; locomotion, for example, deteriorated.

Lazarus: Do you know of any publications describing systematic attempts to reverse these apparently irreversible changes induced by early deprivation in primates?

Sackett: My experiment in behaviour therapy in *M. mulatta* is one in a series of unpublished pilot experiments in which we have also used drugs. We tried to influence maladaptive behaviour in pre-adult monkeys, reared in isolation, using chlorpromazine and amphetamine. Our (preliminary) findings are that animals receiving the tranquillizer (chlorpromazine) show the expected decrease in the total output of behaviour, but the proportion of abnormal and non-social behaviour increases: in other words, the animals appear more abnormal when they are tranquillized because the total number of different behaviours that an animal emits decreases, and abnormal behaviours are preserved at the expense of normal behaviours. With amphetamine, the proportion of abnormal behaviour remains constant but, because of an absolute increase in the frequency of all behaviours, the total amount of abnormal behaviour is increased. The animals get excited, they bite themselves and aggress other animals more, and they rock and huddle more. Further systematic evaluation of the effects of drugs on abnormal behaviours in these animals is needed.

Marks: Although the *TI* monkeys showed normal fear responses at the age of 2-4 months, they had lost these by the time they were a few years old. At what age were appropriate fear responses lost?

Sackett: The incidence of appropriate fear responses to threatening pictures in the picture-isolate (*PI*) animals rose sharply between the ages of 60 and 85 days, with a peak at about 100 to 120 days, and then fell. I assumed that the drop was caused by habituation of the fear response: no harmful consequences occurred if the animal did not show fear to a threatening picture. But the worst thing for the animal is that he is probably learning a maladaptive habit. He shows fear and withdrawal when a picture of a monkey threatens, but nothing happens so he discontinues this behaviour. When he goes out into the "real" world of playroom and laboratory he finds that if he shows no fear in response to threatening from a real animal, he is attacked. It must be terrible for an animal that has developed an image of what a monkey is like from an immobile, two-dimensional screen model, to find that this image is a quite inaccurate representation of a real, behaving animal. Our preliminary data show that the *PI* animals are far more disturbed in real-life situations than total-isolates who have not been shown pictures.

Gelder: You mentioned the absence of appropriate sexual behaviour in the total-isolates. Do they also show *in*appropriate sexual behaviour, and if so, what forms does this take? Do you think there are any parallels between your monkeys and such inappropriate sexual behaviours in man as homosexuality, or fetishism, in which an inanimate stimulus induces sexual arousal?

Sackett: The incidence of auto-erotic behaviour is higher in the *WC* animals than in the animals with peer experience. The male *WC* monkey particularly, although he may have contact with the female once every week for several months and be sexually roused by this, rarely learns to orient himself to the appropriate part of her anatomy. He will mount her head or her shoulders, but he never gets near her vagina. These two examples might be relevant to deviant sexual behaviour in man.

Carstairs: You have described how monkeys, deprived of peer experience, themselves show faulty mothering. If a monkey has had good maternal experience but is isolated from her peers, does she still retain the capacity for good mothering?

Sackett: Probably. Dr. H. F. Harlow has some monkeys treated in this way, but it is still too early to assess their mothering capacity.

Hunt: W. Kesson (1961. *Psychol. Rev.*, **68**, 396-404) formulated the concept of specific inhibitant stimulations in man. These are stimulations that quieten the periodic upsets shown by neonates. An example is oral stimulation, either from the mother's breast or the bottle, or the child may learn how to elicit this stimulation from himself, by sucking his thumb. Could some of the behaviour of the isolated monkeys be an attempt to provide for themselves the specific inhibitant stimulations that quieten similar periodic upsets? This could happen to the monkeys both when they are totally isolated, and after they have been transferred to the playroom if the mother is absent.

Sackett: Monkeys in isolation sleep two or three times as much as monkeys in wire cages: there is nothing to do so they sleep. But within two days of removal from isolation the length of sleeping-time is the same as that of the *WC* animals. This is an example of a major problem in understanding the causes of any abnormal behaviour. It is not necessary to evoke an anomaly within the animal to explain the extra-sleeping time and its "cure"; this is accounted for simply by a response to external stimuli. Similarly, we do not know if self-aggression or self-stimulation are irreversible results of deprivation which involve permanent changes in the animal, or if there is a perfectly reasonable explanation for these behaviours in terms of atypical stimulation.

Hunt: Might the self-stimulatory behaviours—rocking and huddling, sucking various members of the body, masturbation and so on—be good adaptive behaviour for monkeys reared in isolation?

Sackett: Yes. These are the typical responses to any stress situation, where stress is defined as a large change from the circumstances the animal is used to. Even a simple alteration in lighting will induce rocking and huddling in some of these isolated animals.

Miller: If a normally reared animal is presented with a very abnormal circumstance, which gives rise to a great deal of stress, will that animal show self-stimulatory behaviour? An experiment of this sort might provide the answer to Professor Hunt's question.

Sackett: Normally reared animals subjected to stress do show this type of behaviour but to a much smaller extent than the isolates do (Cross, H. A., and Harlow, H. F. [1965]. *J. exp. Res. Pers.*, **1**, 39-49).

Miller: This might be because the isolate experiences more stress but nonetheless reacts in the species-specific way to that stress.

Sackett: Physiological measurements could elucidate whether a deprived animal rocking and huddling after stress is inducing or reducing emotionality, and if this is done in the same way by a normally reared animal. In other words, when the animal rocks and huddles is he showing quiescent or aroused behaviour?

Kaufman: Excessive self-stimulatory behaviour, such as thumb-sucking or handling the genitals, is also seen in baby monkeys raised with the mother for a period of time and then deprived of her presence. Similarly, self-stimulation occurs in the human child at the birth of a sibling who partly displaces the older child from the mother.

Sandler: I am struck by a parallel between the behaviour of the picture-isolates and the development of children born congenitally blind. These children seem unable to make the normal transition, between 4 and 8 months of age, from a so-called passive to an active orientation. They tend to withdraw into themselves, acting in a self-stimulatory way, as the PI monkeys did. It has recently been suggested that the way to deal with this withdrawal, in the absence of vision (which normally acts at this stage of development as an organizer to lead the child's interest to the outside world), is to stimulate the other sensory modalities in these children. But this stimulation must be such that the child can respond and can control input. There has to be an interaction with the environment, and a feedback; simply playing the radio, for example, is no stimulation for a blind child. The results of I. Kohler's experiments (1964. *The Formation and Transformation of the Perceptual World*. Psychol. Issues, Monogr. No. 12. New York: International Universities Press), in which he repeated Stratton's experiments with reversing spectacles, show most convincingly that a child must *act on* stimulus material to build up those aspects of the perceptual world which relate to the stimulus. The images you show the PI monkeys may have no perceptual meaning for them. What is the effect of lack of feedback and, in turn, lack of control of sensory input on the development of the body image—their own and other monkeys'—in your PI animals?

Sackett: You have exactly summarized a major problem in our current research. The hypothesis under test is that in order to develop normal behaviour an animal must learn about the probabilities of input and output. Although some modalities may be qualitatively more important during different developmental stages, we have assumed that an animal reared in a completely non-social environment who learns that he is able to control sensory input some, but not all, the time will be able to learn to adjust to a real social situation. We plan to compare groups of monkeys, raised in three different ways: (*a*) animals with absolutely predictable input—they always know when something will happen; (*b*) animals with absolutely unpredictable input—they never know when something will happen; and (*c*) animals which sometimes can and sometimes cannot predict what will happen. I hypothesize that animals in the last of these three groups will show adequate adjustment to later social experiences, but animals in the other two groups will not.

Dalla Volta: Are there any studies on the influence of early deprivation on non-human primates other than *M. mulatta*? Comparative studies of the more highly evolved primates and man might enlarge our knowledge in this field.

Sackett: The work on non-human primates closest to the studies in our laboratories comes from the Yerkes Regional Primate Center, Emory University, Atlanta, where Menzel and his group have studied behaviour in the chimpanzee (for example, Menzel, E. W., Jr. [1964]. *Psychol. Forsch.*, **27**, 337-365). This work largely supports our findings, particularly concerning sexual and maternal behaviour, although there are some discrepancies. Menzel has a more serious time problem than we do: it takes 15-20 years to complete a study on a chimpanzee. Riesen and his group do not contribute much to this field, because these workers' principal study has been of visual behaviour in chimpanzees reared in the dark (for example, Riesen, A. H. [1960]. *Am. J. Orthopsychiat.*, **30**, 23-36). There is no record, for instance, of social behaviour in these animals.

Hinde: The most aggressive animals in your study were the offspring of inadequate mothers; the next most aggressive group comprised animals partially isolated for 180 days (in the wire cage, with vision of other monkeys but no physical contact), and then totally isolated for the next 6 months. Is that correct?

Sackett: Yes.

Hinde: I am satisfied that for animals in the second category the aggressiveness is a behavioural matter: during the first few months of life all normal babies are involved in aggressive play and gradually learn not to tackle animals bigger than themselves. But what is the nature of the increased aggressiveness of the animals with inadequate mothers?

Sackett: I suggest that during the first 180 days of life the animal learns a social behaviour—aggression—which becomes a permanent personality trait. And it learns this not by being aggressive but by being aggressed, by an aggressive interaction with another animal—the mother.

Carstairs: But do these baby monkeys attack the mother?

Sackett: Never.

Hinde: What mechanism do you postulate has induced this sort of learning?

Sackett: I would postulate that the baby monkey identifies with the mother and learns to be aggressive because she is aggressive. This learning is probably induced by imitation.

Miller: Does such a monkey show aggression only when another animal approaches it, or does it initiate aggression without any provocation?

Sackett: G. D. Mitchell and co-workers (1966. *Psychol. Rep.*, **18**, 567-580) tried to analyse aggressive behaviours in terms of sequences of gestures and their releasers. They used three stimulus animals, an animal younger than the test animal, an age-mate, and a much older (and larger) adult. They found that some aggression-inviting behaviours in younger monkeys or age-mates produced different responses in monkeys raised in different ways. An animal raised with peer experience and by an adequate feral mother expressed aggression almost entirely in threat—by an aggressive display but not by physical violence. Inadequately mothered monkeys with peer experience did not threaten and hardly ever gave any warning before initiating physical violence. And this is exactly what the motherless mothers did to their offspring. A normal mother starts to reject her infant when it is about 100-120 days old (Harlow, H. F., Harlow M. K., and Hansen, E. W. [1963]. In *Maternal Behavior in Mammals*, pp. 254-278, ed. Rheingold, H. L. New York: Wiley) by physically pushing it away from her. This action is usually signalled with some kind of gesture. But the inadequate mother hardly ever signals before aggression; the baby monkey is suddenly bitten or thrown without warning.

Hinde: Nevertheless, all that your evidence actually shows is that animals brought up by inadequate mothers are hyperaggressive. This does not necessarily mean that they have learned this behaviour from the mothers.

Sackett: I agree. Instead of learning to attack, these monkeys may have failed to learn to inhibit physical aggression.

Hinde: I am labouring this point just because we do know something about the way in which normally reared animals learn not to attack (by the early inhibition of aggression as you have said) in terms of conventional learning. But there are no hard data—only theories—about the way in which the deprived monkeys "learn" to be aggressive.

Sackett: Of course we need more experiments before my hypothesis that the baby monkey learns aggression from the mother by imitating her can be accepted. But the data available so far do suggest that this is so. I agree that the process by which this occurs is still unknown—it could be by simple contiguity or a latent effect of early frustration.

Hunt: The deprived monkeys may simply not be learning sequential social behaviour.

Hinde: This is much more likely.

Sackett: I do not agree because in many other behaviours—play behaviours, for example—inadequately and adequately mothered monkeys behave similarly.

Leder: Is aggressive behaviour in the offspring of inadequate mothers a universal or only an average finding?

Sackett: This behaviour is almost universal. Twelve inadequately and twelve adequately mothered monkeys have been tested, at between $2\frac{1}{2}$ and $4\frac{1}{2}$ years of age, in three independent studies (Mitchell, G. D., Arling, G. L., and Møller, G. W. [1967]. *Psychonomic Sci.*, **8**, 209-210; Arling, G. L., and Harlow, H. F. [1967]. *J. comp. physiol. Psychol.*, **64**, 371-377; Sackett, G. P. [1967]. *J. comp. physiol. Psychol.*, **64**, 363-365); in two of these the same and in the third different animals were used. In each situation, almost all inadequately mothered offspring were more aggressive than any of the adequately mothered animals.

Leder: J. M. R. Delgado (1967. *J. nerv. ment. Dis.*, **144**, 383-390) has shown that the number and quality of aggressive behaviours evoked in the same animal depend on whether the animal is the boss-monkey of the colony, or the second monkey, and so on; this behaviour may be modified when the social structure of the group is altered. Are the targets of the aggression of your monkeys dependent on their social rank in the colony?

Sackett: I cannot answer this question because we have almost always studied aggression in a stable group setting, in which there are either only offspring from one sort of mother or only two animals present. Our "neutral" stimulus animal is one that rarely initiates physical contact but does not run away if thus contacted by another animal.

Kaufman: Inadequately mothered offspring, as you have said, can when adult be aroused or provoked to show behaviours that would normally be inhibited by the mother. Delgado described a different set-up in his paper on the fragmental organization of emotional behaviour in the brain of the rhesus monkey (Delgado, J. M. R., and Mir, D. [1968]. *Ann. N.Y. Acad. Sci.*, in press). In his experiments, Delgado stimulated the areas in the brain which subserve aggressive behaviour in animals of different social rank and found that a non-dominant animal does not show aggressive behaviour towards a dominant animal, even if he is close to him, but will attack a less dominant animal. In a hierarchical system a non-dominant animal can be egged on by the dominant animal to become a tyrant towards all the other animals in the group. But Delgado has not done the experiment when the only two animals present are the stimulated animal and a dominant animal. We do not know what would happen in such a situation.

Incidentally, there is a phenomenological similarity (although not necessarily an identity) between the postulated identification of the baby monkey with its inadequate and aggressive mother and the phenomenon of identification with the aggressor in man, as described by Anna Freud (1951. *The Ego and the Mechanisms of Defence.* London: Hogarth).

Sandler: When considering such subjects as the identification of an infant with its mother or the transfer of learned behaviour from one generation to another, learning theorists usually argue from animal behaviour to behaviour in man. But it is also legitimate to argue in the opposite direction. When an individual perceives someone else moving, he first automatically and covertly duplicates the movements himself although these duplicated movements are usually quickly inhibited (Sandler, J. [1961].

Psychosomatic Aspects of Paediatrics. Oxford: Pergamon; Sandler, J., and Joffe, W. G. [1965]. *Psychoanal. Study Child,* **20**, 425-438). As a young infant develops his perception of his own body image he has to develop a capacity for a positive "boundary-setting" between the representations of self and non-self. But in the course of his perception of another, a momentary state of confusion between self and other exists. We might therefore consider the behaviour of the monkeys not only in the context of stimulus-response learning but also from the point of view of an automatic primary identification (to use Freud's term) or adualism (to use Piaget's); and the influence of the momentary confusion between self and object representations must be considerable. An enormous amount of learning must happen when boundaries are still incompletely defined. This type of learning cannot occur with Dr. Sackett's picture-isolates, because there is no interaction between picture and monkey, and thus the distinction between self and non-self cannot be built up. I suggest that, in monkeys, the offspring of inadequate mothers may lack the learning which comes about from this almost reflex and automatic identification with the mother. This is an important part of the process of learning to perceive and to differentiate.

Hinde: Dr. Sackett has described an experimental treatment that produces a result. This is the fact. But the moment one postulates that the baby has *learned* the behaviour from its mother one biases the future course of this research. The true explanation could be that a particular behaviour emerges because the baby did *not learn* to do something else, and one's biased premature conclusions will have sent one on a completely wrong track. It is too early to say that the baby learned its behaviour from its mother; we can only state the results of the experiments.

Sandler: The fundamental disagreement here may be that I regard experimental findings as the pathway to the model we are trying to make rather than as end results in themselves. Unless we theorize about the results and attempt to conceptualize them, and then formulate further testable hypotheses on the basis of our theories, we will make no progress.

METHODS OF ASSESSING THE RESULTS OF PSYCHOTHERAPY

JEROME D. FRANK

Department of Psychiatry and Behavioral Sciences, Johns Hopkins University School of Medicine, Baltimore, Maryland

SINCE this is the first paper concerned directly with psychotherapy in this symposium, I should like, first, to attempt to place the subject in context by sketching in the broadest terms the conditions that psychotherapy purports to treat and its techniques.

PSYCHOTHERAPY IN CULTURAL PERSPECTIVE

At first glance, both the forms of distress and disability considered suitable for psychotherapy and the methods covered by the term are so diverse that they seem to have little, if anything, in common. The types of human misery or malfunctioning treated by psychotherapy range from gross behavioural deficits in deteriorated schizophrenics to tension headaches or general feelings of dissatisfaction with life.

Despite their diversity, however, they do have common features that justify grouping them together. All are characterized by distress in the afflicted person, or in persons close to him, caused by his failure to cope with some aspect of living. At one extreme the failure may be produced by overwhelming stress, as in reactions to disaster which cover the gamut of psychopathological manifestations (Tyhurst, 1957). At the other extreme, some persons seem to sag under ordinary life experiences, presumably due to severe weakness in the coping capacity, as in some simple schizophrenics. The issue is complicated by the fact that usually neither stress nor handicap can be defined independently of each other, and in any particular case the balance between them may largely depend on the meanings of both to the patient, which, in turn, depend on his previous life experience. Since the forms of psychotherapy that I shall consider involve an interpersonal transaction, presumably they are suitable only for those failures in adaptation in which distortions of the patient's perception and behaviour, resulting from his experiences with significant persons, play a major role.

38

As systematic efforts to help patients to change their attitudes or behaviour, all types of psychotherapy involve learning, but, as defined by the conveners of this symposium, they include a great variety of techniques. At one extreme are methods needing, in theory at least, minimal personal contact, such as some of the early token economies; at the other, therapies based on an intimate, emotionally charged relationship between patient and therapist. The former, which may be termed behaviour therapies, concentrate on changing the patient's behaviour, assuming that as it improves his inner experience will change accordingly. The latter, often called interview therapies, seek to enlarge the patient's awareness of himself and his modes of relating to others, leaving his behaviour to take care of itself. Other methods, such as desensitization therapy or methods which place emphasis on problem-solving, range between these extremes. My discussion will focus on interview therapies, broadly defined, since the assessment of changes produced by other forms of treatment will be considered by other participants.

Psychotherapies cannot be understood apart from the cultures in which they function. Attitudes and values of the groups to which patients and therapists belong as well as those of the larger society influence who comes to treatment in what circumstances, who is entitled to conduct psychotherapy, and the nature of its goals. For example, psychoneuroses, the conditions regarded as ideally suited for psychotherapy in the United States, did not exist in the Russian army in World War II. This was not because the patients did not have the symptoms that Americans label as psychoneurotic, but because the Russians interpreted them as evidence of either malingering or organic illness, and treated them accordingly. As to who comes for psychotherapy, the greater its cultural acceptability and availability, the wider the range of people who seek it and the milder their distress; so the demand grows with the supply (Schofield, 1964).

Social attitudes also determine who is qualified to practise psychotherapy. The fact that psychotherapy is a culturally approved institution that, in our society, offers considerable status and other rewards for its practitioners creates disputes among members of different disciplines as to who is entitled to conduct it, as many members of this meeting can testify. But in our rivalry we should not forget that, at least in the United States, psychiatrists and psychologists combined treat far fewer persons than chiropractors and religious healers.

With respect to the assessment of the results of psychotherapy, the values of society, the patient and the therapist determine to a considerable extent what kinds of change are desirable. If the Middle Ages had had an equivalent of psychotherapy, no doubt its goal would have been to instil a sense of guilt, repentance and willingness to submit to the Divine Will, so as to increase the patient's chances of getting to heaven. Twentieth-century American psychotherapy, in harmony with the values of its society, seeks to increase the patient's sense of autonomy and self-direction to enable him to channel his aggressions, and, above all, to become happier.

In periods of social stability the values of the individual and society coincide, but in periods of social change accompanied by conflict of value systems between different groups within a society, the goals of the patient and those about him may sharply diverge. Theoretically, in such periods, the patient's values should prevail; but, especially with those whose personalities are not yet fully formed, the issue is by no means clear-cut. Psychiatrists today are often asked to treat adolescents whose behaviour deviates from the norms of their parents. If an adolescent decides that the values of contemporary society are abhorrent, drops out of college and devotes himself to searching for better guides to his life, often with the help of drugs that alter consciousness, is he moving towards or away from improved mental health? To complicate matters further, we may agree that the patient's values should prevail but, if these lead him into too severe a conflict with society, the result is increased suffering for himself as well as his family and associates. Is he healthier psychologically if he rebels against a "sick society" than if he conforms to it, and how does one weigh the increased suffering he incurs against the gain in his sense of autonomy and self-worth?

To pursue these vast and complex questions further would lead too far afield. For our purposes it is sufficient to recognize that cultural expectations and values of the West today significantly affect the aims and methods of the psychotherapies we shall be considering and the patient's life experiences with which they are intertwined.

ASSESSMENT OF THE EFFECTIVENESS OF PSYCHOTHERAPIES

Problems of design

I should first like to consider whether any form of psychotherapy is more effective than ordinary, helpful life experiences over the same time interval and, if it is, to what extent its effectiveness depends on its specific techniques or on non-specific features of the therapeutic relationship.

Since most, if not all, candidates for psychotherapy have failed to cope with some aspect of life, they suffer from feelings of anxiety, depression and damaged self-esteem that contribute to their distress and hamper their efforts to master their difficulties. All forms of psychotherapy implicitly or explicitly combat the patient's demoralization, revive his hopes and, in general, create a therapeutic atmosphere that will facilitate his ability to recognize and modify his maladaptive patterns of thought and behaviour. This is accomplished mainly by the psychotherapeutic relationship itself, and seems to be based on the patient's confidence in the therapist's competence and desire to help. Every form of psychotherapy is additionally characterized by a specific set of techniques which carry the therapeutic interaction and offer the patient new learning experiences. These techniques are many and various, and any one form of treatment may use several of them. The therapist may serve, to varying degrees, as a model, a provider of instruction and advice, an indoctrinator into a conceptual scheme that enables the patient to reconceptualize his problems, and/or a teacher of methods like free association that enable a patient to widen his self-awareness. Some therapies try deliberately to heighten the patient's emotional tension (Stampfl and Levis, 1967) and others to reduce it (Wolpe, 1961). Since these techniques distinguish therapies from each other, their practitioners are inevitably inclined to attribute the beneficial effects of treatment mainly to the method, rather than to the aspects of the therapeutic relationship that all share.

The question of assessment of any form of psychotherapy, then, can be viewed as twofold: first, are its results superior to no therapy and, second, do they depend primarily on the relationship or on the specific technique? The second question becomes pertinent only if the first can be answered affirmatively. To do this involves disentangling the effects of treatment from all the patient's other concurrent life experiences. For both private and non-private patients, psychotherapeutic interviews represent at best only infrequent, intermittent personal contacts wedged in among innumerable others. What goes on between sessions may be more important in determining outcome than what occurs during them, and the two may interact in complex ways because a change in the patient's outlook or behaviour brought about by psychotherapy inevitably affects the attitudes of others towards him and these may reinforce or counteract the changes induced by therapy. Mere acceptance of the patient for psychiatric treatment, for example, may lead members of his family to change their view of him from a person who is lazy or bad to one who is sick, with concomitant reduction of their pressures on him. Conversely, if the patient's condition contributes to the equilibrium of his family, should he begin to lose certain symptoms or deviant behaviours, this may have repercussions on other family members that lead them to sabotage his treatment. Thus the first problem in the evaluation of psychotherapy is to try to assess the extent to which observed changes are attributable to the treatment itself or to factors outside it, and how the two interact.

The role of treatment is easiest to determine if its goal is highly circumscribed, for example the relief of stage fright or the overcoming of a fetish, or if the criteria of improvement are gross behavioural changes such as getting a patient to keep his clothes on, and when the patient can be observed for 24 hours of the day in hospital. It is most difficult in long-term out-patient therapy with open-ended goals, and the longer the treatment, the greater the opportunity for intercurrent life experiences to influence the outcome.

A special problem with out-patients is that they are apt to seek psychotherapy when they are in the throes of a crisis produced by an abrupt increase in environmental stress which they would have mastered in time with or without treatment; or they may have a cyclic type of illness and then be most likely to seek help when they are at the bottom of a cycle. The presence of a large proportion of such patients in a no-treatment control group might obscure the effectiveness of the treatment because their recovery rate would be so high.

Until recently, most efforts to show that psychotherapy was effective have been inconclusive (Koegler and Brill, 1967; Eysenck, 1965), but this seems to have been due to the inadequacies of the studies. Patients were not adequately defined, therapists were often inexperienced, and measures of improvement were vague. Considering that many of the patients may have been unsuitable for any form of psychotherapy and that many of the therapists were not very competent, the probability of finding a significant difference between treated and untreated patients would be low (Meehl, 1965). As we are learning to define patients, therapists, therapeutic techniques and criteria of improvement with more precision, it is becoming possible to rephrase the question in the only way that can lead to a meaningful answer: what types of therapy, conducted by what types of therapists, produce what type of change in what type of patient?

The patient. As might be anticipated, intelligent young persons who suffer from guilt or anxiety, are willing to reveal their feelings, are psychologically minded and have good ego strengths—in short, patients with strong motivation and good adaptive powers—are good prospects for treatment; but such patients would probably respond favourably to any form of help, so their improvement under a particular form of therapy is not very strong evidence for its efficacy. The demonstration by Gelder (1965) that different types of phobia respond differentially to desensitization therapy is a promising beginning in relating therapeutic outcome to clinical diagnosis.

The therapist. It is reasonably well established that experience helps and that such qualities as genuineness, non-possessive warmth and the ability to show empathy are favourably related to outcome (Truax and Carkhuff, 1967).

That aspects of patient and therapist may reinforce each other is suggested by the findings that patients who are judged to be attractive prospects for therapy do better than those who are not, and that patients who have been prepared for therapy by a special interview not only do better than an unprepared control group but are better liked by their therapists (Hoehn-Saric *et al.*, 1964; Nash *et al.*, 1965).

These findings, although scanty, warrant the conclusion that with some patients and some therapists treatment does have a demonstrably beneficial effect beyond that produced by helpful encounters of daily life (Bergin, 1967).

Specific techniques and the therapeutic relationship. The relative contribution to outcome of specific techniques compared with aspects of the therapeutic relationship shared by all psychotherapies is a knottier problem. To demonstrate the value of a special technique obviously requires, first, a sufficiently precise description of what the therapist actually does, and this can only be determined by direct observation. The therapists' own accounts are too subject to distortion by their theoretical biases. With the advent of electronic recording, and now Videotape, it becomes increasingly possible to describe the therapist's activities objectively. The therapy using the technique in question must then be compared with another therapy, identical in all respects except that the specific technique is not used. Both therapies should be conducted by the same therapists who are equally competent with, and have equal faith in, both. Finally, the criterion of improvement must measure the specific change in the patient's functioning supposedly produced by the technique. If these rigorous conditions are met, then if the therapy containing the technique produces significantly more improvement than the one not containing it, this is strong evidence for the efficacy of the technique. I know of only one published study, of brief desensitization therapy for stage fright, that has accomplished this exacting task (Paul, 1966).

The follow-up interval

It is customarily assumed that the true effectiveness of medical or surgical treatments depends on their ability to produce benefits persisting for a considerable time, and the same criterion has been suggested for evaluating the results of psychotherapy. There may be at least two reasons for this emphasis on long-term results. One is the concept that the primary goal of psychotherapy is stimulating personality growth, which is, after all, a process of indefinite duration. The other is the medical model of the five-year cure. This is appropriate when the illness, for example cancer, is not affected by the patient's continuing interaction with his environment. But a patient's psychiatric condition is continuously affected by the environmental stresses he encounters. In this respect, mental illnesses are analogous to the common cold. The pathogens of this minor but distressing illness are always present in our mucous membranes but have established a kind of truce with their host. Symptoms of a cold appear when the truce is broken by an increase in the virulence of the organisms or a drop in the host's powers of resistance, and this in turn depends on many environmental and internal factors. The discovery of a way of producing permanent immunity to colds would indeed be a medical triumph. In the meanwhile, to hope to achieve a five-year cure for colds seems unduly ambitious. Most of us would be more than satisfied with a remedy that reduced the duration of each cold from, say, a week to an hour. Analogously, a patient with a severe phobia of cancer of the throat received practically complete relief for over a year from brief psychotherapy aimed at helping him to be more assertive in general and, in particular, to overcome intense shyness with women. This soon enabled him to win a wife, who, as might have been anticipated, had a dominating personality; he had a brief relapse, cleared by one interview, after he had lost in a struggle with her (Frank, 1966). Does this indicate that the results of treatment were merely superficial or, rather, that life had faced him with a new stress that he could not readily master?

The longer the interval between the end of treatment and the follow-up evaluation, the greater will be the effect on the patient of life events, including experiences with help-givers (whether or not labelled as psychotherapists) whom he may have encountered. Thus, with the passage of time, the effects of the initial therapy will be increasingly hard to disentangle from other influences. Further, at least one study has shown patients to be very unreliable in their reports of treatment received elsewhere (Paul, 1967). The longer the interval, finally, the greater the difficulty in tracking down patients, and the attrition of the sample may introduce a serious bias into the results.

A further reason for questioning the necessity of routine follow-up studies is that they have repeatedly found that patients' states immediately after therapy are surprisingly good predictors of their condition after an interval of months or years. Thus in a series of patients treated in different ways for interpersonal performance anxiety, all maintained their improvement over a two-year period (Paul, 1967); and in two series of patients treated with brief psychotherapy at Johns Hopkins, three-quarters and four-fifths of those estimated as improved immediately after treatment were still improved one and ten years later respectively.

The immediate beneficial effects of therapy would be expected to endure in patients who have come to treatment in the throes of a crisis. Once they have been helped over it, there is no reason why the symptoms it produced should recur. The symptoms of other patients may have been tied to specific situational stimuli such as snakes or making a speech in public. If therapy makes them invulnerable to these particular stresses, their symptoms should not recur. In still other patients, therapy may have produced changes in viewpoint and effectiveness that increase their ability to cope with life's stresses.

These considerations are not meant to imply that all follow-up studies are pointless. They should always be contemplated in any effort to evaluate the results of psychotherapy, especially if the therapy purports to produce changes in a person's personality and outlook that will enable him to withstand stresses more successfully after therapy than before it. They do suggest, however, that in any particular case the difficulties of follow-up studies should be weighed against the value of the information they might yield. If psychotherapy did no more than shorten the duration of a patient's distress, even though he would recover eventually without treatment, this seems to me to be sufficient justification for it. In general, I believe follow-up studies will throw more light on the natural history of the conditions for which people come to therapy than on the effectiveness of treatment.

Criteria for assessing improvement

Ideally, a patient's progress in psychotherapy should be assessed against a standard based on his optimum mental health, but this ideal has proved to be out of reach so far because, as already indicated, the concept of positive mental health is so contaminated with culturally determined value judgments that no one has yet arrived at a generally acceptable definition of it (Jahoda, 1958). Fortunately, most patients seek psychotherapy for more modest, circumscribed goals—the relief of distress and the overcoming of specific disabilities. In urban or academic centres where psychotherapy is readily available, or even fashionable, a few individuals seek it to achieve greater self-understanding, to combat their existential anxieties, or to achieve other diffuse aims. But these persons represent such a minute fraction of those seeking help that the problem of evaluating the effects of psychotherapy for them need not detain us.

Even the more modest goal of overcoming distress and disability, however, raises certain questions that I shall now consider. These concern the sources of information on which assessment of improvement is based, the multidimensional nature of improvement, and the problem of the validity of criteria.

SOURCES OF INFORMATION ABOUT IMPROVEMENT

All information on which judgments of improvement are made comes ultimately from the patient himself in the form of direct or indirect self-reports or observations of his behaviour.

Patients' self-reports are subject to two sources of error, which may be loosely classed as attentional and motivational (Parloff, Kelman and Frank, 1954). With the best intentions, it is difficult for someone to express his feelings accurately or to give an undistorted report of his relationships with others, especially when he has not been trained to be objective. From a motivational standpoint, the patient's reports are influenced by aspects of the situation in which the ratings are made. The fears or hopes engendered by the prospect of the first interview may lead to transient decrease or increase in symptoms, as with the patient whose toothache disappears in the dentist's waiting room or, conversely, the man whose chest pain is increased by his fear that the physician will discover heart disease. Many patients on first coming to a psychotherapist fear that he may discover evidence of insanity or distrust him on other grounds. This may cause them to conceal, consciously or unconsciously, certain symptoms or difficulties which they reveal as they become more secure; so they may appear sicker when they are actually improving. A patient may exaggerate his difficulties to convince the therapist that he needs help, or minimize them, especially after a period of treatment, as a way of expressing his gratitude. Thus changes in self-ratings after a period of therapy might be due more to a change in what the patient was able or willing to report about himself than to a change in his actual feelings.

A more subtle and pervasive source of distortion of self-reports lies in what has been termed the "demand-character" (Orne, 1962) of the situation in which the ratings are obtained. For example, if a patient is asked to rate his internal state, is subjected to any kind of procedure and then is again asked to rate himself on the same scale, the demand-character of the situation is that his ratings should change. Further, the demand-character of any therapy situation to which a patient submits himself for any length of time is that he accept the therapist's view of mental illness and treatment; so his self-reports are influenced by what has been termed "doctrinal compliance" (Ehrenwald, 1966). It has long been recognized that patients report improvement in terms that fit the therapist's theory, and even dream in these terms.

Despite these limitations of self-reports, symptom check-lists and behavioural inventories afford in general a reliable estimate of improvement and are, indeed, indispensable.

In out-patient therapy, since direct observations of the patient's behaviour outside therapy are impractical, information should also be secured from his relatives. These reports are also subject to attentional and motivational distortions, but these can be reduced by requiring the informants to support their judgments by as much specific evidence as possible. In any case, the relatives' reports serve as useful checks on the patient's statements.

Therapists tend to be more conservative in judging improvement than their patients are, for several reasons. The therapist's judgment must be based only on the small sample of the patient's behaviour that he reports or demonstrates in the interview, and the demand-character of therapeutic interviews favours emphasis on what is going wrong rather than what works well. The therapist judges each patient against an implicit standard of all the other patients he has seen, and may be unwilling to consider a patient improved unless he shows changes that the therapist regards as more fundamental than symptomatic improvement, such as increased maturity. The patient judges progress only by comparison with his own previous state, may include favourable changes outside therapy that he does not report, and is content if he feels and functions better.

Trained raters who do not know what type of therapy the patient has had are particularly useful, especially when their ratings are based on tapes or protocols whose order can be randomized so that the raters do not know which were obtained before and which after therapy.

THE MULTIDIMENSIONAL NATURE OF IMPROVEMENT

The need to evaluate many aspects of a person's functioning in order to determine the effectiveness of psychotherapy arises because psychotherapy is not, in general, a very powerful remedy. If a treatment produces marked improvement, as for example electroconvulsive therapy in many psychotically depressed patients, no extensive measures or elaborate statistical analyses are needed to demonstrate that it has been effective. But psychotherapy is apt to be followed by gains in some areas and not in others. A patient's subjective complaints may worsen as his behaviour improves or *vice versa*, and he may improve in some of his personal or work relationships and not in others. Group therapy may increase a patient's social facility more than his insight; individual treatment may increase his insight but not his social skills. Some criteria of improvement may show changes early in therapy but remain stationary thereafter; others may worsen initially but improve later.

The non-unitary nature of improvement might lead to the too-hasty conclusion that overall ratings of improvement are of no value, and indeed their drawbacks are obvious. Since overall ratings are based on implicit criteria, the rater can shift his standards or the focus of his attention from one patient to the next. He may call one patient improved because he has fewer headaches and another improved because he has found a better job. He may consider a given change, such as loss of a symptom, to represent slight improvement in one patient and marked improvement in another. Nevertheless, in our own research we are not willing to abandon overall judgments of improvement by both patient and therapist since in at least one experimental study overall judgments distinguished quite clearly between experimental and control groups (Hoehn-Saric *et al.*, 1964). This suggests that the weaknesses of a measure of global improvement may also be its strengths. The human brain is a far more sensitive and elaborate computer than any man-made one. In making an overall judgment, the rater can assign weights to different aspects of the patient's improvement in the light of the total picture without having to specify precisely what these aspects are. Thus overall ratings can be used to validate more specific measures. If, for example, a patient reports improvement in his headaches but still rates himself as unimproved overall, this suggests that he did not view the headache as the main reason for seeking treatment or as an important aspect of his distress. Further, the finding that one form of therapeutic intervention leads to more improvement than another, even if the nature of the improvement remains unspecified, may be an important lead to further work. It must be admitted, however, that, in general, overall ratings contribute little to the advancement of knowledge because the data underlying them cannot be made explicit.

When multiple criteria of improvement are used, the fact that patients may change in different directions on different criteria presents an awkward but not insuperable problem. The Gordian knot can be cut by converting the improvement scores on all the tests to standard scores, and classifying a patient as improved if his average standard score has changed significantly (Truax and Carkhuff, 1967).

To obtain an adequate survey of a patient's condition, information is needed first about his bodily or psychic symptoms. Information about these subjective states is customarily obtained through check-lists of symptoms, filled out by the patient or by an interviewer. Improvement includes not only relief of distress but also changes in behaviour, and it is probably useful to distinguish interpersonal behaviour from performance. The former category includes how the patient gets along socially with peers of both sexes and with his parents, siblings and, if married, his wife and children; the latter includes changes in his level of achievement as indicated by changes in status and income.

Many areas of functioning can be covered by a single structured interview. One of special interest because it has been validated in two cultures, London and New York, is the Psychiatric Status Schedule, which covers a large number of factorially derived dimensions of psychopathological behaviour (Spitzer, Endicott and Fleiss, 1967). This schedule is highly reliable, but its value as a measure of improvement in psychotherapy remains to be demonstrated.

The ideal improvement measure would enable comparison of groups of patients while at the same time doing justice to the uniqueness of the individual. Inventories and rating scales accomplish the first aim satisfactorily. Subscales derived by factor analysis and other statistical methods make it possible to follow changes in specific manifestations of psychopathology, while changes in total score take account of the possibility, which proves to be rather rare, that patients may improve in one symptom only to substitute another. But for any particular patient many of the items or subscales are irrelevant, which dilutes the power of the instrument, and for different patients different items may have different weights. How does one compare improvement of a single severe symptom, such as an incapacitating headache, in one patient with improvement of a great number of complaints, that combined produce less distress than the headache, in another?

One criterion suggested by drug evaluation studies (which is based on each patient's uniqueness) is his target complaint (Freyhan, 1959), that is, the complaint for which he comes to treatment. If this improves, then there can be little doubt that the patient is better. But this measure does not resolve the problem of the comparability of patients—how does one equate relief of depression in one patient with resolution of a marital problem in another? And target complaints may change in the course of therapy, as

patients come to see their difficulties in a new light, making it difficult
sometimes to compare the severity of the complaints before and after
treatment. Despite these limitations, target complaints have proved to be
useful criteria for assessing improvement (Battle *et al.*, 1966).

Since many complaints of psychiatric patients are assumed to result
from interpersonal stresses, which in turn reflect the patient's unique way
of perceiving himself and others or conceptualizing his experiences, it would
be desirable to appraise changes in these parameters following therapy.
Many instruments have been devised to describe aspects of the patient's
personal view of the world. Examples are (*a*) the self-ideal Q sort (the
patient arranges a series of cards on which different statements about
personality are written in accordance with how much they resemble his
image of himself; first as he actually is, and then as he would like
to be); this procedure gives a measure of the discrepancy between his
perceptions of his actual and ideal self (Rogers and Dymond, 1954); (*b*) the
Osgood Semantic Differential (Osgood, Suci and Tannenbaum, 1957),
which maps the connotations to him of important persons or concepts in
relation to each other; and (*c*) the Kelly Repertory Grid (Kelly, 1955; Crisp,
1964), which yields an organized picture of the personal constructs by which
he orders his experience; finally, (*d*), projective tests, of which the most
venerable are the Rorschach and the Thematic Apperception Test, yield
information about phantasies and feelings that may lie outside the patient's
awareness.

All the measures so far described require the active participation of the
patient and may be influenced by his conscious intentions. Another set of
criteria, based on direct observation of signs of emotional tension in the
interview, do not require his participation, often lie entirely outside his
awareness and are beyond his control. These include measures of speech
disturbances (Kasl and Mahl, 1965) and a variety of measures of functioning
of the autonomic nervous system such as pulse rate, psychogalvanic reflex
and skin temperature. Although autonomic indices differ from patient to
patient and for the same patient in response to different types of stress
(Lacey, 1959), creating difficulties of interpretation, by and large they do
correlate with the general level of emotional tension.

Since the interview situation in which such measures are made is quite
different from situations the patient encounters in daily life, the extent to
which findings from the various tests represent the patient's typical state
remains an open question. With the advent of telemetry, it has become
possible to monitor the patient's emotional state as he goes about his
daily activities. Comparison of his responses to specific situations before

and after therapy would provide convincing evidence of the effects of treatment.

FACE VALIDITY AND CONSTRUCT VALIDITY OF CRITERIA: THE QUESTION OF "PERSONALITY CHANGE"

Except for measures of attitudes and phantasies, the criteria of improvement just reviewed are valid regardless of any particular theory of mental health or psychotherapy. No one would seriously question that reduction of excessive emotional tension, disappearance of a phobia or restoration of sexual potency constitute improvement, and most members of a given society would agree on criteria of improved interpersonal behaviour and performance. These are the ultimate criteria of improvement and they have face validity. They need no theoretical justification. The demonstration that any particular type of psychotherapy produces improvement in these sorts of criteria, however, does not lead to much gain in knowledge because it casts no light on the therapeutic processes involved or on the validity of the underlying theory. Progress in elucidating the possible differential effects of different techniques, as already indicated, requires criteria of improvement derived from the theory of therapy on which they are based. Some of these criteria, such as relief of a particular symptom through desensitization, have face validity, but others have meaning only in terms of a particular theoretical system—they have construct validity.

Proponents of many therapies are not satisfied with showing that their treatment helps patients to feel and function better; they seek to produce what they regard as changes in the patient's basic personality or outlook on life. Psychoanalysts may wish to help their patients resolve the Oedipus complex or overcome the neurotic process (Kubie, 1963), client-centred therapists aim to produce greater congruence between a person's real and ideal selves, and existential therapists hope to increase the patient's openness to experience. While such conceptualizations are essential for scientific advance, to be of value for research they must be defined operationally, that is, in such a way that criteria based on them can be reliably measured. Validation of such concepts depends on showing that changes in them are systematically related to changes in criteria with face validity. The fact that a given treatment regularly reduces the discrepancy between actual and ideal selves, for example, is significant only if this is accompanied by improvement in comfort and interpersonal effectiveness.

From an operational standpoint, statements that a therapy has altered a patient's personality may mean that the patient has learned to express his problems in the therapist's language (which often is what is really meant by insight) or to voice attitudes and values approved by the therapist. For example, a colleague asserted that he regarded a patient as improved, even though his symptoms were unchanged, because he had become more tolerant of people. Personality change in this sense signifies acceptance of the therapist's value system, at least in part, and is closely analogous to being converted to a religious faith. This may indeed be a powerful therapeutic experience, but it is difficult to define in operational terms.

Statements about personality change may be indirect prognostic statements about the likelihood that improvement will be maintained after therapy stops. If, for example, a patient has gained insight into his problems, the implication is that he will be able to handle them in the future more effectively than he has in the past.

SUMMARY

Assessment of the results of psychotherapy bristles with difficulties, primarily because psychotherapy is not a very powerful remedy, its effects interact with the patient's ongoing life experiences, and its aims involve values of the culture, the patient and the therapist. Some headway has been made in identifying characteristics of the therapist, such as his ability to empathize, that are related to his effectiveness, and certain circumscribed symptoms have been shown to respond better to some types of psychotherapy than others. But disentangling the effects of the therapeutic relationship from those of specific techniques remains a formidable task. Findings concerning the long-term effects of psychotherapy are difficult to interpret, but psychotherapy is worth-while even if it produces only short-term benefits. Measures of improvement must include both the subjective state and behaviour. While overall estimates are of some value, estimates of change in specific symptoms and behaviour patterns are essential, and possible distortions introduced into the patient's reports by his attitudes toward the therapist and treatment situation must be taken into account. Indices of autonomic tension, which cannot be deliberately influenced by the patient, have considerable promise as measures of improvement, but the determinants of such indices are complex. Advances in knowledge of the psychotherapeutic process require not only measures whose validity is self-evident, but also those whose validity is derived from particular theories of therapy.

REFERENCES

BATTLE, C. C., IMBER, S. D., HOEHN-SARIC, R., STONE, A. R., NASH, E. H., and FRANK, J. D. (1966). *Am. J. Psychother.*, **20**, 184–192.
BERGIN, A. E. (1967). *Int. J. Psychiat.*, **3**, 136–150.

CRISP, A. H. (1964). *J. psychosom. Res.*, **8**, 327–335.
EHRENWALD, J. (1966). *Psychotherapy: Myth and Method, An Integrative Approach.* New York: Grune and Stratton.
EYSENCK, H. J. (1965). *Int. J. Psychiat.*, **1**, 97–144.
FRANK, J. D. (1966). *Am. J. Psychother.*, **20**, 564–575.
FREYHAN, F. A. (1959). *Am. J. Psychiat.*, **115**, 577–585.
GELDER, M. G. (1965). *Proc. R. Soc. Med.*, **58**, 525–529.
HOEHN-SARIC, R., FRANK., J. D., IMBER, S. D., NASH, E. H., STONE, A. R., and BATTLE, C. C. (1964). *J. psychiat. Res.*, **2**, 267–281.
JAHODA, M. (1958). *Current Concepts of Positive Mental Health.* New York: Basic Books.
KASL, S. V., and MAHL, G. F. (1965). *J. Pers. soc. Psychol.*, **1**, 425–433.
KELLY, G. A. (1955). *The Psychology of Personal Constructs*, vols. 1 and 2. New York: Norton.
KOEGLER, R. R., and BRILL, N. Q. (1967). *Treatment of Psychiatric Outpatients.* New York: Appleton-Century-Crofts.
KUBIE, L. S. (1963). In *Counterpoint, Libidinal Object and Subject*, pp. 106–120, ed. Gaskill, H. S. New York: International Universities Press.
LACEY, J. I. (1959). In *Research in Psychotherapy*, pp. 160–208, eds. Rubinstein, E. A., and Parloff, M. B. Washington, D.C.: American Psychological Association.
MEEHL, P. E. (1965). *Int. J. Psychiat.*, **1**, 156–157.
NASH, E. H., HOEHN-SARIC, R., BATTLE, C. C., STONE, A. R., IMBER, S. D., and FRANK, J. D. (1965). *J. nerv. ment. Dis.*, **140**, 374–383.
ORNE, M. T. (1962). *Am. Psychol.*, **17**, 776–783.
OSGOOD, C. E., SUCI, G. J., and TANNENBAUM, P. H. (1957). *The Measurement of Meaning.* Urbana, Ill.: University of Illinois Press.
PARLOFF, M. B., KELMAN, H. C., and FRANK, J. D. (1954). *Am. J. Psychiat.*, **111**, 343–351.
PAUL, G. L. (1966). *Insight vs. Desensitization in Psychotherapy.* Stanford, Calif.: Stanford University Press.
PAUL, G. L. (1967). *J. consult. Psychol.*, **31**, 333–348.
ROGERS, C. R., and DYMOND, R. F. (eds.) (1954). *Psychotherapy and Personality Change.* Chicago: University of Chicago Press.
SCHOFIELD, W. (1964). *Psychotherapy, the Purchase of Friendship.* Englewood Cliffs, New Jersey: Prentice-Hall.
SPITZER, R. L., ENDICOTT, J., and FLEISS, J. L. (1967). *Compreh. Psychiat.*, **8**, 321–343.
STAMPFL, T. G., and LEVIS, D. J. (1967). *J. abnorm. Psychol.*, **72**, 496–503.
TRUAX, C. B., and CARKHUFF, R. R. (1967). *Toward Effective Counseling and Psychotherapy: Training and Practice.* Chicago: Aldine Publishing Co.
TYHURST, J. S. (1957). In *Symposium on Preventive and Social Psychiatry*, 15–17 April 1957, Walter Reed Army Institute of Research, pp.149–168. Washington, D.C.: U.S. Government Printing Office.
WOLPE, J. (1961). *J. nerv. ment. Dis.*, **132**, 189–203.

DISCUSSION

Miller: In my experience, both experimental and personal, I have seen two different sorts of errors which can easily occur in assessing the results of psychotherapy. The first is "regression to the mean" which could also be called a criterion error. By this I mean that because a person's psychological adjustment fluctuates around a mean, he is more likely to start psychotherapy when his adjustment has moved to its lowest (that is, poorest) level.

After this, additional spontaneous fluctuations will be towards the mean, in other words the patient's adjustment will tend to improve. To the extent that patients initiate therapy when they are feeling unusually ill, regression to the mean will introduce an artefact biasing the assessment in favour of therapy. The possibility of an opposite type of error is illustrated by my own experience with brief psychoanalysis. I did not benefit much immediately but there was "a sleeper effect" of gradual, cumulative changes over a number of years. This sort of artefact will cause one to underestimate the results of therapy if one tries to measure them too soon.

Kubie: There are also patients who are so depressed that they cannot seek therapy because they do not believe there is any help for them. They come to therapy only when they are *least* disturbed by their emotional problems. Inevitably therefore they become worse as soon as treatment starts. In this situation the therapist naturally becomes as discouraged as the patient. But this initial set-back may be the necessary beginning of the therapeutic process. If patients always came into therapy at their lowest ebb, our lives would be much easier; but perhaps less useful.

I have studied the problems of assessing the results of psychotherapy and have argued about them with Professor Frank for many years. During the past nine years I have (by design) been involved almost exclusively in writing and research, and in looking back over the previous 40 years of work; but I have had no patients in analysis. I think this has enabled me to become more objective in thinking about the assessment of results. Further, I have spent much of my life challenging any excessive claims made for psychoanalysis or any other form of psychotherapy. We cannot answer the questions implicit in Professor Frank's presentation without first deciding what constitutes the criteria for change in human psychology. I have discussed this question for many years, but I have not published my ideas about it because I am not satisfied with them. One tentative answer is that the only true criterion of change in human psychology is a change that leads to continuing change. This may sound redundant and circular but it is basic.

Some differentiations are essential prerequisites for assessing the results of psychotherapy: differentiations, for example, between symptomatic changes and alterations in the underlying personality. In psychiatry, as in all medicine, the relief of certain symptoms may be helpful even if one has not removed their cause. Thus a patient who is confined to one room by claustrophobia lives a desperately sick life, although the process of illness may itself not be as "sick" as the life is. If the restrictions imposed on such a patient by the claustrophobia are lessened, this frees him from prison and every external aspect of his life begins to change. This example illustrates one of the ways in which our nosological system is totally inadequate. It does not differentiate between a sick personality, a sickness as a process, and a sick life. We lump all three together as though they were the same thing.

We will have to learn how to attach quantitative values to the changes induced by therapy, so as to enable us to define not only the criteria of change but also how to measure them. Because we cannot measure something does not mean that it does not exist. I know of no way of measuring education: yet education exists. We are no more precise about our concepts of education than we are about the various sorts of therapy in psychiatry, whether this is psychotherapy or somatic therapy or a combination of both. We need to analyse all data—subjective, objective and autonomic; but here again we meet difficulties. Some patients make magnificent changes within the therapeutic relationship, while their behaviour in their lives outside continues as before. Other patients, who seem to be unable to make any changes in the therapeutic situation, are regarded as miraculously improved by their relatives and friends in the world outside. These differences add to the difficulty of correlating therapeutic changes with subjective, objective and autonomic data. To organize such data requires an institute for the basic study of psychological, psychoanalytic and psychotherapeutic processes.

One hears about measuring "tension"—a metaphor borrowed from the physical sciences. The word "tension" is now misused to imply that a special kind of energy explains a familiar but purely subjective experience. It is not surprising that with this underlying conceptual confusion we have been unable to measure "tension" differences.

Another confusing aspect of change comes about because we fail to differentiate between changes that occur in the price we pay for the same symptomatic manifestations in varying circumstances and changes in the underlying neurotic process itself. An individual with a height phobia who moves from New York to a flat plain in the Middle West, where there are no heights, will lead a comfortable life. His life changes, but he is not a changed man. Nor is his neurosis changed. His altered external environment has lessened the price he will have to pay for his neurosis; and of course this will help him. Yet if we regard this change as an indication of successful therapy, we deceive ourselves. If such an individual moved from his flat plain to the Rocky Mountains, his height phobia would reappear.

In assessing results we need a more basic framework for characterizing disease processes. Our current system of nosology is wholly misleading. I have sometimes challenged my colleagues with a paper called *"The Life*

Expectancy of the Concept of Schizophrenia" (unpublished). That such a totally invalid term could ever arise is a sad commentary on the intellectual clarity of our predecessors; that it persists is an equally sad commentary on ourselves.

With these enormous quantities of data, S. S. Kety has stated (personal communication) that the only way of dealing with so many items is by randomization. I do not agree. What is more urgently needed is agreement on an objective definition of (*a*) what constitutes psychotherapy, (*b*) what are its essential ingredients as a process, and (*c*) whether it can be measured or not.

Marks: To take up your comment that patients may behave in one way in the psychotherapeutic situation and quite differently outside therapy, the only way to try to deal with this difficulty is to use multiple ratings from different sources, including patients, therapists, and observers in different life situations.

Carstairs: Professor Frank, in your zeal to keep your presentation brief, you defined your terms very briefly. Notably, you said that the cue for a patient's need for psychotherapy is that a person is in distress. But this definition may need some qualification. The villagers in Sicily, who have recently (December, 1967) suffered from an earthquake, are undoubtedly in distress, but do they need psychotherapy? This question is also implicit in some of Dr. Kubie's comments.

Frank: Being in distress is one of the necessary cues for psychotherapy, but the distress must also involve other people. J. S. Tyhurst (1957. In *Symp. Prev. Soc. Psychiat.*, pp. 149-168. [April 1957, Walter Reed Army Institute of Research.] Washington: US Government Printing Office) has shown that subjects involved in external disasters do manifest psychiatric illnesses; the people in Sicily did, in fact, show the full gamut of psychiatric illness and some of them have responded well to brief psychotherapy.

Carstairs: But surely this is not the first thing they need?

Frank: No, of course not. The external stresses must also be reduced.

Kubie: What of the middle-aged man who has had a life-long, successful, compulsive work drive? His neurosis has been rewarded from childhood, yet a compulsive work drive is just as much a neurotic symptom as a compulsive work block, although the fate and consequences are profoundly different. The patient pays heavily for a work block every day of his life. The patient with a compulsive work drive pays nothing until he breaks down with a typical involutional depression. He has never before noticed, or at least never admitted, internal distress. But has he not needed help?

Frank: Not until he breaks down; he is functioning well until this time.

Kubie: He may be coping all right, but his family will be paying heavily for this.

Frank: Then he is causing distress to others.

Kubie: But he does not admit it.

Frank: We see many patients who do not admit they are ill but are brought to the psychiatrist by someone else. Another aspect of this interesting syndrome—the compulsive work drive—is that it is a good illustration of the different categories of stress that exist at different stages of life. Because an individual magnificently handles the stresses peculiar to one stage of his life it does not mean that he will automatically be able to handle stresses at another. Dr. Kubie's comments suggest that we should try and catch people before they break down, but surely we have enough work treating those who are actually in trouble without looking for prospective candidates who may need psychotherapy in the future.

Kubie: There is a pre-clinical phase in the story of the neurotic process and the psychiatrist should surely try to study and treat this phase. If we do not (even if we are short of personnel who are adequately trained to deal with the fully evolved neurotic state), we will be abandoning the principle by which all somatic medicine has made its major contributions: namely, the principle of early recognition, early diagnosis and appropriate early treatment. This has been not only the principle of preventive medicine but also one of its essential tools. The rejection of this principle in psychiatry has been one of the major obstacles to progress by which early psycho-diagnosis and psychotherapy are used to arrest the neurotic process before it has had time to destroy a life. One obvious way of helping to solve this problem is to train more people—non-medical behavioural scientists as well as medically qualified psychiatrists.

A programme of early preventive treatment for the neuroses contains intrinsic difficulties, apart altogether from the external problem of the bottleneck due to shortage of trained personnel to implement it. Some neurotic processes cause a patient psychological suffering and pain from the onset, and patients thus affected seek help and seek it early. They know they are in trouble because their inner experience has taught them that an insidious process of illness is at work. But, unfortunately, in many other neurotic processes the patient is wholly unaware that he is threatened with neurotic disorganization of his development—his thinking, living, plan-ning, interpersonal relationships and so on. He does not suffer. People around him (friends, family, work or school associates, teachers, students) may suffer, but the individual himself may not be aware of this. Sometimes a wise or loving friend or relative, teacher or doctor, may be able to make such an individual aware of his need; but this is only a derivative awareness, not the awareness that comes directly from inner suffering. Because these patients do not suffer, they come only reluctantly for help. A third group of neurotic illnesses are actually rewarding. The most striking example in this group is the compulsive work drive which wins advancement, high marks in school, job and educational opportunities, high pay and rewards of every kind. Any hints that reach the individual that something may be wrong are vague, indeterminate and intermittent. These hints alone rarely persuade him that he needs help. Although the rewards for such a "sufferer" are so great that it is almost impossible to persuade him that he is in need of help, it is practically certain that if he remains unpersuaded he will develop an involutional depression in late middle-age. (This is a very common, although not the only possible, result of the compulsive work drive. It leads to the *cliché* that people break down from overwork.) I cannot accept the defeatist attitude that we should turn our backs on problems of this kind merely because we are shorthanded. Even if we cannot cure all these patients, and thereby forestall later disaster, our obligation as scientists is to study the pre-clinical phases of the neurotic process.

Marks: Professor Frank, surely your comments on the lack of importance of a five-year follow-up after psychotherapy need qualification. The length of follow-up depends on whether one is rating an illness with the natural history of the common cold or of one of the incurable forms of cancer. A five-year follow-up may be inappropriate for the common cold, but it is extremely important in assessing the results of the treatment of malignant disease, and the same thing applies to psychological disorders. Brief follow-up is of little value in assessing the results of treatment of a naturally fluctuating condition such as agoraphobia, which has a relatively low cure rate over five years but may show wild fluctuations within that period. But for a condition without this natural fluctuation, for example some of the more specific animal phobias, a shorter follow-up tells us all we need to know about the effects of treatment. We should pay attention to the clinical variables in the disease process in planning follow-up studies.

Malan: We are confusing the issues. It is true in the sense you describe that a long follow-up of, say, the common cold is useless, but a five-year follow-up of the tendency to *catch colds* is very useful. The parallel between this situation and what happens in psychological illness is exact: a patient reacts to stress by producing symptoms, but one is not concerned so much with his symptoms as with his *tendency to react to stress* by getting them.

Frank: I agree with all this. I was not decrying long-term follow-up studies but pleading for the value of short-term studies as well. From the standpoint of personal suffering, to give an agoraphobic patient even a short period of freedom from his symptoms is worth-while.

Gelder: The length of time the treatment takes is also important. If this is only two or three days we might be satisfied if the short-term results were reasonable, even if the patient later relapsed. But if a treatment lasts for two or three years, we need evidence of more lasting improvement to convince us that the treatment has been worth-while. It might be useful to introduce a concept of "cost-effectiveness" into our schemes of evaluation, that is, to relate length of treatment to duration of improvement. This concept could also include the cost to the patient—in terms of time and loss of income—as well as to the psychiatrist.

Concerning the value or otherwise of classical diagnostic groupings, although I agree that they have severe limitations they do have one advantage, namely that the little we know about the natural history of the neuroses is described in terms of these classical diagnoses. Recorded follow-up studies (for example, Greer, H. S., and Cawley, R. H. [1966]. *Aust. med. Ass.*, Mervyn Archdall med. monogr. No. 3; Ernst, K. [1959]. *Die Prognose der Neurosen. Monographien aus dem gesamtgebiete der Neurologie und Psychiatrie,* **85.** Berlin: Springer Verlag) have used these classical diagnostic groupings. Therefore we cannot dispense with them when we compare the outcome of the untreated illness with the results of different treatments.

Kubie: They serve a purpose for the records of the various State Boards of Mental Hygiene but are misleading for scientific purposes.

Bandura: Evaluation of the results of psychological procedures is often obscured by the use of such concepts as "cure", "spontaneous remission" and "relapse". These terms may be appropriate in describing the course of general medical diseases but are misleading when applied to behavioural changes that are governed by social variables. For these, the pertinent issues are whether a given treatment can successfully induce a change in behaviour, whether the established changes generalize to extratherapeutic situations, and whether the changes are maintained over time. It is important to distinguish between these three processes because they are governed by different variables. The fact that established changes may no longer be present some time after treatment has been discontinued does not necessarily mean that the method is inadequate. On the contrary, it may be exceedingly powerful for inducing changes, but the gains may have been short-lived because the proper maintaining conditions have not been arranged. Similarly, enduring behavioural changes may be achieved but these do not transfer to extratherapeutic situations, thus supplementary procedures are needed to ensure optimum transfer. Follow-up studies should therefore be designed to provide information on whether therapeutic failures reflect a weak treatment, inadequate maintaining conditions in the client's social environment, or deficient transfer training.

PSYCHODYNAMIC ASSESSMENT OF THE OUTCOME OF PSYCHOTHERAPY

D. H. Malan, E. H. Rayner, H. A. Bacal, E. S. Heath and
F. H. G. Balfour

Tavistock Clinic, London

Professor Frank has described (p. 40) the difficulties inherent in evaluating the results of psychotherapy. These difficulties are due to the fantastic complexity of the various factors concerned—mainly in connexion with the interactions between the patient, the environment and the therapist—which may introduce the many fallacies and biases that bedevil our work. My own view is that, in spite of all these problems, the only thing we can do is to decide what we think are the most important factors affecting our results and then devise ways to measure them as best we can. Thus we can see if our estimate of the importance of any particular parameter is correct. Then, of course, we must apply scientific caution to our results.

I shall now present briefly some of the results of our work at the Tavistock Clinic in which we are attempting to deal with the problem of assessing the results of brief dynamic psychotherapy. A disadvantage of many of the methods of assessing therapeutic results is that, with the data available, one cannot evaluate the system of "patient-environment" as a whole, as the following example shows.

Severe depressive symptoms first occurred in a woman after eight years of marriage at the birth of her first child. Her past history and present comments about the child showed that she was over-dependent on her husband (for instance, she insisted that he telephone her every evening if he was away from home) and that she regarded the child as an intruder between them. This woman was not treated, but at follow-up three years after our initial assessment she was symptomatically much better. At the follow-up interview she volunteered that the improvement occurred rather suddenly when her son first went to nursery school; in her own words, "I had him in smaller doses and I felt more relaxed." This improvement even reflected itself in her sexual life with her husband, which had also improved to some extent at this time. If we applied a method such as the self-ideal correlation (see Rogers and Dymond, 1954) to this patient, she would almost certainly rate herself as nearer to her ideal self in the sense that she is now much more comfortable than she was three years before. But this method of assessment cannot take into account the fact that the improvement had occurred when the stress in her life was reduced. Moreover, the self-ideal correlation tells us nothing about the patient's ability to withstand stress in an adaptive way, without developing maladaptive patterns (symptoms), which is what interests us in dynamic psychotherapy. The patient does not know that this is the sort of information we want and so will not include it in the self-assessment.

In our follow-up studies of patients treated by brief psychotherapy at the Tavistock Clinic we have tried to make considerations such as these central to the assessment of the patient. Our initial assessment of the patient is made to as deep a level as we are able to see. Then, before the follow-up interview, we formulate and record criteria for a fully satisfactory improvement. In the example given, we would have aimed for improvement not only in the woman's symptoms and in her relationship with her husband, but also in her over-dependence on her husband and her ability to cope with situations of jealousy. We then match the findings at follow-up with the criteria laid down beforehand. In this study four assessors made an independent judgment on the follow-up material, obtained by interview, to try to match the findings at follow-up with the criteria originally laid down.

Two questions need to be asked about any method of assessment: first, is it reliable? And, second, is it valid?

Reliability of the method

We divided the four judges into two teams of two. All four judges first made independent scores, and then each team of two met independently of the other team to make a written consensus assessment of the results. While we were practising, we started with a basic 5-point scale for "dynamic improvement", from 0 ("essentially unchanged") to 4 ("apparently resolved"); but we soon found it necessary to introduce half points (0·5, 1·5 and so on) and to extend the scale at each end—negative scores meaning "worse", and a score of more than 4 meaning "apparent resolution" of very severe psychopathology.

For the present purpose, I shall consider only those patients who had "brief" psychotherapy (arbitrarily defined as fewer than 40 sessions), and for whom we were able to obtain satisfactory follow-up information. There were 22 such patients (nine others had brief psychotherapy but refused follow-up or could not be traced, and eight went on to longer therapy). Fig. 1 shows the mean score for improvement as judged by the two members of Team *A*, plotted against the mean score judged by Team *B*.

If all mean scores given by one team had been identical with those given by the other team, all would have fallen on the continuous straight line in

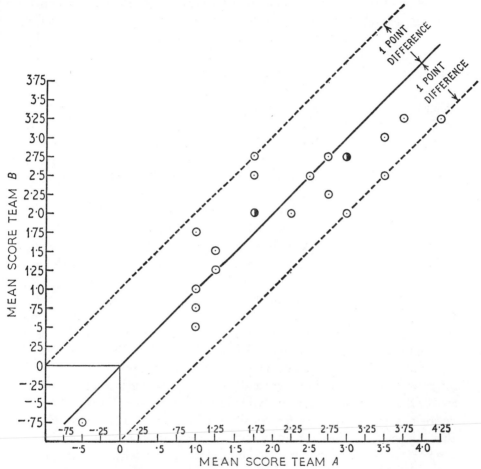

FIG. I. Mean score for improvement (Team *A*) plotted against mean score for improvement (Team *B*). Number of patients: 22; Kendall's correlation coefficient (τ_b): $+0\cdot77$; ◐: 2 scores at same position on graph.

the figure. All scores that differ between the two teams by no more than one whole point on the basic 5-point scale fall on or between the two dotted lines. A glance at the figure will show that in fact all 22 mean scores differ by no more than 1 whole point, and that 12—just over half—differ by no more than one quarter-point. Kendall's rank correlation coefficient (τ_b)

is $+ 0 \cdot 77$ between the mean scores of the two teams. We consider this a satisfactory degree of agreement.

Validity of the method

To the question "Is the method valid?", we can only answer "Of course we cannot say, but at least it gives meaningful results." Fig. 2, which refers to the same 22 patients, shows the mean score for "improvement" made by all four judges, plotted against the "transference-parent ratio". This ratio is a measure of the attention paid by the therapist to linking (a) the transference relationship to (b) the patient's relationship with his parents. It was calculated from the written accounts of the therapies (which were dictated from memory) as follows: the number of interpretations in which a link was made between transference and parent was counted, and this was divided by the total number of interpretations recorded in that therapy. The fact that the transference-parent ratio is a *proportion* and not an *absolute number* at least partially eliminates two variables that might confuse the issue, namely (1) length of therapy, and (2) fullness of recording.

Kendall's rank correlation coefficient between the two variables plotted in Fig. 2 is $+ 0 \cdot 30$ which is significant at the 3 per cent level (one-tailed test). This is a replication of the result published in *A Study of Brief Psychotherapy* (Malan, 1963).

Fig. 2 shows several interesting features: (a) half the points lie on or close to the straight line AA, suggesting that there is a type of patient in whom the outcome is really dependent on the amount of attention paid to this type of interpretation; (b) the upper left-hand area of the diagram is empty, which means that no patient who received a reasonable proportion of these interpretations failed to improve; and (c), in contrast, the lower right-hand area of the diagram is not empty, which means that some patients who did not receive many of these interpretations did improve. There is considerable independent evidence that a number of the patients in the lower right-hand part of the diagram (but excluding the two best results on the extreme right of the diagram) improved as a result of life experiences several years after termination of therapy, and that the therapy that they had may not have been responsible. (The follow-up assessments were made between 4 and 8 years after the termination of therapy.)

Conclusion

At the least, these results show that this method of assessment is self-consistent according to what we understand about this kind of therapy.

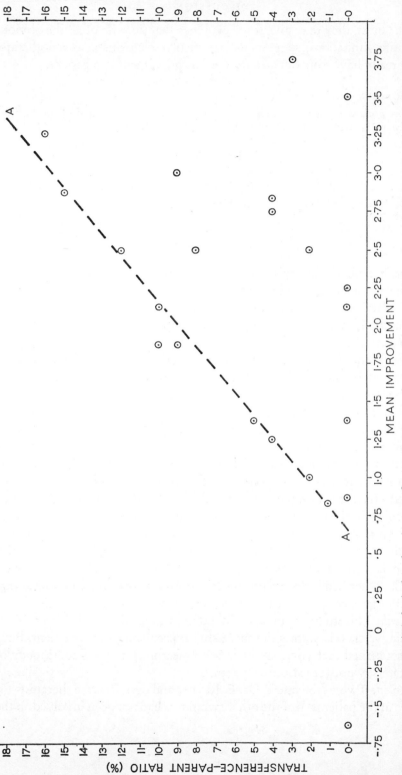

FIG. 2. Mean improvement (4 judges) plotted against transference–parent ratio for 22 patients treated in less than 40 sessions. The transference–parent ratio is the ratio of the number of transference–parent interpretations to the total number of interpretations recorded, expressed as a percentage.

At the most, they may give some evidence that (in spite of all the obvious scientific limitations) suggests that particular elements in psychotherapy may really have something to do with improvement in a patient.

ACKNOWLEDGEMENTS

This work was generously supported by the David Matthew Fund of the Institute of Psycho-Analysis and by the Mental Health Research Fund.

REFERENCES

MALAN, D. H. (1963). *A Study of Brief Psychotherapy*. London: Tavistock.
ROGERS, C. R., and DYMOND, R. F. (eds.) (1954). *Psychotherapy and Personality Change*. Chicago: University of Chicago Press.

DISCUSSION

Frank: Since the therapists in this study were all using a similar technique (the technique of dynamic psychotherapy), would not the number of the particular interpretations you have described depend more on the communications of the patient than on the therapist?

Malan: Yes.

Frank: So this parameter is not independent of the type of patient being treated—who might also be the type of patient who would recover spontaneously.

Malan: Of course that is true. My only claim for these data is that they are compatible with the hypothesis that a case record containing a large number of transference-parent interpretations (interpretations of identification, by the patient, of the therapist and a parent) tends to be the case record of a patient who recovers. The data *prove* nothing about causality or the effectiveness of therapy. Clearly the behaviour of the therapist varied according to the patient he was treating, and the number of transference-parent interpretations depended as much on the patient as on the therapist. In other words, the patients who stimulated their therapists to record this particular type of interpretation were the patients who tended to improve. On the other hand, these data are also consistent with the hypothesis that the transference-parent interpretations tended to cause improvement.

Frank: This study is a most useful attempt to tackle the problem. Your predictive criteria were quite successful in predicting improvement, but I am concerned that you may have been measuring the self-consistency of the raters, who were also the therapists.

Malan: Two of the raters, Dr. E. Rayner and myself, were therapists for some of the patients But the other two raters had not been involved in the therapy at all; the only information they were given was the initial assessment material and follow-up material. The high level of agreement suggests that contamination through knowledge of what had happened in therapy was minimal.

Miller: Were the two raters without previous knowledge of the patients grouped together in the same team, or were they divided, one in each team?

Malan: They were together in team *B*.

Foss: One possible fallacy in your results may be connected with the different durations of different therapies: the time that a therapy lasts may be correlated with recovery. But it is also possible that as a therapy gets longer its content changes and the therapist may tend to make a particular type of interpretation more often. Do transference-parent interpretations tend to occur more often in the longer therapies? If so, what you are studying may be the correlation between length of therapy (directly associated with changed content, that is, with a particular type of interpretation) and favourable outcome.

Malan: The transference-parent interpretations did tend to occur more often in the longer therapies. But it is also true that (*a*) the total number of sessions, and (*b*) the passage of time correlated positively with outcome, but not significantly so. We have not yet studied whether the *difference* between the correlation coefficient given by these interpretations and that given by the other two variables is significant.

CONTROLLED TRIALS IN BEHAVIOUR THERAPY

I. M. MARKS AND M. G. GELDER

Institute of Psychiatry, The Maudsley Hospital, London

WITH any treatment we need to ask whether it works, in which patient it works and what the effective ingredients are in that treatment. Controlled trials can help us answer each of these questions, but controlled trials of psychological treatments are especially difficult to organize because it is not easy to specify the procedure or the target effect which is intended. This is particularly true for the interview therapies discussed so ably by Professor Frank (pp. 38–53). Certain behaviour therapy techniques can be studied more readily because their procedures and aims can be specified fairly clearly. This has led to many controlled experiments in recent years and our report concerns such experiments where groups of subjects treated by a behavioural method were contrasted with groups of subjects with similar problems who were treated by a control procedure. Studies are excluded which only used subjects as their own controls.

It is rather a sobering thought that the only behavioural technique which has so far been subjected to adequate controlled scrutiny has been desensitization, and most of this paper will deal with results of this scrutiny. A handful of controlled trials have examined the conditioning treatment of enuresis, and aversion in smoking, and controlled studies of aversion in homosexuality are in progress, but it is too early to evaluate these.

Desensitization of phobic disorders has proved a valuable testing ground for the development of methods of controlled study which can be used in any psychological technique. Phobic disorders can be defined and measured more readily than most disorders, and desensitization consists of an assembly of techniques which can be systematically dismantled to examine their contribution to the total effect.

At least 17 controlled trials of desensitization have now been completed and it is perhaps the only psychological technique for which we can give fairly complete answers to the questions posed earlier—whether it works, and if so in whom, and which aspects of the procedure are responsible for the effects.

DOES IT WORK, AND IF SO, IN WHOM?

Studies with volunteer subjects

Most controlled investigations of desensitization have dealt not with patients but with volunteer subjects who have been found on special inquiry to have circumscribed phobias. These investigations have been of undoubted value in determining the mechanisms by which desensitization works, but their results have to be confirmed in a patient-population because

TABLE I
CONTROLLED STUDIES OF DESENSITIZATION IN VOLUNTEERS

Study	*Fear treated*	*Number of subjects in desensitized group*	*Length of follow-up (months)*
Lazarus (1961)	Acrophobia, claustrophobia	16	9
Lang, Lazovik and Reynolds (1965)		23	8
Davison (1968)		8	0
Lomont and Edwards (1967)		11	0
Schubot (1966)	Snake phobia	15	0
Melamed and Lang (1967)		7	7
Leitenberg *et al.* (1968)		10	0
Ritter (1968)		15	0
Bandura (1968)		12	1
Rachman (1965)	Spider phobia	3	3
Paul and Shannon (1966)	Stage fright	20	24
Donner (1968)	Test anxiety	14	3
Kondas (1967)	Test anxiety	12	5
	Mean =	12·5	5

patients may differ from volunteers in important respects. Furthermore, at least a year's follow-up is essential to differentiate transient effects from more useful lasting changes. At the Maudsley Hospital fewer than 2 per cent of patients seeking psychiatric help complain of isolated phobias. Later we shall inquire whether these psychiatric patients are helped by desensitization, and whether its efficacy can extend to patients with wider problems.

Table I shows 13 studies with volunteers in which a group which received desensitization was compared with a control group. All but three of the studies dealt with student volunteers, so the populations sampled have been rather homogeneous. Surprisingly few different kinds of fear have been treated—eight studies dealt with snake phobias, two with test anxiety and one each with spider phobia, acrophobia and claustrophobia, and stage fright. Several of the studies have had rather small numbers of desensitization subjects, and follow-up has often been short, though a year's follow-up is usually regarded as a reasonable aim in clinical investigations.

Despite these limitations nearly all the investigations show a striking uniformity in their results. Each showed desensitization to produce more

TABLE II
CONTROL PROCEDURES CONTRASTED WITH DESENSITIZATION IN VOLUNTEERS

	Number of studies
Relaxation	4
Graduated exposure	5
Flooding	1
Visualizing non-phobic scenes	2
Suggestion and hypnosis	1
Insight psychotherapy	2
Drug/placebo	1
Modelling	1
No treatment, or period on waiting list	11

change in the treated fear than did the corresponding control treatment, which included relaxation, graduated exposure, flooding, visualizing non-phobic scenes, suggestion and hypnosis, insight psychotherapy, drug/placebo, and no treatment or a period on a waiting list (Table II). The one exception is Professor Bandura's study, in which live modelling produced superior results (1968). These findings provide a strong case for studying the effect of desensitization in phobic patients. Moreover, comparisons with the various control groups throw light on the mechanism by which desensitization acts (*vide infra*).

Studies with patients

So far the only investigations of desensitization to include control groups of patients have been published from the Maudsley Hospital (Table III).

TABLE III
CONTROLLED STUDIES OF DESENSITIZATION IN PHOBIC PATIENTS

Study	Fear treated	No. of patients in desensitized group	Length of follow-up (months)	Control procedure
Cooper, Gelder and Marks (1965)	Mixed phobias	41	12	Mixed treatment without desensitization
Marks and Gelder (1965)	Mixed phobias	31	12	Mixed treatment without desensitization
Gelder and Marks (1966)	Agoraphobia	10	12	Hospitalization
Gelder, Marks and Wolff (1967)	Mixed phobias	16	12	Insight psychotherapy
Marks, Gelder and Edwards (1968)	Mixed phobias	14	9	Hypnotic suggestion

Four controlled investigations have been completed. The first was a retrospective investigation of 77 patients and their controls (Cooper, Gelder and Marks, 1965; Marks and Gelder, 1965). These 77 patients comprised 41 phobic patients (31 of whom were reported by Marks and Gelder, 1965),

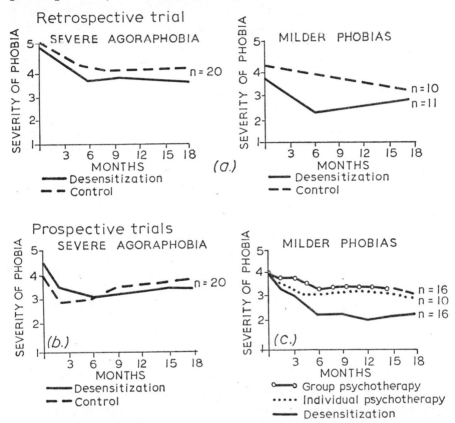

FIG. 1. The course of phobic disorders in three controlled trials of desensitization. Ordinates: severity of phobia graded from 1 (absent)–5 (severe); abscissae: time in months; n=numbers of patients in the various groups. (a) 41 patients; including data from Marks and Gelder (1965); (b) 20 patients; based on data from Gelder and Marks (1966); (c) 42 patients; based on data from Gelder, Marks and Wolff (1967).

10 patients with obsessive rituals, 13 with writer's cramp and 13 with various other neurotic problems. This study was useful in directing attention to the type of disorder which could most profitably be studied in more detail. Although many studies of psychological treatment ignore the type of problem being treated, this is not the best way to proceed, for it is known from investigations by Ernst (1959), Greer and Cawley (1966) and others that the *untreated* course differs in different types of neurosis. Results of

the retrospective study of 77 patients (*vide supra*) showed that isolated phobias responded significantly better to desensitization than to the control treatment of hospital care; complex phobic disorders such as agoraphobia did rather better, but not significantly so; while obsessive neuroses and a group of other miscellaneous neuroses did no better with desensitization than with control treatment (Fig. 1a).

The prospective studies concerned patients with a variety of phobic disorders. In the first prospective trial (Gelder, Marks and Wolff, 1967, Fig. 1c) 42 patients with focal phobias or with milder agoraphobia were treated as out-patients. Desensitization was compared with two matched control groups who received group or individual psychotherapy. Ratings were made by three independent raters. At the end of treatment all raters agreed that the phobias of patients who received desensitization had improved significantly more than those of the psychotherapy control groups. Over a year's follow-up, desensitization continued to show better results, but the difference diminished with time. This emphasizes the importance of the time at which treatments are compared.

Desensitization specifically improved phobias rather than other complaints. But once the treated phobias diminished, improvement also followed in work and leisure adjustments that had formerly been hampered by the phobias. These observations were possible because multiple ratings had been made of eleven items about patients' complaints and social adjustment. Multiple ratings of directly observable items are thus of great value: inferences can be drawn from multiple ratings, but kept separate from observations.

A third investigation of 20 in-patients with severe agoraphobia showed the danger of extrapolating too widely from findings on volunteer subjects In these patients desensitization did not produce significantly more improvement than did the control treatment of supportive hospitalization (Gelder and Marks, 1966, Fig. 1b).

Fig. 1 summarizes the results of these three studies. In two separate groups of severe agoraphobics desensitization conferred no significant advantage over other forms of treatment, whereas in two separate groups of patients with more focal phobias, including mild agoraphobia, desensitization did produce significantly more improvement than did the control procedures. The type of patient being treated was clearly a crucial variable.

Psychophysiological measures of anxiety and clinical ratings of anxiety were related to the outcome of desensitization in 36 patients from the three studies just described. Results showed that the results of desensitization were poorer in patients with very high levels of free-floating anxiety.

The findings point to an important limitation in the value of desensitization in psychiatric patients, since few patients need treatment for focal phobias alone but also for general background anxiety. The best results with desensitization are obtained where patients closely resemble the volunteers used in the studies cited earlier. Unfortunately this similarity is found in only a small minority of psychiatric patients. In this minority, however, desensitization is a useful treatment even though it is often a lengthy and very boring procedure.

ACTIVE COMPONENTS OF DESENSITIZATION

Granted that desensitization is useful in focal phobias, what ingredients of desensitization are responsible for its effects? Table IV shows the main processes involved. The procedure of desensitization consists of graduated exposure to phobic stimuli along a hierarchy while the patient simultaneously has a contrasting experience such as relaxation. Usually he is relaxed and visualizes a series of images of phobic situations, and later also goes out to meet those situations in practice. The patient expects to improve, is encouraged by the therapist at all stages, and develops a relationship with the therapist.

TABLE IV

PROCESSES INVOLVED IN DESENSITIZATION

(1) Graduated exposure to phobic stimulus along hierarchy (in visual images and in practice)
(2) Simultaneous contrasting experiences (e.g. relaxation)
(3) Expectation of improvement
(4) Verbal reinforcement
(5) Relationship to therapist

All these processes have been studied in desensitization. Table V summarizes the results for these and other variables which have been contrasted with the desensitization assembly of procedures. The full desensitization procedure consistently gives better results than relaxation alone (Table Va), exposure to phobic stimuli along a hierarchy without relaxation (extinction) (Vb), exposure to phobic stimuli without a hierarchy (flooding or implosion therapy) (Vc). Desensitization also gave better results than the visualization of non-phobic scenes (Vd).

Desensitization produced better results than suggestion under hypnosis (Ve), than a drug/placebo (Vf), or than an intense relationship occurring with insight psychotherapy (Vg). But significant improvement also occurred in some control groups receiving hypnotic suggestions (Marks, Gelder and Edwards, 1968), a drug/placebo (Paul and Shannon, 1966), exposure (Schubot, 1966) or brief insight psychotherapy (Paul, 1967).

TABLE V

PROCESSES WHICH HAVE BEEN COMPARED WITH DESENSITIZATION (CONTROLLED TRIALS IN PHOBIC SUBJECTS)

Process	Results	Population	Type of fear	Study
a Relaxation	Desensitization better	Students Students Students+children	Snake phobia Spider phobia Test anxiety	Davison (1968) Rachman (1965) Kondas (1967)
b Exposure: visualization of phobic scenes along a hierarchy (extinction)	Desensitization better	Students Students Students Students+children	Snake phobia Spider phobia Snake phobia Test anxiety	Davison (1968) Rachman (1965) Lomont and Edwards (1967) Schubot (1966) Kondas (1967)
c Flooding (exposure without hierarchy—implosion)	Desensitization better	Students	Spider phobia	Rachman (1965)
d Visualization of non-phobic scenes	Desensitization better	Students Students	Snake phobia Snake phobia	Lang, Lazovik and Reynolds (1965) Davison (1968)
e Suggestion and hypnosis	Desensitization better (but hypnosis group also improved)	Psychiatric out-patients Students	Mixed phobias Snake phobia	Marks, Gelder and Edwards (1968) Lang, Lazovik and Reynolds (1965)
f Drug/placebo	Desensitization better (but placebo group also improved)	Students	Stage fright	Paul and Shannon (1966)

Condition	Result	Subjects	Phobia	Reference
g Relationship to therapist: (1) Psychotherapy	Desensitization better	Psychiatric out-patients / Volunteers	Agoraphobia / Acrophobia, claustrophobia	Gelder, Marks and Wolf (1967) / Lazarus (1961)
(2) Therapist absent, tape recorder used	Desensitization better (but psychotherapy group also improved)	Students	Stage fright	Paul and Shannon (1966) / Paul (1967)
	Desensitization works without therapist but { bit better with therapist / bit worse with therapist }	Students	Test anxiety / Snake phobia	Donner (1968) / Melamed and Lang (1967)
h Verbal reinforcement (expectation of improvement)	Desensitization significantly worse without reinforcement or expectation of improvement	Students	Snake phobia	Leitenberg *et al.* (1968)
i Conventional hospital care	No significant difference	Psychiatric in-patients	Agoraphobia	Gelder and Marks (1966)
j Live modelling with exposure	Live modelling + exposure better (but desensitized group also improved)	Volunteers	Snake phobia	Bandura (1968)
k Passage of time (no treatment controls)	No significant improvement in any study. Desensitization significantly better	Volunteers	Snake phobia	Bandura (1968)
		Children	Snake phobia	Ritter (1968)
		Students	Snake phobia	Lang, Lazovik and Reynolds (1965)
		Students	Snake phobia	Leitenberg *et al.* (1968)
		Students	Snake phobia	Davison (1968)
		Students	Snake phobia	Rachman (1965)
		Students	Snake phobia	Melamed and Lang (1967)
		Students	Rat phobia	Cooke (1966)
		Students	Stage fright	Paul and Shannon (1966)
		Students	Test anxiety	Donner (1968)
		Students + children	Test anxiety	Kondas (1967)

Significant results have even been obtained when desensitization was given by tape recorder with no therapist present during the procedure, and no consistent effects resulted from the presence of the therapist during tape-recording sessions. However, in the only study that has examined the role of expectation of improvement (Table V*h*), the effect of desensitization was significantly impaired when this element was removed from the treatment situation (Leitenberg *et al.*, 1968). Students in this study were simply told that it was an experiment on fear, and they were not praised when they reported a decrease in their fears during the sessions.

Desensitization had no significant advantage in agoraphobic in-patients (Table V*i*, and *vide supra*). This was not because conventional hospital care is such an effective treatment but because severe agoraphobics are resistant to any treatment. The nature of one's clinical material is one crucial factor which determines results.

Desensitization consistently gives significantly better results than simple observations of subjects over a period of time—so-called "spontaneous improvement" (Table V*k*). All these studies involved focal phobias in volunteers, not patients.

Only one procedure has been superior to desensitization, namely live modelling with exposure along a hierarchy (Table V*j*). In the study using this procedure (Bandura, 1968) the subjects were volunteers with fears of snakes, and it will be of interest to see how far these findings can be repeated in patients, especially those with diffuse phobias and generalized anxiety.

To summarize these results, desensitization has produced better results than relaxation alone, exposure alone along a hierarchy, exposure without a hierarchy, visualization of non-phobic scenes, suggestion under hypnosis, drug/placebo, psychotherapy, or no treatment. Though desensitization is effective in the absence of a therapist, its effect is significantly impaired when subjects do not expect to improve and do not receive verbal reinforcement for reports of calmness.

Although some improvement was occasionally obtained with simple exposure to phobic images, suggestion-hypnosis, insight psychotherapy or a drug/placebo, this was never as great as with the full desensitization procedure. Desensitization is thus an assembly of techniques several of which may contribute to improvement when used alone, but which produce the maximum effect when combined together.

The fact that relaxation alone and exposure to phobic images alone are less effective than the two together supports the view that a process of counterconditioning is involved. However, there is little evidence that a new response takes the place of the earlier phobic one. After successful treatment patients rarely state that when they think of phobic images they experience relaxation instead of tension; that repeated exposure to phobic images alone is not enough to reduce the phobias suggests that extinction or habituation is only one aspect of the mechanism of improvement; that verbal reinforcement significantly improves the results argues that operant conditioning plays an important part in the method. As the patient constantly monitors small changes in his affect during treatment and his reports of calmness are repeatedly reinforced by approval, so his fear is gradually diminished and he becomes more willing to meet the phobic situation. Professor Neal Miller (1966, 1968) has clearly shown how autonomic responses are subject to operant or instrumental control. Fear seems no exception to this rule.

Indirect light on the mechanism of desensitization also comes from controlled trials of techniques other than desensitization (Table VI). The value of modelling, or vicarious conditioning, has already been noted and five studies on volunteers with focal fears have shown that modelling is useful in reducing fear (VIa). Modelling is more effective in children when combined with exposure to the phobic object along a hierarchy, as occurs during desensitization (Ritter, 1968; Bandura, 1968).

Particularly interesting results have been obtained with flooding, or implosion therapy (TableVIb). The aim of this method is that the patient experiences the phobic stimulus as vividly and for as long as possible until, finally, he or she is unable to feel fear any more. In Hogan and Kirchner's (1967) study this produced significant decrease in avoidance of rats, and similar results were obtained in another three studies (Table VIb). Flooding produced significant effects even when the therapist was absent and the instructions were given by tape recorder (Kirchner and Hogan, 1966). One study (Rachman, 1966) did not yield useful results with flooding, but here the subjects were not allowed to visualize their phobic images for longer than two minutes. Lang (1968) adduced physiological evidence that it is important for desensitization patients to experience phobic anxiety during treatment in order for improvement to occur. Hogan and Kirchner's results further emphasize the potential importance of anxiety experiences for improvement during desensitization. However, such intense phobic anxiety as occurs in flooding has hitherto been regarded as harmful rather than beneficial.

Flooding or implosion procedures may well throw light on broader problems than desensitization, such as why some patients in psychotherapy improve after abreaction, which may be a reliving of past experiences or

TABLE VI

PROCESSES OTHER THAN DESENSITIZATION WHICH REDUCE FEAR (CONTROLLED TRIALS IN PHOBIC SUBJECTS)

Process	Results	Population	Type of fear	Study
(a) Modelling	Significantly decreased avoidance	Children (3–5 yrs.)	Dog phobia	Bandura, Grusec and Menlove (1967)
		Children (3–5 yrs.)	Dog phobia	Bandura and Menlove (1968)
		Children (5–11 yrs.)	Snake phobia	Ritter (1968)
		Students	Snake phobia	Geer and Turteltaub (1967)
		Students	Snake phobia	Hart (1966)
(b) Flooding (implosion)	Significantly decreased avoidance	Students	Rat phobia	Hogan and Kirchner (1967)
		Psychiatric in-patients	Snake phobia	Wolpin and Raines (1966)
		?	Snake phobia	Larsen (1965)
	No improvement	Students	Spider phobia	Rachman (1966)
(c) Cognitive manipulation	Significantly decreased avoidance	Students	Snake phobia	Valins and Ray (1967)
		Students	Snake phobia	Hart (1966)

may be non-specific. Further controlled study of this method is clearly important.

Finally, two studies in students with snake phobias have shown that cognitive manipulation can effectively decrease avoidance of a phobic stimulus (Table VIc). The subjects studied by Valins and Ray (1967) were given false auditory feedback of their heart sounds while watching slides of snakes. They were led to believe that their heart rates did not increase on seeing the snakes. This procedure led to significantly decreased avoidance of snakes. Hart's (1966) subjects were simply asked to prepare a tape recording supposedly to help teach other students with snake phobias to overcome their fears. This procedure of cognitive rehearsal alone reduced their avoidance of snakes when compared with control procedures. These studies confirm the findings of Leitenberg and co-workers (1968) that cognitive processes may be quite important in desensitization. They open up important areas of research which may broaden our understanding of psychotherapeutic processes.

CONCLUSIONS

The only behavioural technique which has yet had adequate controlled clinical study is the desensitization of phobic disorders. Both psychiatric patients and volunteers with focal problems benefit from the method, but the treatment is often time-consuming and is applicable to only a small minority of patients. Desensitization has been a useful model for the assessment of psychological techniques and valuable clinical knowledge is accumulating from its study. One promising feature is the interchange of ideas between laboratory and clinic. Parallel lines of research of this kind can do much to advance our knowledge of psychological treatment.

SUMMARY

Desensitization is the only behavioural technique that has been subjected to adequate controlled scrutiny. Thirteen of the controlled studies of desensitization in phobic disorders have been in volunteers, mainly students with isolated fears. Nearly all investigations showed desensitization to produce more change in the treated fear than did the corresponding control treatments, which included relaxation, graduated exposure, flooding, visualizing non-phobic scenes, suggestion and hypnosis, insight psychotherapy, drug/placebo, and no treatment or a period on a waiting list. Only live modelling with guided exposure has produced superior results.

There have been four controlled trials of desensitization in psychiatric patients with phobic disorders. Desensitization yielded superior results to other treatments in patients who have circumscribed phobias without severe generalized anxiety, but is not particularly useful in patients with high levels of free-floating anxiety. Less than 2 per cent of psychiatric patients have focal phobias suitable for desensitization, and in this minority desensitization is useful even though it is a lengthy and boring procedure.

Desensitization is an assembly of techniques several of which may contribute to improvement if used alone, but which yield maximum benefit when combined together. Evidence suggests that counterconditioning is involved, and operant conditioning by verbal reinforcement may also be important.

Techniques other than desensitization that have been shown in controlled trials to reduce fear include modelling procedures, flooding (implosion) and cognitive manipulation. These methods may lead to more powerful and rapid methods of ameliorating phobias.

ACKNOWLEDGEMENTS

Dr. J. H. J. Bancroft and Mr. A. Mathews made helpful comments on the manuscript. This work was partly supported by a grant from the Medical Research Council.

REFERENCES

BANDURA, A. (1968). This volume, pp. 207-213.
BANDURA, A., GRUSEC, J. E., and MENLOVE, F. L. (1967). *J. Pers. soc. Psychol.*, **5**, 16-23.
BANDURA, A., and MENLOVE, F. L. (1968). *J. Pers. soc. Psychol.*, **8**, 99-108.
COOKE, G. (1966). *Behav. Res. Ther.*, **4**, 17-24.
COOPER, J. E., GELDER, M. G., and MARKS, I. M. (1965). *Br. med. J.*, **1**, 1222-1225.
DAVISON, G. C. (1968). *J. abnorm. Psychol.*, **73**, 81-99.
DONNER, L. (1968). Unpublished Ph.D. thesis, Rutgers State University.
ERNST, K. (1959). *Monogrn Gesamtgeb. Neurol. Psychiat.*, **85**, Berlin: Springer Verlag.
GEER, J., and TURTELTAUB, A. (1967). *J. Person. soc. Psychol.*, **6**, 327-331.
GELDER, M. G., and MARKS, I. M. (1966). *Br. J. Psychiat.*, **112**, 309-319.
GELDER, M. G., MARKS, I. M., and WOLFF, H. H. (1967). *Br. J. Psychiat.*, **113**, 53-73.
GREER, H. S., and CAWLEY, R. H. (1966). *Aust. med. Assoc.*, Mervyn Archdall med. Monogr., No. 3.
HART, J. D. (1966). Unpublished M.A. thesis, University of Wisconsin.
HOGAN, R. A., and KIRCHNER, J. H. (1967). *J. abnorm. Psychol.*, **72**, 106-109.
KIRCHNER, J. H., and HOGAN, R. A. (1966). *Psychotherapy: Theory, Research and Practice*, **3**, 102-104.
KONDAS, O. (1967). *Behav. Res. Ther.*, **5**, 275-281.
LANG, P. J. (1968). In *Assessment and Status of the Behavior Therapies*, ed. Frank, C. M. New York: McGraw-Hill. In press.
LANG, P. J., LAZOVIK, A. D., and REYNOLDS, D. J. (1965). *J. abnorm. Psychol.*, **70**, 395-402.
LARSEN, S. R. (1965). Unpublished Ph.D. thesis, Stanford University (cited by Lang, 1968).
LAZARUS, A. A. (1961). *J. abnorm. soc. Psychol.*, **63**, 504-510.

LEITENBERG, H., AGRAS, W. S., BARLOW, D. H., and OLIVEAU, D. C. (1968). *J. abnorm. Psychol.*, **73**, in press.

LOMONT, J. F., and EDWARDS, J. E. (1967). *Behav. Res. Ther.*, **5**, 11–25.

MARKS, I. M., and GELDER, M. G. (1965). *Br. J. Psychiat.*, **111**, 561–573.

MARKS, I. M., GELDER, M. G., and EDWARDS, G. (1968). *Br. J. Psychiat.*, in press.

MELAMED, B., and LANG, P. J. (1967). Paper presented to Midwestern Psychological Association Convention, Chicago, May, 1967. (Unpublished.)

MILLER, N. E. (1966). In *Proc. XVIII Int. Congr. Psychol.* (Moscow, 1966). Printed report at Congress, awaiting publication.

MILLER, N. E. (1968). This volume, pp. 294–309.

PAUL, G. L. (1967). *J. consult. Psychol.*, **31**, 333–348.

PAUL, G. L., and SHANNON, D. T. (1966). *J. abnorm. Psychol.*, **71**, 124–135.

RACHMAN, S. (1965). *Behav. Res. Ther.*, **3**, 245–251.

RACHMAN, S. (1966). *Behav. Res. Ther.*, **4**, 1–6.

RITTER, B. (1968). *Behav. Res. Ther.*, **6**, 1–6.

SCHUBOT, E. D. (1966). Unpublished Ph.D. thesis, Stanford University.

VALINS, S., and RAY, A. A. (1967). *J. Pers. soc. Psychol.*, **7**, 345–350.

WOLPIN, M., and RAINES, J. (1966). *Behav. Res. Ther.*, **4**, 25–37.

DISCUSSION

Lazarus: It is interesting that the agoraphobic group in your study did significantly less well than other phobic patients. This may be partly explained by errors in the desensitization procedure. We must be absolutely clear about what we are trying to desensitize the patient to. Agoraphobia is not a homogeneous disorder. Clinically, an agoraphobic individual is a person who is often housebound because of anxiety; she is unable to venture out alone because of the fear of moving about freely. The usual procedure in desensitizing these patients is simply to ask them to imagine themselves venturing, alone, farther and farther away from home. And often, after a considerable expenditure in time and money, the results of this procedure are almost worthless. But if we do a thorough behavioural analysis of the patients (Wolpe, J., and Lazarus, A. A. [1966]. *Behaviour Therapy Techniques: a Guide to the Treatment of Neuroses.* Oxford: Pergamon) we often find that their basic fears are not of open spaces at all, but of many other things—contamination, public scrutiny, social disapproval or sexual promiscuity, for example. The underlying fears in two agoraphobic patients who recently consulted me were that unpleasant endogenous bodily sensations such as stomach cramps, fatigue, or palpitations would lead quickly to their death. After the presenting global phobia has been broken down into these smaller and more specific areas of anxiety, a combined regime of desensitization and *in vivo* excursions may be very successful.

Marks: The phobias of the patients in the studies I described were dissected in this way, but this did not seem to improve the results of therapy.

I know of no controlled trials which show that a series of severely house-bound individuals can be significantly helped by deconditioning. The results in uncontrolled trials are not very convincing because agoraphobia is a fluctuating condition.

Lazarus: The treatment of *severely* incapacitated housebound patients by desensitization alone may give poor results, even if the main phobia is dissected into smaller parts. The point about agoraphobic patients is that they seem to need a broad spectrum of behaviour therapy. Such patients require several techniques in addition to desensitization. We may use assertive training and various modelling and rehearsal procedures to help them, as well as other forms of environmental manipulation, marriage counselling, and family therapy. A most important aspect of our therapy is teaching spouses, parents, siblings and friends to stop reinforcing dependent behaviour. We probably all agree that desensitization alone has poor results in complex phobias.

Hunt: Dr. Marks, would you comment on the control procedures used in comparative studies designed to investigate desensitization? It is some-times difficult to assess how the patient is seeing the control situation (when placebos are used for control groups, for example). Could you also com-ment on the influence on control procedures of such non-specific factors as the enthusiasm of the therapist?

Marks: The value of the control groups in the studies I described varied widely. As regards enthusiasm, in G. L. Paul's study (1967. *J. consult. Psychol.*, **31**, 333-348) the bias of the therapists was in favour of insight psychotherapy, so the results were contrary to the bias. But in several of the other studies bias was in favour of desensitization. Concerning expectations of treatment, in all but one of the studies the subjects in the desensitization groups expected to improve; and some of the waiting-list controls prob-ably expected not to improve until they received treatment. In several of the other studies, the phobics in the control groups did not expect to receive treatment and were not contacted at all; they were then compared to the treated phobics. This is a more satisfactory arrangement and the results in these studies could not have been due to expectations about deferred treatment. Another problem about the results in some of the trials was that desensitization was significantly superior to some, but not all, control procedures. For example in Paul's study (1967, *loc. cit.*), at the two-year follow-up the overall results for the desensitization group were not significantly superior to the results for the placebo group. But the results were significantly better compared with groups who were treated by in-sight psychotherapy, and with untreated control groups. A similar result was noted by P. J. Lang, A. D. Lazovik and D. J. Reynolds (1965. *J. abnorm. Psychol.*, **70**, 395-402). Nevertheless, the overall trend in results is fairly impressive.

Hinde: In treatment by habituation, do all therapists expose their subjects to the stimulus for a standard length of time, or does this period vary with different therapists? Evidence from animal studies (for example, for the chaffinch [*Fringilla coelebs*], see Hinde, R. A. [1960]. *Proc. R. Soc. B.*, **153**, 398-420) shows that the length of time for which an animal is exposed to, say, a frightening stimulus is a really crucial variable in establishing habituation of the species-characteristic fear response. If the periods of exposure are too short the intensity of the animal's response may be increased rather than decreased.

Marks: In most of these studies the period of exposure, which I agree may be crucial, was short—usually only a few seconds and never more than a few minutes. S. Rachman (1966. *Behav. Res. Ther.*, **4**, 1-6) has studied the effect of "flooding" female subjects who had spider phobias. He asked these women to imagine their phobia at maximal intensity for two minutes; they did not improve. But some other studies by R. A. Hogan and J. H. Kirchner (1967. *J. abnorm. Psychol.*, **72**, 106–109) in subjects with rat phobias showed rather different results. These patients continuously visualized themselves in very frightening situations with rats (rats attacking them, gnawing their insides out, and so on) for as long as they could bear it; in practice this was for about 4 minutes. The subjects showed panic during this period, but finally their ability to experience fear was exhausted and after this treatment they were said to avoid rats less, although there was no follow-up in this study. At the moment we do not know the optimum period of exposure. This may be a function of the intensity of the phobia and the anxiety of the subject outside the phobic situation.

Kubie: The conditioning approach to phobias may be too superficial. A phobic patient almost never has a single phobia, even when deconditioning to one object appears to be successful. Although the patient usually presents with one manifest phobia, a whole series of underlying fears exist, and transitions can occur from one form to another. The manifest content of a phobia may alter in the same way as the content of dreams changes. A phobia finally focuses on one particular object, but when one cures that particular fear another one comes to the surface. This is not a basic underlying change but a gradually evolving process. Even apparently simple, single phobias have a multiple pathology and, if we do not take a detailed history from phobic patients before studying the effect of deconditioning, we may be comparing completely different groups. Similarly, one could give one particular medicine to one hundred pyrexic patients and find that it cures some of them, but not others. Such a result is meaningless because we are dealing with many different disease processes. Unless we are treating the same disease process when we apply a constant technique, our scientific evaluations will be invalid.

Marks: We have studied this important problem. Our adult patients with animal phobias (fears of snakes, spiders and dogs for example) had all had their phobia in that form since early childhood; it had run true to type for 20 or 30 years (Marks, I. M., and Gelder, M. G. [1966]. *Am. J. Psychiat.,* **123**, 218–221).

Kubie: It is difficult and may take a long time to determine to what extent a current phobia is a screening process covering underlying masked neurotogenic conflicts and other symptoms.

Marks: We checked the histories of most of these patients with relatives and, as far as we could see, the manifest phobias were not screen phobias. Some of the patients, especially the agoraphobics, may show the changing symptomatology you describe, but this does not happen in patients with more specific phobias.

Gelder: Most clinicians who use behaviour therapy techniques today start with a full psychodynamic and psychiatric evaluation of the patient, his family and his past history. We do not ignore the complexity of the situation, but we may find one symptom that is limiting the patient's life and, if so, we try to deal with this by using behavioural techniques. These techniques do not preclude full assessment of the patient and the whole situation in which he finds himself.

Kubie: I am not against the use of desensitizing and deconditioning techniques. If one can do anything to alleviate the symptoms that disrupt a patient's life one has done something for him. But, as scientists, our task is to study the psychopathology which hides behind the symptom. If one finally breaks through the manifest symptoms in any patient, one invariably finds their multiple symptomatic predecessors. These predecessors have often been repressed and are difficult to uncover because they are loaded with pain. During their discovery further disorganization of the patient's psychological processes often occurs.

Miller: Dr. Marks, how much do such isolated phobias as spider and snake phobias interfere with a person's life? Snakes and spiders can surely be avoided without undue difficulty.

Marks: Almost all the *volunteers* who have been studied have not been seriously hampered by their phobias. But the *patients* were quite severely incapacitated which, of course, was why they came for treatment; their phobia seemed, at least to them, to be their overriding problem. Many of the patients had given up their jobs for fear of encountering the phobic situation on the way to work; or they could not venture out of their homes by themselves and needed help with shopping, taking children to school and so on; and some of these patients also had depressive episodes, and panic attacks even at rest.

Miller: This is important because high motivation promotes cure. An agoraphobic who reaches a psychotherapist is already a highly selected, resistant patient. His friends, people in his social environment, and the patient himself will all have tried to cure him and failed. This is a patient who does not respond to "easy" forms of therapy. Many agoraphobic patients may benefit from attempts at therapy by friends and relations (reassurance or exhortations to pull themselves together) but these patients do not reach the therapist. On the other hand, a patient with a snake phobia may not have been screened so thoroughly for non-responsiveness to rigorous but non-professional attempts at therapy because his phobia has not interfered so extensively with his life.

Sandler: Behaviour therapy and desensitization techniques certainly have a part to play in the spectrum of psychotherapy, but I am uneasy about one aspect of your presentation, Dr. Marks. In the study in which patients were desensitized with tape recordings, with the therapist present only at the beginning and end of the sessions and not during the desensitization process, improvement occurred but was not as great as when the therapist was present throughout. You interpreted these results as showing that the patient-therapist relationship was not the overall determinant in improvement. I question the logic of this interpretation because the relationships of the patient to various factors in his environment are extremely complicated. You do not have a situation in which the therapist is simply present or absent. You may not have allowed for the phantasy about the therapist, and for the patient's relationship to the institution and to the invisible therapist. It is an oversimplification to conclude from these results that the relationship to the therapist plays only a subordinate role. I am sure you are well aware of this and I would be interested to hear your comments.

Marks: We must be clear about what we mean by "relationship". This is not a mystical event but something that happens between patient and therapist. H. Leitenberg, W. S. Agras, D. H. Barlow and D. C. Oliveau (1968. *J. abnorm. Psychol.*, **73**, in press) have clearly shown that in a relationship in which the patient is not expecting to improve, and in which when he says he feels better he is not rewarded but simply told to proceed to the next item, he does significantly worse than when improvement is verbally reinforced. In other words, it is the nature of the transaction between therapist and patient that is vital: it is not merely the presence of the therapist but what he is doing. This continuing reinforcement of what the patient reports is one crucial variable in desensitization. Of course many other variables are also important, and they all interact.

LEARNING TO SOLVE EMOTIONAL PROBLEMS:
A CONTROLLED STUDY OF SHORT-TERM
ANXIETY-PROVOKING PSYCHOTHERAPY

PETER E. SIFNEOS

Department of Psychiatry, Massachusetts General Hospital, and Department of Psychiatry, Harvard Medical School[*]

In this paper, the follow-up observations of a selected group of patients seen in the Psychiatric Clinic of the Massachusetts General Hospital will be presented. All patients received a specialized type of psychotherapy, which we call "anxiety-provoking" (Sifneos, 1966, 1967). Its main features are: brevity, limited goals, and the attempt to increase anxiety in order to bring about these goals.

In our evaluation of this treatment, we have been impressed by the observation that, although most of the patients had only moderate symptomatic relief, they showed a restoration of their self-esteem and described psychotherapy as "a new learning experience".

More recently, 28 patients who received anxiety-provoking psychotherapy were seen, both before and after the therapy, by an independent evaluator. Most of these patients claimed that they had acquired a higher degree of self-understanding, had learned new ways to deal with their emotional problems, and, in addition, had developed new adaptive attitudes in their everyday lives. Most striking of all was the claim made by 19 patients (68 per cent) that they were utilizing what they had learned in therapy in attempts to solve new problems arising in their daily lives.

In choosing patients for treatment, we use the following selection criteria: the history of one meaningful relationship with another person, a circumscribed chief complaint, above-average intelligence, ability to express affect during evaluation interviews, and motivation for psychotherapy. Because it is considered a crucial prognostic criterion, motivation for psychotherapy (Sifneos, 1968) is further assessed as follows: the patient must have realistic expectations of the results of therapy and a willingness to give a truthful account, to participate actively in the treatment and to introspect; curiosity and a willingness to change, explore, and experiment are important dimensions, as well as the realization that the symptoms are

[*] Present address: Department of Psychiatry, Harvard Medical School Beth Israel Hospital, Boston, Massachusetts.

psychological in origin; and, finally, the patient should be willing to make tangible sacrifices.

The technical requirements of this kind of psychotherapy involve face-to-face interviews once a week, each lasting about 45 minutes. The therapist encourages the establishment of rapport, and attempts to create a "therapeutic alliance" early—often during the first treatment session. He utilizes the patient's positive feelings—his expectations that the doctor will help him—explicitly as the foundation for this alliance. By using anxiety-provoking techniques, by concentrating on a circumscribed area of un-resolved emotional conflicts such as are usually associated with the patient's symptoms, by continuing the concentration on these areas and by-passing character traits such as passivity and dependence, the therapist helps the patient to identify an emotional conflict which becomes the problem to be solved. The therapist encourages its solution and in so doing helps the patient to develop new problem-solving techniques which can effectively be utilized by him in the future. The treatment ends early.

CONTEXT OF THE STUDY

In an attempt to evaluate our results more systematically, we have set up a controlled study which is now only partially completed. The number of patients is small. Our findings are therefore preliminary.

When the new patient comes to the clinic he is seen by several inter-viewers, all members of an evaluation team composed of doctors and social workers. The main task of this team is to gain a psychodynamic under-standing of the subject's emotional difficulties and to assess the selection features already mentioned.

During the evaluation interviews the patient is asked to identify an area of emotional difficulty which he considers most important. As a result of this selective process, a compromise may be reached between what the patient chooses as important and what the evaluating interviewer considers to be the problem. Psychotherapy is always presented to the patient as a joint venture for the therapist and himself, in which the patient is to learn problem-solving techniques. If an area of conflict can be agreed upon, treatment will be undertaken.

Those patients who fulfil the selection criteria are seen by two independent evaluators. A psychodynamic formulation about the patient's psycho-pathology, as well as specific predictions about changes to be expected if the patient's emotional conflicts are to be resolved, is made by the evaluators.

The patients are then matched according to age and sex, and are desig-nated alternately as "experimental" and "control", as shown in Table I.

The control patients wait while their experimental counterparts are treated. When the therapy with the experimental group is completed, both groups are re-evaluated, after which the control patients are taken into treatment. Both groups are seen in follow-up interviews by the original evaluators.

TABLE I

DESIGN OF STUDY

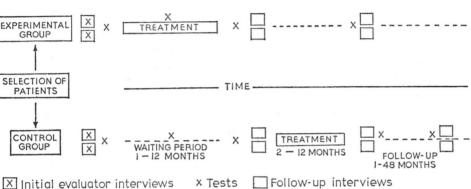

Recently, psychological tests, particularly for attention and memory tasks, were given to patients to try to assess whether improved performance resulted from the treatment. The patients performed experimental tasks while listening to tape-recorded interviews depicting other patients in states of anxiety, depression, aggression and so on. Improved performance in these tests when treated subjects were compared with controls and with an outside sample would suggest that the therapy had lowered the patients' susceptibility to stress and helped to improve tasks involving attention and memory.

These tests, in addition to the Minnesota Multiphasic Personality Inventory tests, are conducted by an independent research group and I am unable at this time to give a final report on their results. Preliminary findings suggest that there will be significant differences between the experimental and the untreated control groups.

RESULTS

Table II shows the status of 35 experimental and 36 control patients. In the control group, after a waiting period of any time from 3 months to 1 year, two control patients were lost. Table III shows the findings on the remaining 34 patients. The following changes were noted: almost half

(45 per cent) showed moderate symptomatic relief and 18 per cent changed their expectations of the results of therapy.

Table IV shows the observations on 14 experimental and 18 control patients. The results for the experimental group and the control group *B* are similar.

TABLE II

DESCRIPTION OF STATUS OF EXPERIMENTAL AND CONTROL PATIENTS

Experimenta	*Number of patients*	*Control*	*Number of patients*
(A) *Waiting period*		(A) *Waiting period*	
		(a) Did not complete waiting period	2 (5)*
None		(b) Completed waiting period but no longer interested in therapy	7 (20)
(B) *Therapy*		(B) *Therapy*	
(a) Lost after completing therapy	14 (40)*	(a) Lost after completing therapy	4 (11)
(b) Still in therapy	7 (20)	(b) Still in therapy	5 (14)
(c) Completed therapy and tests	14 (40)	(c) Completed therapy and tests	18 (50)
Total	35 (100)	Total	36 (100)
(8 male, 27 female)		(6 male, 30 female)	

* Figures in parentheses are percentages (approximate).

The evaluators made psychodynamic formulations and specific predictions as to a minimum needed for assessment of the results of the treatment, as suggested by Malan (1959, 1963). Table V shows the findings on 14 experimental and 13 control patients. No patients in the control group

TABLE III

CONTROL GROUP: 34 PATIENTS SEEN AFTER WAITING PERIOD

	Patient reports	*Evaluator reports*
(1) Improved self-esteem	4 (12)*	4
(2) New adaptive attitudes	2 (6)	2
(3) Change in expectations of results of therapy	6 (18)	6
(4) Self-understanding	2 (6)	2
(5) Moderate symptomatic relief	15 (45)	14
(6) Learned new ways to solve emotional problems	0	0
(7) Use of problem-solving techniques	1 (3)	1
(8) Psychodynamic change	—	0

* Figures in parentheses are percentages (approximate).

showed any psychodynamic changes by the end of the waiting period. After therapy the majority in both groups showed "moderate" or "complete" resolution of their emotional conflicts with evidence of self-understanding, new learning, and the acquisition of problem-solving abilities.

TABLE IV

RESULTS IN EXPERIMENTAL AND CONTROL GROUPS

		Experimental (Number = 14)		Control A* (Number = 18)		Control B† (Number = 18)	
		Patients	Evaluators	Patients	Evaluators	Patients	Evaluators
(1)	Improved self-esteem	13 (93)*	13	2 (11)	2	17 (94)	17
(2)	New adaptive attitudes	13 (93)	13	0	0	17 (94)	17
(3)	Positive feelings for therapist	12 (85)	11			17 (94)	17
(4)	Change in expectations of results of therapy	11 (78)	11	3 (16)	3	15 (83)	15
(5)	Self-understanding	11 (78)	11	0	0	16 (88)	16
(6)	Moderate symptomatic relief	9 (64)	9	7 (39)	8	14 (77)	14
(7)	Learned new ways to solve emotional problems	9 (69)	9	0	0	15 (83)	15
(8)	Use of problem-solving techniques	10 (71)	9	1	1	14 (77)	14
(9)	Need more therapy	3 (21)	1			2 (11)	3

*A: After waiting period but before therapy
†B: After waiting period and psychotherapy.

* Figures in parentheses are percentages (approximate).

At present it is difficult to assess the permanence of these changes. Only long-term follow-up will determine this. We recently mailed questionnaires to 23 patients who had finished psychotherapy between one and a half and three and a half years ago. Four experimental and six control patients answered the questionnaires. Of these, three were controls and one experimental with "moderate" resolution and three were controls with "complete" resolution. They all claimed that they utilized what they had learned during psychotherapy to solve emotional problems arising in their everyday lives. The remaining three were experimental patients who were rated as having "a valuable false solution". Of these, one claimed new learning and problem-solving, but another did not. The last patient answered that he was unable to use what he learned to solve new problems.

TABLE V

(I) PSYCHODYNAMIC FORMULATIONS AND PREDICTIONS IN EXPERIMENTAL
AND CONTROL GROUPS

	Experimental group	Control A*	Control B†
No change	0	13	0
Valueless false solution	1	0	0
Valuable false solution	4	0	2
Moderate resolution	5	0	7
Complete resolution	4	0	4
Total	14	13	13

*A: After waiting period but before therapy.
†B: After waiting period and psychotherapy.

(II) TOTALS: EXPERIMENTAL AND CONTROL GROUP B

Valueless false solution = 1
Valuable false solution = 6
Moderate resolution = 12
Complete resolution = 8
Total = 27

	Valueless false solution	Valuable false solution	Moderate resolution	Complete resolution
Self-understanding	0	2	12	8
New learning	0	5	11	8
Problem-solving	0	2	11	8
Total	1	6	12	8

DISCUSSION

The number of our patients is too small for us to draw unequivocal conclusions. Further, the research design requires tightening. One may also suspect the presence of bias in the patients, as well as in the evaluators, in favour of obtaining good results. Although our evidence is not conclusive in supporting our hypothesis, we are in agreement with Frank (1967) that this cannot be interpreted as proof that our hypothesis is false, only that further studies are needed.

Certain aspects of short-term anxiety-provoking psychotherapy may be peculiar to our clinic, and may play a special role in facilitating the learning process. Our clinic is a division of the Academic Department of Psychiatry of the Massachusetts General Hospital—the largest teaching hospital of the Harvard Medical School. Further, it is staffed primarily by full-time residents in psychiatry, and draws patients from greater Boston—an important education centre in the United States. More than 50 per cent of the population of the clinic is composed of students, and about 60 per cent of the patients have had a college education. The whole atmosphere is permeated with learning.

The extensive preparation of the patient as part of his evaluation has already been described. From the onset of the psychotherapy, therapist and patient must agree on the emotional conflict as a problem which must be defined and solved during the treatment, even though there might be differences of opinion between them, and even though this new problem may differ from the one that had been discussed during the evaluation interviews. As the therapy progresses, both the patient and the therapist may have to change or redefine a problem, depending upon available new information. One should not look upon this too rigidly. One concentrates primarily on the specific area of emotional conflicts (as long as this does not have to do with certain primitive character traits, such as passivity and dependence), and focuses on *how* to go about defining and solving an emotional problem that is important. It should be emphasized also that if the therapist has different views from the patient on the problem to be solved, he should be able to give evidence of this, citing concrete examples from material that has already been discussed during the course of the treatment.

McGuire (1968) has utilized Bruner's (1963, 1966) educational views and has emphasized the importance of structuring and sequencing information during psychotherapy, as major determinants of the patient learning-and-problem-solving strategy of self-study (McGuire and Sifneos, 1967). It should be noted that this differs from the usual expectation of symptom relief, when the patient presents passively a problem which must be solved by someone else (the abscess-surgeon paradigm). In our situation, the patient must learn that his symptom is only the end-result of an emotional conflict which he must define and solve himself, with the help of his therapist. Thus, *there should be motivation for change, not motivation for symptom relief.*

Because so much time has been spent during the evaluation in assessing the strength of character of the patient, the therapist takes it for granted that the patient is able to solve many of his own problems, and that only a few need the therapist's assistance. This attitude facilitates the creation of an atmosphere where learning can take place. The therapist, in his role as teacher, must first take advantage of the patient's wishes to please him. These positive feelings, which predominate at this stage, are utilized to set up a therapeutic alliance. It is of interest that such feelings persist in most of

4*

the patients whom we have seen at follow-up. The examination of the patient's feelings for the therapist is pursued vigorously, explicitly, and early, and this facilitates the clarification of differences between old family conflicts and the actual doctor-patient relationship which Alexander (1963) calls corrective emotional experience.

For the patient to become aware of such feelings—"alive" so to speak—during the interview, is a new experience for him which facilitates the development of the anxiety-provoking stage of psychotherapy, when the patient must be confronted with his anger and fear. Such painful feelings, which are obviously evaded, must also be brought into the open during the interview. The therapist, having established his role as an ally of the patient, is able to stimulate and increase the patient's desire to understand the conflicts underlying his symptoms, as well as to experience the unpleasant affects responsible for them and induced by anxiety-provoking questions of the therapist. As Semrad (1966) emphasizes, keeping the patient's energies within the problem area is the crucial technical procedure in short-term psychotherapy. Despite the awareness of pain, the patient, by identifying with his therapist, gradually becomes convinced that he must face up to his own difficulties. As his curiosity rises, so his motivation increases.

When the problem is finally solved he feels satisfied. On the cognitive level, this satisfaction is similar to that which one experiences when one masters a complicated mathematical problem. Further, the realization of the patient that he has been able to resolve something with which he had previously been struggling unsuccessfully increases his self-esteem. In addition, there is a decrease in tension, resulting from relaxation of the therapist's probing, which reinforces the patient's rewards (Dollard and Miller, 1950). This also contributes to the patient's sense of well-being. Things start falling into shape.

All the ingredients are now present for further trial and error experimentation in new areas of emotional difficulties. If such experiments are successful, it may indicate that new intellectual, emotional, and therapeutic learning has taken place. This may be one reason why insight sometimes follows after, rather than precedes, clinical improvement (Brady, 1967). No wonder, then, that insight becomes a valuable asset to the patient who is willing to utilize it in the future.

The ability to solve new emotional problems long after treatment has terminated constitutes, in our opinion, the most important single evidence that new learning has taken place during psychotherapy, particularly if the patient is able to give us concrete examples of this.

A 19-year-old control patient put it as follows: "It was like not knowing how to read. During the waiting period, I was looking forward to having the doctor read stories to me. Therapy was like learning to read. Now I read my own books." Another young woman had this to say: "One thing that I discovered during the treatment was that I was angry at my father when he remarried. I was completely unaware of this because all my hostility had been directed at my stepmother. When my *fiancé* decided to go to visit his mother in Europe recently, I started to resent her because I thought she had designs on keeping him away from me. I quickly changed and became angry at him, and I thought of breaking off our engagement. I knew that it was the same story with my father all over again. There was also another thing however that I was able to figure out. I realized that I had employed all this anger as a way to evade my sad feelings. My *fiancé* and I had a good talk together, after which I felt better."

It is possible that such statements about new learning may be the result of suggestions from the therapist, whom the patient parrots and imitates, and may be a source of error for research purposes (Levi, 1967). A distinction should be made between imitation and identification. The former involves paying lip-service or repeating the therapist's words without understanding what they mean. Identification, on the other hand, is a dimension of the learning process which involves motivation and selectivity, and encourages independence. It gives the patient an opportunity to make free choices.

From our experience gained from teaching medical students (Sifneos, 1962), we have discovered that identification with their teachers plays an important role in learning. For example, a student may act as a surgeon on a Friday—the last day of his surgical rotation—but on the following Monday, having started ophthalmology, he acts as an eye specialist, only to change into a dermatologist two weeks later. During the last three years of the medical course, lectures and seminars in psychiatry, which were scheduled during the medical rotation, were actively boycotted by the students, although some of them expressed interest in psychiatry. When the same students took their regular psychiatry rotation, they admitted that they remembered very little of what had transpired during any earlier conferences that they had attended. The students would not allow this interference with their identification with the personnel of the medical faculty; thus their refusal to switch identifications proved to be a hindrance to their learning of psychiatry.

The timing of termination is crucial in short-term psychotherapy. It is the patient who usually suggests ending the treatment because the work that had been outlined at the beginning has been accomplished. The difficulties of separation from someone whom the patient likes must be counterbalanced by the pride he feels from the knowledge that the therapist trusts his newly reinforced problem-solving ability.

It appears, then, that this kind of psychotherapy helps to set in motion a process of learning and problem-solving which seems to continue after treatment has finished.

SUMMARY

Preliminary follow-up observations of experimental and control patients who received short-term anxiety-provoking psychotherapy demonstrate that, in the majority, self-esteem is increased and new adaptive attitudes and self-understanding have been developed. Further, it appears that psychodynamic changes during psychotherapy are the result of learning new ways to handle emotional conflicts. A process of learning and problem-solving is set in motion. These methods are utilized to solve new problems after the treatment has finished.

ACKNOWLEDGEMENTS

The author wishes to thank Drs. M. T. McGuire and H. Blane for their innumerable valuable suggestions.

REFERENCES

ALEXANDER, F. (1963). *Am. J. Psychiat.*, **120**, 440–449.

BRADY, J. B. (1967). *Archs gen. Psychiat.*, **16**, 304–310.

BRUNER, J. S. (1963). *On Knowing, Essays for the Left Hand.* Cambridge, Mass.: Harvard University Press.

BRUNER, J. S. (1966). *Toward a Theory of Instruction.* Cambridge, Mass.: Harvard University Press.

DOLLARD, J., and MILLER, N. E. (1950). *Personality and Psychotherapy.* New York: McGraw-Hill.

FRANK, J. (1967). In *Comprehensive Textbook of Psychiatry*, pp. 1305–1310, eds. Freeman, A. M., and Kaplan, H. I. Baltimore, Maryland: Williams and Wilkins.

LEVI, L. (1967). *Forsvarsmedicin*, **3**, Supplement 2, 72–90.

McGUIRE, M. T. (1968). *Am. J. Psychother.* **22**, 218–232.

McGUIRE, M. T., and SIFNEOS, P. E. (1967). *The Teaching of Problem Solving Methods in Psychotherapy.* [Paper presented at the VII International Congress of Psychotherapy, Wiesbaden, Germany, August, 1967.] In press.

MALAN, D. H. (1959). *Br. J. med. Psychol.*, **32**, 86–105.

MALAN, D. H. (1963). *A Study of Brief Psychotherapy.* London: Tavistock.

SEMRAD, E. V. (1966). *Am. J. Psychother.*, **20**, 576–599.

SIFNEOS, P. E. (1962). *Am. J. Psychiat.*, **118**, 832–836.

SIFNEOS, P. E. (1966). *Psychiat. Q.*, **40**, 271–282.

SIFNEOS, P. E. (1967). *Am. J. Psychiat.*, **123**, 1069–1074.

SIFNEOS, P. E. (1968). *Psychiat. Q.*, in press.

DISCUSSION

Miller: Will you clarify your definition of anxiety-provoking psycho-therapy?

Sifneos: Anxiety-provoking therapy describes a technique in which the therapist provokes anxiety by various means; maintaining silence, for example, or raising questions about subjects the patient wants to avoid. Since we do not use reassurance, this form of treatment is quite different from supportive psychotherapy.

Hunt: Do you focus on the problem expressed by the patient?

Sifneos: Yes, but in addition, at a deeper level, we focus on the emotional conflicts underlying the symptoms. This causes anxiety.

Miller: In other words, instead of trying to analyse resistances slowly, you plunge right at them?

Sifneos: To some extent.

Leder: All the patients in your series were intelligent and strongly moti-vated for psychotherapy. Were these the conditions for admission to your trial? Did you accept only those patients who already understood that verbal interaction—talking—was a form of therapy that could help them? Or were there any patients in your series who understood nothing about this form of psychotherapy and thought the cause of their symptoms was physical?

Sifneos: Intelligence and motivation for psychotherapy are two of our selection criteria. Many of the patients are college students, they are psychologically sophisticated, and one might think that they are too healthy to need therapy; Franz Alexander, in discussing a paper of mine (Sifneos, P. E. [1961]. In *Current Psychiatric Therapies*, pp. 168-175. New York: Grune & Stratton), emphasized this. But he was impressed by the suffering and incapacitation of some of these patients when he read their case histories. One does not have to be in a mental hospital to be mentally ill.

Leder: But you are using the evaluation of the patient by the therapist, not the patient's evaluation of himself.

Sifneos: Yes, and obviously this approach involves the re-education of the patient.

Foss: This form of therapy resembles imaginal desensitization except that the steps are not graded. I assume you would conclude that the reason the patients said they had learned new ways of solving problems was because they had achieved some insight. But in the early stages of therapy you actually told them you were going to teach them new ways of solving their problems, and they may have simply repeated this back to you. This worries me.

Sifneos: We are well aware of this problem. The only way of checking our conclusion is to examine the way in which a patient can utilize, in the problems they have to face after therapy has finished, what he or she has learned. This was done in the example I described in my presentation (this volume, pp. 94-95). Another patient put it this way: "I have an internalized dialogue. I ask myself the questions which I imagine my therapist would have asked me. I give my own answers and then I try to apply the results of this exchange to the new situation." This is the kind of evidence we are looking for to confirm that new learning has taken place during psychotherapy.

Marks: What instructions were given to the control patients before they were put on the waiting list? Were they told they would be given treatment in, say, six months, or a year, or any definite time?

Sifneos: We did not specify an exact time, but we reassured them by telling them that it would not be long—a matter of three or four months. Since many clinics in Boston have a waiting list most patients assume that they will have to wait.

Hunt: Could we translate "ways of problem-solving" in your language to "strategies" in mine? Problem-solving implies a method of setting about various problems, whereas strategies embody a more general concept because a different strategy can be developed to deal with each different problem as it arises. Are you in fact teaching your patients new strategies for dealing with their problems?

Sifneos: Yes.

Gelder: I have two questions about the high drop-out of patients in this study. First, was the drop-out rate different in the treatment and control groups and, if so, would this affect the results? And, second, were the dropouts related to the time when anxiety was provoked? Did any patients leave therapy because they could not tolerate the anxiety it induced?

Sifneos: We lost no patients during psychotherapy, so drop-out was not related to the anxiety induced; all the losses occurred after the treatment was finished. Some of these patients were students who graduated and left Boston and were lost in this way.

Frank: I would like to be cynical and suggest that, since you put such emphasis on learning to solve problems, the students who were not successful in this might not want to come back for follow-up. They might think they had flunked the course!

Kubie: One of the difficult problems of follow-up studies on patients with emotional problems is that the subjects who respond to questionnaires or invitations to visit fall into two groups: those who come back because they are angry, and those who come back because they are grateful. Further, subjects who stay away or refuse to reply fall into the same two groups. Some stay away because they are grateful and feel well; some may be anxious about seeing their therapist again, for fear of rekindling the old problems. Therefore it is impossible to evaluate the distribution of success and failure (however we define these) solely by studying those patients who drop out spontaneously and those who readily maintain contact.

Sifneos: Most of the patients who maintained contact with us had been very positive towards their therapists. So they may have been coming back to please the therapist (or us, representing the therapist).

Kubie: What was the sex distribution among therapists and patients?

Sifneos: As one would predict, most of the patients were female and the therapists male.

Kubie: I would not have predicted that. The first time I studied the gender distribution among my patients, 90 per cent of them were men. They have never been predominantly women (Kubie, L. S. [1950]. *Bull. Am. psychoanal. Ass.*, **6**, 6-10).

Malan: In the first twenty patients that we treated with brief psychotherapy (described in Malan, D. H. [1963]. *A Study of Brief Psychotherapy*. London: Tavistock) we found a significant positive correlation between (*a*) the willingness of the patient to return for follow-up, and (*b*) the extent to which the transference had been dealt with in therapy. Further, in these twenty patients, acting-out about follow-up before the patient eventually kept an appointment was an accurate predictor of relapse. These results have probably not been reproduced in the next thirty patients; but this may be because follow-up has been much longer for them, which may lead to a quite different state of affairs.

BASIC ASPECTS OF LEARNING IN THE PSYCHOLOGY AND PSYCHOPATHOLOGY OF THE CHILD

A. Dalla Volta and G. Mansueto Zecca

Institute of Psychology, Faculty of Medicine, University of Genoa

In this short paper we can deal with only a few basic psychological and psychopathological aspects of learning in the child, paying particular attention to some of the characteristics of the thinking processes often neglected in psychology—characteristics whose investigation could help to improve psychotherapeutic techniques. We have intentionally omitted from this presentation the different forms of conditioning; these are discussed elsewhere in this volume as techniques of behaviour therapy rather than as normal processes of development. We are here concerned with teaching the individual child how to learn—so-called "learning to learn"—by means of direct or indirect psychological interventions. Such interventions may increase the efficiency of learning in a child whose learning difficulties are due to mental disturbance.

THE HIERARCHY OF THE LEARNING PROCESSES

Learning by problem-solving

Learning by problem-solving has a central position among the learning processes. This process implies the existence of difficulties which can usually be overcome, provided maladaptive habits have not been formed. Problem-solving involves attempts to deal with almost unperceived frustrations (microfrustrations); the individual concerned has to intervene actively to overcome these obstacles, and usually he succeeds only after trial and error. In other words, he cannot make use of innate patterns of species-specific responses but must develop new responses. The microfrustrations which accompany the processes of learning are therefore a positive factor contributing to the enrichment of behaviour.

Overprotective techniques discourage problem-solving in every field and substantially reduce the capacity for learning. Similarly, oppressive and over-exacting techniques aggravate the frustration of learning beyond the normal tolerance of the individual concerned (Dalla Volta, 1961, 1965).

Motor and perceptual learning. These constitute the primary bases of learning through problem-solving in that they confront the individual, from birth, with the reality of his environment and with elementary and basic problems. The solution of these problems is essential for adjustment within the family and in society. This form of learning is a normal process which takes place in the ordinary contacts of the child with his surroundings. Motor and perceptual learning are intensified when the child is able to enjoy a great variety of stimuli. Psychological counselling may increase contact with these stimuli and thus prepare the way for an adequate development of the symbolic parts of the thinking process.

Symbolic learning. The highest manifestations of mental activity in man are not directly linked to reality. Symbolic learning in its logical form (reasoning) is another important form of learning. Through reasoning, man—withdrawing himself as much as possible from the reality of his environment—can resolve many different sorts of problems, within the limits of his own capacity. The function of reasoning as a voluntary process is to direct and coordinate the total behaviour.

The development of mental life is essentially linked to thinking. Memory establishes lasting connexions with past experience and guarantees continuity in spite of innumerable modifications. The importance of reasoning is bound up with the tools it is able to utilize increasingly with advancing age, namely, the recollection of experiences, of concepts and of symbols. In particular we must consider the acquisition of language, because of its intimate relationship to the development of thinking in the child.

Assessments of mental age from the results of intelligence tests are not, in general, useful in early adolescence (or, in some cases, for a few years afterwards). This is because the yearly increase in points on the intelligence-test scales is so small in adolescence compared with this increase in childhood that one cannot construct corresponding ranks for adolescents. Scales of intelligence for measuring the capacity for the rapid solution of problems would be more connected with the characteristics of the subject's learning processes than with his intelligence quotient. The mature, symbolic form of learning that develops slowly with intense and sustained motivation cannot be assessed by routine intelligence tests. If scales for the extensive measurement of logical symbolic thinking were available we would see a continuous development of learning throughout childhood and adolescence.

Just as motor and perceptual learning precede the major development of symbolic learning, so the latter opens the way for dealing with new problems, which are foreseen but not yet related to the reality of the environment. The most characteristic example of this progression is the solving of technical problems, at all levels. These are invariably preceded in thought by a preparatory, symbolic elaboration. Even the most modest achievements in a child's activities in play have a similar basis. It is an essential task in education for the teacher to understand the slow development of the child's symbolic thinking as expressed in his behaviour, in order to help him to adapt thought to reality as much as possible.

The child is not mature enough for abstract thinking as an aim in itself. He knows phantasy only as pure abstraction. But phantasy, which has an important function in childhood, must be gradually reduced with advancing age.

Learning by imitation. This type of learning is included in the section on learning by problem-solving since current psychological theories connect the two.

Imitation is copying what another person has already learned. When we say that children often imitate other children or adults, we are concerned only with short-term and insignificant behaviour which leaves no permanent trace on the child's personality. A process of problem-solving by trial and error must usually precede imitation if this kind of learning is to have permanent effects.

Imitation as we understand it may be used as a technique of psychotherapy inasmuch as the child invariably tries to copy the behaviour pattern of his peers. His efforts sometimes fail, and similarly he may be unsuccessful in his attempts to imitate adult behaviour. Although it is always easier to solve a problem when there is a pattern to copy, the imitation of what has been learned by others is not always a simple task.

Psychoanalytic theory considers that identification is an unconscious mechanism for learning, but this does not exclude the possibility that the intervention of problem-solving by trial and error may also be important in learning by imitation.

MOTIVATION AND SYMBOLIC THOUGHT

The capacity to think logically develops gradually, as shown by the enrichment of behaviour which occurs as the child grows older. But the most complete manifestations of mental activity belong to later adolescence and more particularly to adulthood, and are perfected throughout the course of life. This gradual progression in the capacity for logical thinking is determined by the interaction of, on the one hand, maturational processes connected with the biological substratum of the organism and, on the other, the processes of learning and the continual accumulation of knowledge.

Before the child reaches maturity, logical thinking, more than any other mental activity, must pass through a long preparatory period. This period may be studied from very different points of view. Jean Piaget (Piaget, 1947; Piaget and Inhelder, 1966) in particular has carefully described the first cognitive structures which, from the second year of life, allow objects to be represented through differentiated meanings—language —and mental images.

The authors, who follow this line, have studied the various forms through which the child's capacity for this type of representation evolves. This point of view, however, is not particularly connected with the motivation which animates these thought processes, and has a fundamental importance in the slow, preparatory development of logical thinking. This will be seen in the examination of characteristic psychopathological behaviours (see pp. 106–109).

We define motivation, from a functional point of view, as the process which initiates a behaviour or activity and maintains and directs it in relation to definite goals. Thus, two fundamental and inseparable aspects of motivation must be distinguished: (a) an energizing aspect, concerned with the mobilization of energy for animating behaviour; this energy must be more or less strong and sustained, depending on the characteristics of the goals; and (b) a directional aspect, concerned with the goal pursued. Motivated activity directed towards solving problems meets frustrating obstacles, but these are normally overcome by trial and error, and this process is an essential determinator of learning.

Motivation in the thought processes conforms to the general pattern of all motivated activities. Internal factors determine the beginning of the thought, the sequences in which it takes place, and the solution of the problem—the goal—which is itself internal. It is therefore necessary to make a choice, which often gives rise to frustration but generally leads to relaxation after the state of tension which accompanies the thinking process has been resolved.

Thinking may need strong and sustained motivation at certain times whereas, at others, the process is broken off and restarted after a period of rest.

MOTIVATION FOR THINKING IN THE CHILD

The child does not apply himself to abstract thinking, since he is not a thinker, and logical reasoning tires him easily. Detachments from his environment because of the problems he is called upon to solve, especially those bound up with systematic learning in school, are frequent, of short duration, and often partial. Even a normal child does not show, in symbolic thinking, the intense sustained motivation that would permit him to resolve his problems in orderly sequences, overcoming the associated obstacles and frustrations.

These observations accord with the child's need for frequent interruptions in the course of his more exacting activities. Thus primary problems alternate with others which could be called "accidental"—that is, they are provoked by insignificant events. When these alternations are expressed in speech, as they often are, they may be classified as "silly speeches" and may worry the child's family. This is particularly so when a child is especially gifted, because the contrast between his "silly" and more logical speech is so marked. Because of this instability and inconstancy, the expressions of thought in the child, even when logical, often show remarkable similarities with psychotic thought patterns which, also, are broken up into characteristic sequences. The difficulty in resuming reasoning after the breaks that are necessary when a child is dealing with a lengthy and difficult internal psychic task also tends to make his logical thinking resemble psychotic thinking. In both, the subject rarely returns to his starting point after a rapid flight of ideas.

During the first years of life the child, in his frequent phantasies, probably learns the schemes that will be operating for many years in the gradual formation of his logical and mature thinking.

From a psychoanalytic standpoint, we could paraphrase these comments and speak of fluctuations involving progression and regression in the thought processes (Klein *et al.*, 1952). However, compensating phantasies in the child may operate side by side with logical thinking, often tending to dominate the latter. This phenomenon can be observed even in normal children, especially when too-strict school discipline forces them to remain sitting at a desk for hours, although this is a completely inefficient way to study. The flights from reality in phantasy already mentioned may take the form of playing games, including sports, and, in older children, sexual day-dreaming.

In short, a fundamentally important function of all the characteristics (already described) of the thinking processes in childhood is that they slow down the development of logical thinking. This protects too-rapid matur-ation of the child's emotional behaviour. In order for thinking to develop it has continually to overcome obstacles, and a long period of prepara-tion is necessary before it can achieve its full potential.

These characteristics of the development of the child's thought, which often seem inconsequential but in fact are essential features, are often neglected by the psychologist. Inadequate intervention often accentuates and makes pathogenic rather than constructive the frustrations that accompany problem-solving.

LANGUAGE AND THINKING

As we have said, the goal of thinking is the solution of problems. This is also the goal of language. During development, through an increasing capacity for conceptualization, thought becomes more widely generalized and therefore richer in meaning. Symbols, consequently, can contribute a notable economy because of their universal validity. Language is funda-mentally a tool for the expression of our thoughts, and thus functions as a means of communication between individuals. But exactly because of this function it is itself influenced and transformed by thinking.

Psychological theory thus confirms the spontaneous technique of many mothers, who follow, correct and direct the language of the child, starting from his simplest expressions and gradually reaching more complex ones. Such interventions, when made in an attractive and natural way (for example, during play) and in new and pleasurable environmental situations, may be of the greatest importance, whether they operate directly, enriching and giving greater mastery of language, or indirectly, providing a more efficient tool for thinking because of greater refinement of language.

A close functional relationship between language and thinking exists in the child, who may express in words (generally while at play) prolonged sequences of thought which evidently refer to present situations. This clearly shows the part which linguistic symbols play in the thinking processes. Moreover, in early childhood, words have not become firmly established in the child's mind as part of his thought processes, and the trying out of new concepts in "thinking by talking aloud" is an important part of the development of his thinking, and one which should not be discouraged by his family. This activity should be controlled only when it is excessive and the soliloquy is connected more to phantasies than to situations in real life. Indeed, in mentally retarded children, thinking by talking aloud may be actively encouraged in the course of play by creating simple problematic situations, and resolving them gradually with the child, using childish phrases.

Although thinking aloud may occur in subsequent years, thinking tends more and more to become an inner process without manifest motor expression. Nonetheless, electromyography has demonstrated the constant participation of peripheral structures in the central activities of thinking.

LEARNING PROBLEMS AND THEIR TREATMENT
IN PSYCHOLOGICAL DISORDERS IN THE CHILD

Study of the motivational aspects of learning in childhood gains support from systematic investigation of the characteristics of the learning process in psychopathological conditions in the child.

Borderline mental deficiency

We are here concerned only with high-grade mental deficiency (intelligence quotient not less than 70), in children without overt signs of brain damage. In these cases, motivation tends to be weak and unsustained; the child is, therefore, easily tired when forced to perform an activity which needs attention and sustained application. The development of language is retarded and we may presume that the balancing action of phantasy is insufficient in consequence; phantasy cannot act adequately to encourage the development of patterns of logical thinking, which therefore remain deficient.

The technique for achieving maximum efficiency and sufficient social adjustment in these children so that they may be as productive as possible is to single out modest goals which are attainable without sustained application or fatigue. Because these goals avoid prolonged frustration, and are to some extent gratifying, they succeed in arousing sufficient interest and, consequently, in increasing the level of the child's motivation.

This type of treatment must be started early, before the frustrations bound up with the excessive demands of the environment (especially in the scholastic field) give rise to the habit of failure, to the point of altering the mechanism of motivation irreversibly. Once this happens it is no longer possible to stimulate interest and achieve social adjustment.

In our present industrial society, the goals that can be attained by high-grade mental defectives are limited. Agricultural work is one of the most suitable jobs for these subjects. And light industry, particularly industry connected with handicrafts, provides an environment in which, at least to some extent, the subject is spared derision and punishment for his mistakes and failures.

Minimal brain damage

Children with minimal brain damage may have interests, even strong ones, but these are of short duration, so that success in the achievement of their goals varies. The movements of progression and regression (Klein et al., 1952) in short periods of time, typical of the normal child, are accentuated so that the instability already described is evident in every behaviour in these abnormal children.

The technique designed to encourage adjustment must be applied early in these subjects also. Although the pre-school-age child may be allowed to gratify his excessive need of movement freely, our technique must include gradually increased disciplinary measures, in order to obtain some control over the movements and needs of these subjects. Short-term goals should be aimed for initially, because it is easier to promote motivation for these; but more long-term aims must be gradually encouraged until, between early and late adolescence, the child's capacity for motivation towards long-term goals is established.

Excessive imposed limitation of the need for movement, particularly in children of school age, may induce intense and prolonged "phantasy-thinking" which tends to become habitual and is a considerable obstacle to scholastic learning.

In contrast to mentally deficient children, whose personalities change very little during their lives, children with minimal brain damage may, after first adolescence, develop various types of psychopathic personality if they have not been suitably treated in infancy or childhood. The technique already described, if applied early, correctly and consistently, generally leads towards normalization. Chlordiazepoxide (Librium) or similar drugs can be very useful in these children, but the best results are obtained with stimulant drugs, such as dexamphetamine. By eliminating hyperkinesis, these drugs improve behaviour at home and in school. For the most satisfactory results, it has been shown experimentally (Dalla Volta, 1958) that cooperation of both family and school is needed.

Neurosis

In neurotics, various emotional processes disturb the functioning of intelligence to varying degrees, although these emotional disturbances are often episodic or at least of short duration. But motivation in neurotic subjects may be very strong in aiming at normal and long-term goals. The spontaneous healing of neurosis in the child is not rare.

The technique for the treatment of neurotic children is strictly individual and must therefore be developed for each particular subject. Nevertheless, the distinguishing characteristic of this treatment is that it should be predominantly indirect in so far as it is often aimed more towards the family and the environment than towards the child. Modifications in the environment (for example the separation of the child from his family in especially serious cases) can reduce or even eliminate neurotic symptoms. Separation therapy is a type of learning therapy, since the new environment into which the child is introduced must be one that favours the breaking of maladaptive habits and the formation of adaptive ones.

Refusal to go to school, a frequent neurotic syndrome in children, is often connected with unfavourable situations that can be easily modified. Psychological treatment of the child (perhaps with the help of such drugs as meprobamate) is of course also necessary to reduce the feelings of insecurity and inferiority that are usually present. To try to compensate for such feelings the child often seeks comfort in day-dreaming.

Nevertheless, one must not remove all obstacles and thus avoid every frustration. The size and extent of the obstacles must be carefully weighed against each individual's capacity for tolerating frustration, and gradually increased in order to increase this capacity, which is always reduced in neurotic subjects.

Schizophrenia

Problems in learning in schizophrenics are particularly difficult to resolve This is partly because of the different meanings given to the term "schizophrenia" in different countries, and partly because we are dealing with chronic syndromes which slowly become modified with time. We follow here the European concept of schizophrenia as a well-defined mental disorder, already well-characterized in the child, although the identity between psychotic syndromes in childhood and psychoses in the adult is not universally accepted.

The frequent alternations of periods of improvement and apparent remission with periods of deterioration make it difficult to give general suggestions for the techniques to be followed in promoting learning in schizophrenic children. The basic treatment usually consists of permitting the relatively free expression of abnormal behaviours, and at the same time entrusting the direction of the treatment to one person in the family who is able to establish a particularly intense relationship with the child. Some instruction in orderliness, to make the subject relatively tolerable in environments outside the family, must be an important part of the treatment.

In the patients we have been able to follow for many years, a strong and anxious concern for schooling is often shown: the children want to study and succeed. In the face of failure they display crises of anxiety. Systematic learning, however, is not possible. The best results have been obtained by integrating attendance at school (with reduced hours and requirements) with private teaching.

Although drugs are always necessary to promote the learning processes in these children, we must not forget that the children are psychotic. We have used reserpine as routine drug therapy for many years, since reserpine and similar drugs may be used safely over long periods. At times of hyperexcitability we have found chlorpromazine useful.

Epilepsy

Our research on epileptic children has been restricted to subjects without pronounced specific symptoms but with behaviour disturbances of various kinds. These included patients with a history of such clinical manifestations as *petit mal*, psychomotor attacks and so on.

Behaviour disorders of every kind occur in epileptic children, and these disorders are often of the same type but more severe than those that occur in neurotic subjects or children with minimal brain damage. Symptoms of the dissociative type are often seen.

Similar behaviour disorders are frequently seen in children with electroencephalographic changes suggesting epilepsy in the absence of its clinical manifestations.

Behaviour disturbances may be aggravated during the initial period of administration of anti-epileptic drugs; similarly, the common anti-epileptic drugs do not always improve disordered behaviour in epileptics.

The technique for encouraging learning in these subjects is not very different from the one we follow for children with minimal brain damage. But one must be aware of the greater aggressiveness and irritability of epileptics, and the sedative effect of anti-epileptic drugs when they are first administered. Later in therapy, drugs which specifically regulate the paroxysmal cerebral activity can aid the learning processes.

Difficulties in learning in epileptics may also be linked with such emotive factors as the child's fear of attacks and awareness of his own slowness and awkwardness. These factors may provoke serious and repeated blocking of motivation for the systematic activities of the school environment.

CONCLUSIONS

This brief outline of alterations in the motivation for learning in children with behaviour disorders of various types shows that in such children there is an aggravation of the usual deficit in strong and sustained motivation, characteristic of thinking in the normal child. This aggravation explains the increased inconsistency and instability of the goals of learning in childhood.

Further research is needed on the motivation of the thinking processes in normal children, as well as in those with behaviour disorders, because this motivation, more than any other criterion, allows us to evaluate the complex areas of symbolic thought and the child's ability to learn and therefore to adjust himself in the family and in his social environment.

The acquisition of knowledge in these areas may provide us with the best guide for psychological interventions in the most common behaviour disorders of childhood, and help us to limit as much as possible the associated formation of maladaptive habits.

REFERENCES

DALLA VOLTA, A. (1958). In *Proc. Int. Congr. appl. Psychol.*, vol. 13, pp. 333–346, ed. Canestrelli, L. (Rome, 1958).
DALLA VOLTA, A. (1961). *Riv. Psicol. norm. patol. appl.*, **55,** 384–405.
DALLA VOLTA, A. (1965). *Annali Neuropsich. Psicoanal.*, **12,** 45–68.
KLEIN, M., HEIMANN, P., ISAACS, S., and RIVIERE, J. (1952). *Developments in Psycho-analysis.* London: Hogarth Press.
PIAGET, J. (1947). *La Psychologie de l'Intelligence.* Paris: Armand Colin. (1959. *The Psychology of Intelligence*, London: Routledge & Kegan Paul).
PIAGET, J., and INHELDER, B. (1966). *La Psychologie de l'Enfant.* Paris: Presses Univer-sitaires de France.

DISCUSSION

Frank: I was interested in your discussion of the relationship of phantasy to the different phases of learning in children. This may be relevant to one of the pitfalls in treating schizophrenics: the use of phantasy in these patients may make them worse because they cannot relate phantasy to reality. In contrast, some learning theorists may have neglected the free flow of phantasy that is encouraged in psychoanalysis. Might this sort of phantasy be a useful preliminary to our behaviour therapy techniques?

Dalla Volta: I purposely stressed that J. Piaget and other psychologists have studied the structure of the learning and thinking processes during normal development but have neglected the phantasies that retard and accelerate these processes. Phantasy is fundamental to the development of learning (and to teaching) in children, particularly because the whole process of learning continues over a long period of time.

Foss: The underlying processes in imaginal desensitization and in phantasy may be related. In imaginal desensitization the patient forms an image of a stimulus that normally induces fear or anxiety; in some kinds of phantasy one may make an image of something which is pleasant and reinforcing, or which leads to reinforcement. So when we look at the consequences of behaviour therapy, we should consider what might happen when reinforcement is given without the behaviour that usually leads up to it. This would be the behavioural equivalent of phantasy. Do you agree with this, Professor Frank?

Frank: We seem to be using the word "phantasy" to refer to several types of mental processes that cannot be sharply distinguished but lie on a continuum. At one extreme are structured, goal-directed efforts to solve problems, rehearse behaviours or evoke specific images, as in a behaviour desensitization hierarchy; at the other are unstructured reveries, indulged in for their own sake or intruding involuntarily into awareness, pleasant or disturbing, coloured by wishes and fears, some of whose sources may lie outside consciousness. I was speaking more of the latter end of the continuum, that is, of the type of phantasy that is so much a part of psychoanalytic theory and practice, and a much broader concept than the imaginal phantasies you have described, which are at the other end of the continuum. Whether the term "phantasy" should be used for that type of process is questionable. In any case, the childhood phantasies described by Professor Dalla Volta seem to lie somewhere in between these two extremes.

Foss: But would you agree that the goal-directed phantasies you described involve imagined reinforcement?

Frank: Yes. But in psychoanalytic phantasies thoughts are allowed to come into consciousness as they will. We do not yet understand the value of this, but it may loosen up or rearrange the thought processes in some way.

Hunt: The first type of process could be described as the rehearsal of a behaviour in imagination, in anticipation of the future.

Frank: The therapeutic value of that sort of phantasy is easy to understand. My question concerned phantasy that is not closely related to reality or even to consciousness; the sort of process that occurs in dreams and during the free associations fostered by the psychoanalytic situation, when environmental stimuli are sharply reduced and the patient often has his eyes shut. Are we overlooking the value of this "phantasy through free association" in our behavioural models?

Lazarus: The use of unstructured phantasy is not necessarily inconsistent with a behavioural model. In the classical desensitization process an item— for example a picture of the patient's mother calling him stupid—is presented to the patient and he is asked to indicate distress by signalling. After the completion of various scenes, there is an "inquiry phase", but by then much spontaneous phantasy is lost. The more modern behavioural techniques involve examining various associations during and immediately after each desensitization item. Although this may temporarily disrupt relaxation, it often has distinct advantages. For example, a patient may respond to this immediate inquiry with a related or (apparently) unrelated phantasy; and thus new dimensions for more basic desensitization may be discovered.

Sifneos: Phantasies, as visualized images, can be used creatively and serve a double role. An artist in analysis (Sifneos, P. E. [1964]. *Revue fr. Psychoanal.* **28**, 591-608) used his phantasies both as a source of inspiration for his painting and for some of the detail in the actual composition of the pictures. He obtained gratification because he felt that he did not have to be inspired from the outside world—his phantasies to him were a sort of "built-in" inspiration. And there was additional gratification when his pictures sold well and he was rewarded financially. In other words, phantasies can be used both as a source of creativity and as a tool in the execution of an artistic work.

Professor Dalla Volta, you have implied that phantasy is a tool for learning in normal children. A young child, when left alone for a long period of time, may select and pursue certain phantasies which both facilitate learning and serve as a defence against loneliness. Is that correct?

Dalla Volta: This is the function of phantasy in normal young children.

Sifneos: Don't you think that phantasy serves this purpose in adult life?

Dalla Volta: I do not know. In children, but not in adults, the pattern of logical thinking resembles the formation of phantasies, which may explain the different functions of phantasies in childhood and adult life.

Miller: Problem-solving sometimes occurs through a phantasy of wishful thinking. For example, a man held up in a traffic jam of cars all waiting to make a left-hand turn (in a country where cars drive on the right) may wish that he were driving on the opposite side of the street. A phantasy of how easy it would be for him to turn off the main road if he were in fact driving on the opposite side and in the opposite direction may stimulate him to figure out how to do this: he must drive straight ahead (past the left turn) in the right-hand lane, and then turn round and come back on the other side of the road where it is easy to make the turn (Dollard, J., and Miller, N. E. [1950]. In *Personality and Psychotherapy*, p. 112 and Fig. 8. New York: McGraw-Hill). In this form of problem-solving, wishful thinking about the goal leads to constructive thinking about how to achieve it and, ultimately, to success in achieving it. Since phantasy can have various functions one cannot state dogmatically that it is always useful or always harmful.

PSYCHOTHERAPY: PLACEBO EFFECT AND/OR LEARNING?

STEFAN LEDER

Psychoneurological Institute, Warsaw

EVERYONE appears to know what the word psychotherapy means, yet so many definitions exist that different authors may mean quite different things by this term. Nevertheless, most definitions (Wolberg, 1954) appear to have a common denominator—the assumption that "influencing" plays a crucial role in the psychotherapeutic process. But, as influencing means to induce, promote and direct modifications of attitudes, cognitive schemata and overt behaviour by communication signals addressed primarily to the emotions, it is probably a universal and phylogenetically old mode of interaction in human society, based on passive learning from persons who are symbols of leadership and authority.

Hence the questions arise: is there anything specific and characteristic in the process of influencing in psychotherapy? Do different ways of exerting influence exist in this form of treatment? And in what ways are influencing and learning related? The answers must probably take account of such factors as the goals of the influencing, the structure of the situation in which it is put into effect, and the expectations and roles of the participants in the interaction.

The aim of influencing in psychotherapeutic interactions is usually described as being primarily to relieve the symptoms of emotional disturbance and inadequate reactions. The structure of the setting is determined by many sociocultural factors and the means by which influencing occurs are predominantly verbal signals. The expectations and roles of the participants are determined by the fact that therapists are in a position of leadership because of their professional knowledge and experience, and are perceived as symbols of power and wisdom. Patients on the other hand seek help because of their inability to help themselves in their state of anxiety, discomfort and distress. As this state seems to be characterized by the patients having inadequate cognitive schemata, either because they lack information cues or because they perceive them in a distorted fashion, the therapist may be the decisive source of important signals for the patient.

These factors thus create the conditions of psychotherapeutic interaction at the initial stage, when influencing the patient means satisfying his most important present needs. These needs are for cognitive information and emotional contact and they may be optimally met by the therapist in an active and directive manner through his use of several verbal and non-verbal techniques of communication. These may include reassurance, explanation, advice, persuasion, suggestion, acceptance, sympathy, understanding, and enabling the patient to unburden himself of emotionally loaded content-material. The achievement of this goal (meeting the needs of the patient) is facilitated (a) if the therapist has, and acts within, a conceptual framework, because this enables him to feel more secure (and thus superior) to the patient in their interaction; and (b) if the patient is in an optimum state of expectancy and faith.

At this stage of the psychotherapeutic process the patient is storing up important cognitive and emotional cues in the framework of a therapeutic relationship, which is a specific form of human interaction and differs from others in which influence is exerted. This type of learning (that is, passive learning) occurs not only in and through the relationship with the therapist, but also in many social settings in which other non-specific factors contribute to the satisfaction of the patient's need for emotional support and cognitive information. The result of this whole process is a growing feeling of security and consequent reduction of symptoms. This probably constitutes the so-called placebo effect. But it is this that enables the patient to continue the learning process—to learn how to learn—and creates the conditions for the next step. This is experimentation with new behaviours in different social settings, where the developing interactions can modify the patterns of behaviour and types of reaction of all participants.

This assumption may be illustrated from one of our own studies (Leder *et al.*, 1967), on the mechanisms of the placebo effect in patients with neurotic disorders who stayed in our in-patient clinic, that is, within a therapeutic community, for eight weeks. They were treated by a combination of individual and group psychotherapy, consisting of twice-weekly individual and twice-weekly group therapy sessions, a once-weekly ward-group meeting, occupational and sociotherapy, gymnastic-training therapy, and, in selected cases, drugs; (no drugs were given before the third week). The evolution of symptoms is shown graphically in Fig. 1. Most of the reduction in symptoms in these patients occurred spectacularly during the first two weeks, and especially during the first week, after admission. During the third week no further significant improvement was seen, and during the week before discharge (the seventh week) there was even some reappearance of symptoms. We therefore conclude that after two weeks of intensive complex treatment in a clinical setting an important modification of the emotional state and cognitive schemata has been brought about in these patients; usually there was no definite alteration in their attitudes and strategies for solving life problems and conflicts, and therefore no far-reaching integration of new feeling, thinking and behaviour, at this stage.

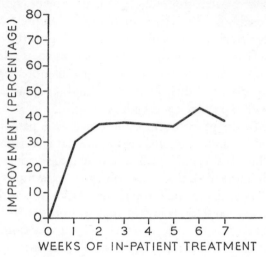

FIG. 1. Symptomatic change (symptom reduction shown as a percentage) in a group of neurotic patients during in-patient treatment.

The formulation of the need to achieve these and other goals is the result of the sophistication of the therapists, who express these goals in different terms according to the different theoretical constructs they follow. By imposing their own goals and interpretation of the causes of the disturbances and of effective mechanisms of the psychotherapeutic process, the therapists continue to influence patients in the next stage of the interaction, but now use modified techniques for the achievement of their aims. These aims usually include some kind of personality change in the patient (that is, a modification of many aspects of his functioning) which necessitates a change on a higher level of integration. The patient must not only learn new attitudes—he must also unlearn some of his former inadequate cognitive schemata, motivations, strategies for solving conflicts, and patterns of interpersonal interaction. These changes cannot be satisfactorily brought about by passive learning, but require active relearning, a primarily social process.

Active relearning consists of exploratory activity such as labelling facts and dilemmas, formulating alternative hypotheses and solutions and experimenting with their verification, and drawing conclusions from rewarding and punishing experiences. It is a process combining emotionally loaded behaviour with cognitive analysis. The promotion of a process of this nature demands not only the operation of more specific, modified and elaborate therapeutic techniques than in the preceding phase of passive learning, but also their operation in differently structured settings. Hence the need to complement the patient-therapist relationship with group therapies and intermediary treatment settings such as the day hospital. In these settings relearning is enhanced and facilitated by the different structures and situations, and by the need to play many different roles, especially if the development of new cognitive schemata and behaviour through imitation, analysis and probing proves rewarding for the patient and his surroundings. Consequently, the therapist is usually much less directive and active in his interaction with the patient than in the first phase of treatment. His role is more that of a catalyst of the activity of the patient than a source of information; conversely, the role and importance of other members of the group, and of the social surroundings, increase. These changes also imply that the verbal techniques of the therapeutic interaction play a relatively smaller role than before and they usually consist more of interpretation and other techniques stimulating the problem-solving activity of the patient.

Thus the way of influencing the patient has changed its character—the cues are primarily addressed to the intellect, while emotional support and contact are gradually withdrawn. As a result of these mechanisms the patient learns greater awareness, understanding and control. This process is known as "acquiring insight". The content of insight is differently described according to the different concepts of the therapists, but all agree that it interprets the causal relationship between psychosocial factors and the inadequate or maladaptive functioning of the patient. In most cases insight seems to facilitate reorientation, that is, the development of new attitudes, which is probably the crucial variable for the outcome of the psychotherapy.

The results of one of our studies (Leder, Kluczek and Kuliszkiewicz, 1969) seem to confirm the scheme outlined above. In this investigation we evaluated the results of treatment in our in-patient clinic, comparing the assessments on initial referment, discharge, and at a follow-up examination carried out at an average of 21 months after discharge. We used four measures in this study: physical and mental symptoms, insight, reorientation, and social changes. The assessment, judged by two independent

raters, was based on the results of clinical examination and the answers of
the patients to 48 closed and 3 open questions. Fig. 2 shows the results for
the whole group of 148 patients. Symptom reduction shows a greater

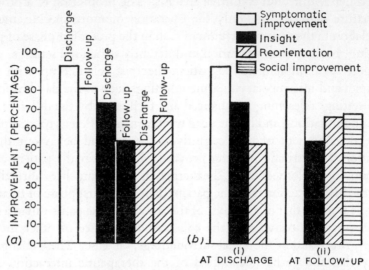

FIG. 2. Results of treatment at discharge and follow-up (148 patients).
Results drawn to show (a) change in each measure compared at discharge
and follow-up; and (b) comparison of changes in all measures at the stage at
which the evaluation was made—(i) on discharge and (ii) at follow-up.

improvement than the other measures on discharge as well as at the follow-
up assessment. Symptom reduction and insight tend to decrease and
reorientation to increase with the passage of time.

We next compared the results of treatment in two groups of patients,

TABLE I

RESULTS OF TREATMENT AT DISCHARGE AND FOLLOW-UP

Group	Number of patients	Stage of evaluation	Symptomatic improvement: marked or moderate	Insight: present	Reorientation: marked	Social improvement: marked
P	72	Discharge	66 (91·6)★	55 (76·3)	36 (50)	
		Follow-up	59 (81·9)	44 (61·1)	50 (69·4)	54 (75)
P+F	76	Discharge	72 (94·3)	54 (71)	41 (53·9)	
		Follow-up	61 (80·2)	36 (47·3)	50 (65·7)	47 (61·8)
All patients	148	Discharge	138 (93·2)	109 (73·6)	77 (52)	
		Follow-up	120 (81)	80 (54·0)	100 (67·4)	101 (68·2)

★Figures in parentheses are percentages.

those given complex therapy (as above) without drugs (group P) and those who were also treated with drugs (group $P+F$) (Table I). The results on all measures do not differ significantly in the two groups, even though the group $P+F$ consisted of patients with a much poorer prognosis, assessed according to many variables. The relationships between the measures and their trend towards improvement or deterioration between consecutive evaluations are also identical in both groups.

In the third step of our analysis we divided the whole population studied into four subgroups according to the degree of symptom improvement at the follow-up assessment, as compared with the initial assessment of symptoms (Fig. 3). The results differ significantly ($P< 0·02$) for the measures of insight, reorientation and social changes between the group with marked symptomatic improvement and the groups with moderate reduction or no reduction of symptoms. All the measures described are of course much higher in the group with marked symptomatic improvement (Fig. 3a).

What is our explanation of the results in this and in our first study ? We assume that the reduction of symptoms begins immediately after the patient has been admitted to the clinic, when he at once feels more secure as a result of the influence of various non-specific factors in the therapeutic setting which meet his needs for emotional contact and cognitive information. This stage of passive learning merges with the next stage, which begins in the second or third week of his stay, when the systematic planned application of therapeutic influencing in terms of a conceptual framework promotes active relearning and some of its results, namely insight and reorientation. Thus evaluation on discharge assesses changes which result from both passive learning—the placebo effect—and active relearning.

The decrement in the rate of symptom reduction at the time of the follow-up evaluation may partly be the result both of the action of new traumatic factors in the life situation of the patient and of a reduction of the placebo effect. In the patients in whom the rate of symptom reduction has fallen at follow-up the placebo effect may have been primarily responsible for the initial improvement; the higher rate of symptom reduction compared with the other indices is certainly evidence in favour of the existence of such a group of patients. The decrease in insight may result from the cessation of the systematic learning experience in a therapeutic setting with clearly defined goals, and may also be promoted by the reappearance of symptoms. The relationship between insight and the other measures seems to confirm that insight may be helpful but is not essential for the development of reorientation. The increase in the measure of reorientation at the

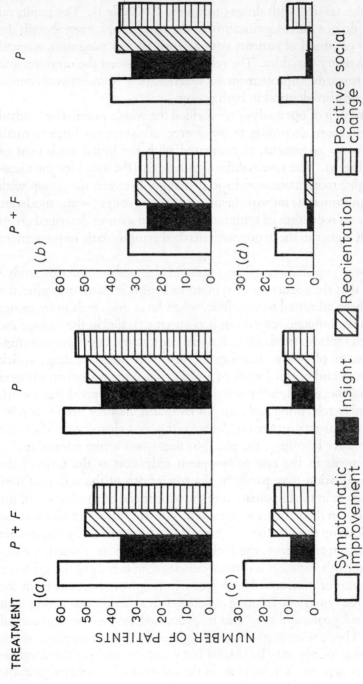

FIG. 3. Assessment of improvement in the measures described, for 148 patients divided into four subgroups according to the extent, at follow-up, of their symptomatic change after treatment. Symptomatic change for patients in the subgroups ranges from (a): marked and moderate symptomatic improvement (grouped together), through (b): marked symptomatic improvement; (c): moderate symptomatic improvement to (d): no significant symptomatic improvement or change. P: patients treated with complex therapy alone; P+F: patients treated with complex therapy plus drugs.

follow-up assessment seems to be the result of rewarding social experimentation with new attitudes and modes of behaviour which were developed during the stay at the clinic and promoted after discharge through symptomatic improvement, increased insight or positive social changes, separately or in combination.   The direction of the changes in two of the criteria— symptom reduction and reorientation—in the time between discharge and follow-up in the group showing marked improvement is such that these two measures have tended to approximate by the time of the follow-up evaluation. We also found a low rate of reorientation in the groups with moderate improvement or no change. These two findings tend to refute the hypothesis that there is no causal relationship between symptom reduction and reorientation, and that the evolution of both is caused by a change in some hypothetical variable responsible for the development and course of neurotic disorders. If reorientation is thus the most important variable for lasting symptomatic improvement after the placebo effect has disappeared, this would also explain the lack of differences between the patients treated with and without drugs. As drugs were used in such a way as to underline their auxiliary role, they probably facilitated reorientation by reducing symptoms in patients with a poorer prognosis, thus equalizing the chances for change in both groups—those with marked and those with little improvement.

   In conclusion, I must stress that the border between the two stages of the psychotherapeutic process is quite fluid, and that both passive learning and active relearning often occur simultaneously, while the therapeutic techniques aimed at promoting them also merge into each other. The decisive factors seem to be the formulation of the goals by the therapist, the techniques he uses, and the setting in which the processes operate. Probably most therapists agree that the first stage of the process, in which the most important present needs of the patient are met through his passive learning, is necessary in the treatment of all persons who seek help and support. On the other hand, most schools of thought agree that the further stage of active relearning plays a decisive role only in the long-lasting successful treatment of neurotic disorders. The personalities of the patients, with their different capacities for learning and relearning, may in fact be a more important variable than the clinical diagnosis; unfortunately, we still cannot evaluate and predict these capacities. Another important problem is the character of the neural mechanisms which operate in the learning process and whether they differ in passive and active learning. An impressive amount of evidence points to the crucial role of classical and instrumental conditioning, but I am inclined to believe that some central mediating process of "programming" is also an important mechanism in the functioning of human consciousness and plays a major role in active learning.

SUMMARY

The implications of the definitions of psychotherapy for the understanding of the nature of the psychotherapeutic process are discussed. The characteristics of interpersonal relationships, reciprocal interaction and influencing in psychotherapeutic settings are reviewed. On the basis of the literature and some of our own studies the following hypothesis is formulated: in the first stage of the psychotherapeutic process, satisfaction of the needs of emotionally distressed patients for emotional contact and cognitive information constitutes the "placebo effect" and is a passive form of learning. In the second stage of the process, the achievement of other goals, formulated by the therapist, presumes that modifications in the patient occur on a more integrated level; this may be achieved through the operation of different therapeutic techniques. The process thus becomes one of active relearning. It is concluded that the psychotherapeutic process is one of passive learning and active relearning, determined by different goals, characterized by different stages and levels, and put into effect by different techniques.

ACKNOWLEDGEMENTS

The ideas presented in this paper are the result of studies and discussions by the Research Team of the Psychotherapeutic Unit of our Institute, and have been largely inspired and stimulated by the work of many authors, especially Frank (1961), Goldstein (1962), Cameron and Magaret (1951), Dollard and Miller (1950), Wolberg (1966), Marmor (1966), Mjasichev (1960), Knobloch (1967), Corsini (1955), Breger and McGaugh (1965), Frank and Rosenthal (1956), and others.

REFERENCES

BREGER, L., and McGAUGH, J. L. (1965). *Psychol. Bull.*, **63**, 338–358.
CAMERON, N. A., and MAGARET, A. (1951). *Behaviour Pathology.* Boston: Houghton Mifflin.
CORSINI, R. J. (1955). *J. abnorm. soc. Psychol.*, **15**, 406–411.
DOLLARD, J., and MILLER, N. E. (1950). *Personality and Psychotherapy.* New York: McGraw-Hill.
FRANK, J. D. (1961). In *Contemporary Psychotherapies*, ed. Stein, M. Chicago: The Free Press of Glencoe.
FRANK, J. D., and ROSENTHAL, D. (1956). *Psychol. Bull.*, **53**, 294–302.
GOLDSTEIN, A. P. (1962). *Therapist-Patient Expectancies in Psychotherapy.* Oxford: Pergamon Press.
KNOBLOCH, F. (1967). In *Gruppenpsychotherapie in Klinik und Praxis*, ed. Höck, K. Jena: Fischer.
LEDER, S., BEKKAREWICZ, B., BIGO, B., and KOSEWSKA, A. (1967). Unpublished.

LEDER, S., KLUCZEK, M., and KULISZKIEWICZ, D. (1969). *Psychiatria, Neurol., Neurochir.,* *Warsaw,* in press.
MARMOR, J. (1966). In *Psychoneurosis and Schizophrenia,* ed. Usdin, G. Philadelphia: Lippincott.
MJASICHEV, W. N. (1960). *Licznost i Newrozy.* Leningrad: Lenunivizdat.
WOLBERG, L. R. (1954). *The Techniques of Psychotherapy.* New York: Grune & Stratton.
WOLBERG, L. R. (1966). *Psychotherapy and the Behavioral Sciences.* New York: Grune & Stratton.

DISCUSSION

Krasner: How do you measure insight in the second (active) part of your therapy? And can you distinguish insight from learning the theoretical concepts of the therapist? Insight and agreement with the therapist may represent the same thing.

Leder: What most therapists mean by insight is that the patient understands what we think about him; in other words, he has learned our lesson. And therapists from different schools mean different things by insight. But what is important is not the exact meaning of the word insight, but that the patient is enabled to accept that there is a causal relationship between his inadequate functioning and sociopsychological factors in his past life. If he can appreciate this then he has some insight, even if all he has learned is that his symptoms are not somatic in origin but based on emotional disturbances. This is only minimal insight but it is something because it may reduce the emotional distress of the patient.

Krasner: You have shown that a patient who achieves insight does not necessarily also make helpful social changes in his life. How are insight and social change related, and to which would you give priority if you had to select one or the other?

Leder: In most cases there seems to be a correlation between insight and social changes although, if I had to make a choice, I would choose the latter. At follow-up, 21 months after treatment has been discontinued, the patient may have no insight but still be symptomatically improved and coping better with life. Insight is undoubtedly helpful for some patients (and for all therapists) but although it may be important for the patient to understand the cause of his symptoms this may not be the most decisive factor in his improvement. Some patients improve without gaining any insight. Although we try to give insight, our main goal is to help the patient to function better in society.

Sifneos: Might not insight follow rather than precede learning? And could the relearning process you describe be followed by insight which has meaning for both therapist and patient?

Leder: Insight may only appear some time after improved social functioning, but it is more likely that it is the admission of insight by the patient, not the insight itself, that is delayed. A man may fear that if he accepts the explanations given by the therapist they will oppose his own system of values, or motivation, or attitude; he resists insight. We may suspect that a patient has achieved some insight during therapy, but he cannot verbalize this until later when he is less under the therapist's influence. In my view insight follows learning, but at the same time it facilitates further learning, relearning, and experimenting with new and more appropriate solutions, thus improving the social functioning of the patient.

Sifneos: I am intrigued by what you call passive learning, in other words, symptomatic improvement. In our series, 40 per cent of the control group (patients waiting for treatment) showed symptomatic improvement. Does simply telling a patient that he will be getting therapy produce this effect?

Leder: The waiting list has the same function as the first stage of treatment I described: both induce passive learning. During the first week that a patient is admitted to our clinic the regime is the same as in subsequent weeks and the patient develops no cognitive awareness of his problems. He exists in a setting where there are no night nurses or ward rounds, where no one asks him how he is feeling, and where the other patients may be dancing when he feels he is dying. Nonetheless, even in this first week, marked symptom reduction occurs because most patients perceive the situation as a therapeutic environment in which somebody is trying to help and understand them. And a patient who is put on a waiting list for future treatment may feel the same sort of security with an associated reduction in symptoms.

Marks: The role of insight may also depend on the particular psychological problem involved. In certain circumstances insight may precede and in other circumstances it may follow change. J. H. Cantela (1965. *Behav. Res. Ther.*, **3**, 59-64) made an interesting observation on the desensitization of phobic subjects (not patients) in whom insight followed symptomatic improvement. These subjects did not discuss their problems during the desensitization sessions but, as the phobia improved, they started to make remarks showing insight about the way in which the phobia had originally been acquired. In these cases insight seemed to be secondary to the symptomatic improvement induced by another process. In other circumstances, of course, insight may play a more primary role.

Frank: Dr. Leder, I am basically in agreement with your formulation of the two stages of treatment except that your concept of passive learning m ay be misleading. In drug trials, for example, it is not until after the first two weeks, when the almost invariable placebo effect of any new drug has been allowed for, that its real action can be assessed. I do not know whether your initial improvement really is passive learning or if it is just a non-specific response (which does not involve learning) to cues in the situation. The patients may not be learning anything new, but showing already existing patterns of behaviour in response to cues that would ordinarily elicit relief.

Miller: In other words, it is the performance of behaviour already learned, rather than new learning, that is induced in the first phase of therapy by the novel therapeutic situation.

Frank: The novelty itself may be the relevant factor. K. Rickels, C. Baumm and K. Fales (1964. In *Neuro-psychopharmacology*, vol. 3, pp. 80-84, eds. Bradley, P. B., Flügel, F., and Hoch, P. H. Amsterdam: Elsevier Publishing Company) have shown that when a placebo pill is switched to one differing in colour, shape and size, psychiatric out-patients respond with a new surge of improvement. Learning may not be the right word for what is happening in Dr. Leder's first stage of treatment.

Bandura: Initial changes in a patient's condition may primarily reflect a change in the environmental demands imposed upon him rather than true passive learning. When a patient first enters treatment people in his immediate environment are likely to display a more tolerant attitude toward his deviant behaviour, and this has a stress-reducing effect.

Frank: One factor that may have contributed to this early relief of symptoms (before the start of specific therapy) in Dr. Leder's, and others', patients is an artificial increase in symptoms before the patient comes to the clinic because of his apprehension about what he will find there. We have certainly suspected this in many of our patients.

Lazarus: We have been assuming that a placebo is medically and psychologically inert and yet produces a favourable response in the patient. Are there any published data on patients who respond adversely to placebos? I would surmise that if such negative placebo reactors exist they might get worse rather than better during the initial phase of therapy, or while waiting to start treatment, because their expectations are not realized at this stage. My own clinical data show that some patients do react adversely to the initial stages of behaviour therapy. Dr. Leder, have you observed any particular types of personality or individuals with particular behaviour patterns who show an adverse response in the first stage of treatment?

Leder: Some of the confusion about passive learning and placebo responses may depend on definitions. A patient asks the therapist (or magician or anyone) for help. He may be asking for emotional contact and cognitive

5*

information, or simply for something to take, but he feels ill and he expects help. Thus, whatever the therapist does will probably be helpful because of the patient's expectation. If the therapist gives the patient two apparently different sorts of chemically inert pills—yellow and red, say,—he will either be told or he will assume that the pills of one colour (probably the red) will be better for him. So the patient is already a passive recipient of an information cue that has changed his concept of what will happen to him. He has taken in some new information and if this helps him he will store it. Passive learning is a conscious intake and storage of information which results in changes in the recipient's emotional state. This is quite different from the learning associated with insight and consequent problem-solving.

Lazarus: But are there patients who, presumably full of hope, take the red pill and come back complaining of side effects and saying that they feel much worse?

Leder: In our study we gave no drugs for the first two weeks in hospital, and then the patients were randomly allocated into two groups, receiving either placebo for one week followed by an active drug for one week, or *vice versa.* Some patients became more ill on both placebo and active drug during the first two weeks on drugs in hospital. My clinical impression is that this small group of patients felt that nothing could help them, and until their attitude about this changed they were indeed negative placebo reactors. But if their attitude could be changed they were then able to respond positively to both placebo and active drug. These observations suggest that there are no negative or positive placebo reactors but that the same personality can react differently to placebos in different situations.

Krasner: There may be no placebo reactors *per se*, because the concept implies that the placebo reaction is primarily a function of the reactor. But it may be the conditions of the experiment rather than the characteristics of the subject that give rise to placebo effects. If we knew enough about the variables of this type of situation we might find that most individuals are potential placebo reactors.

Frank: L. D. Hankoff, N. Freedman and D. M. Engelhardt (1958. *Am. J. Psychiat.*, **115**, 549-550) have shown that placebo reactors probably do exist *per se*. These workers studied placebo reactions in a group of chronic schizophrenics discharged from hospital, and found that those who had reacted to a placebo had a significantly better chance of remaining out of hospital than those who had not. At this level of massive distrust, the ability to respond to a placebo may be a sign of being able to trust someone —that is, the doctor. Nonetheless, I agree with you, Professor Krasner, that environmental factors are more important than personal factors in the

development of placebo reactions. Some of the patients who react negatively to a pill may do so because they were expecting psychotherapy and
a pill was not what they wanted; they might have responded well to
psychotherapy.

Krasner: I would hypothesize that the important variable in the chronic
schizophrenics who respond to a placebo may simply be the ability to
respond at all. In other words, the behavioural characteristic that these
patients have in common is their ability to respond to any kind of environmental stimulus.

Bandura: What is meant by "specific" and "non-specific" influences?
Does non-specific refer to unknown, non-contingent or ubiquitous
influences? Dr. Leder, how are you using these terms?

Leder: I regard therapy as specific when the therapist finds a framework
in which he can systematically use his particular therapeutic techniques to
deal not only with the symptoms known to the patient but also with some
of his underlying problems. The therapist devises a way of changing the
patient's total behaviour. Non-specific factors include emotional contact, information and placebos, all of which meet the needs of the patient in distress.

Bandura: Experiences within the patient-therapist relationship are often
treated as non-specific influences, and contrasted with various learning
procedures that are referred to as specific. It is difficult to conceive of non-
specific influences in psychotherapeutic interchanges because each expression by the patient elicits some type of response from the therapist, and this
response inevitably creates a specific reinforcement contingency that has a
specific effect on the patient's behaviour. Recent studies of psychotherapeutic processes conducted within a framework of social learning (Ayllon,
T., and Michael, J. [1959]. *J. exp. Analysis Behav.*, **2**, 323-334; Harris, F. R.,
Wolf, M. M., and Baer, D. M. [1964]. *Young Children*, **20**, 8-17; Lovaas,
O. I., Freitag, G., Gold, V. J., and Kassorla, I. C. [1965]. *J. exp. Child
Psychol.*, **2**, 67-84) show that therapists' interpersonal responses have
specific and predictable effects on their clients' behaviour. Grossly deviant
behaviour in both children and adults—including self-destructiveness,
hypochondriacal and delusional preoccupations, infantile and regressive
response patterns, extreme withdrawal, chronic anorexia, psychogenic
seizures, psychotic tendencies and countless other disorders of long-standing
—have been successfully eliminated, and reinstated and removed for a
second time, by altering the amount of interest, attention and solicitous
concern displayed by the therapist toward the deviant activities. Relationship experiences may thus be potentially both helpful and harmful. Therapists who provide relationship experiences through indiscriminate positive

interest may be creating social reinforcement contingencies that have injurious consequences. This consideration suggests that therapeutic practices must be evaluated carefully in terms of their specific effects upon clients.

Miller: I agree with this. Your comments on non-specific influences remind me of the classical Hawthorne effect (Roethlisberger, F. J., and Dickson, W. S. [1939]. *Management and the Worker*, Cambridge, Mass.: Harvard University Press). Industrial psychologists at the Hawthorne Plant studied the effect on work output of a number of changes in work conditions. They found that almost any change in any direction—for example either an increase or a decrease in illumination—increased work output; their results clearly were not specific to the direction of the change. The authors concluded that any change made the workers feel the management was taking an interest in their welfare and that this feeling made them work harder. Similarly with placebo effects: the specificity may be to the feelings of the patient about his relationship with the doctor who is giving him a pill and trying to help him, rather than to the pill itself.

Marks: L. C. Park and L. Covi (1965. *Archs gen. Psychiat.*, **12**, 336-345) describe a study on the effect of placebos on subjects who were told that they were being given a sugar pill, with the comments: "Do you know what a sugar pill is? A sugar pill is a pill with no medicine in it at all. I think this pill will help you as it has helped so many others." Several subjects immediately felt better and assumed that the pills did contain an active ingredient. This "placebo improvement" was not likely to have been due to the subjects' expectations of improvement, but was presumably caused by their feeling that something was being done for them.

Foss: This material suggests a research method. In behaviour therapy reinforcement is usually given immediately after (that is, contingent on) the desired behaviour. But if the reinforcement were given non-contingently to the behaviour one is trying to modify, although it might not modify the behaviour it might modify the patient's attitude to the physician. This approach might enable one to study the distinction between the effects of the transference situation and the specific effect of therapy on symptoms.

Bandura: An interesting methodology has been devised to assesss the contribution of relationship factors and specific reinforcement contingencies to the changes observed in psychotherapy. In this procedure the therapist maintains the same relationship with his client but systematically alters the reinforcement from a response-contingent to a time-contingent basis. For example, in his treatment of mute autistic children, O. I. Lovaas (1966. In *Early Childhood Autism*, pp. 115-144, ed. Wing, J. K. Oxford:

Pergamon) demonstrated that, when rewards are made conditional on progress in the learning of language, autistic children display a uniformly high level of verbal responsiveness; by contrast, when the same rewards are given, but after a certain amount of time has elapsed so that the rewards are independent of the children's behaviour, there is a marked drop in the amount and accuracy of verbalization. These behavioural changes are particularly striking considering that the interpersonal relationship factors and the total amount of extrinsic reward remain the same in all phases of treatment; the only factor that is changed is the arrangement of the reinforcement contingencies.

Foss: But does the transference remain strong and positive and constant throughout these changes?

Bandura: Presumably the therapist maintains the same level of social responsiveness during the time-contingent and response-contingent phases of treatment. This could be easily checked by observers who rate the amount and type of social reinforcement exhibited by the therapists while they are applying the different contingency systems.

Marks: C. B. Truax and R. R. Carkhuff (1967. *Toward Effective Counselling and Psychotherapy.* Chicago: Aldine) have shown, in Rogerian psychotherapy, that certain behaviours in the therapist are followed by changes in the patient and others are not. Improvement does not depend on the therapeutic relationship as such but on what is done with it.

Lazarus: The active ingredients in most forms of therapy are thought to be a function of specific techniques applied within a warm, empathic patient-therapist relationship. Initially it was assumed that the patient-therapist interactions were more important than any specific technique, but recently the pendulum has swung in favour of the influence of techniques. Support for the importance of technique variables is to be found in the success of such mechanistic procedures as self-administered desensitization, often using computers, tape recorders and other devices for automated desensitization (Migler, B., and Wolpe, J. [1967]. *Behav. Res. Ther.,* **5,** 133-135). With some of these techniques the therapist is almost completely excluded. Reversal studies also have shown the importance of specific methods. For example B. M. Hart and co-workers (1965. In *Case Studies in Behaviour Modification,* pp. 320-325, eds. Ullmann, L. P., and Krasner, L. New York: Holt, Rinehart & Winston), treating a four-year-old child who cried excessively, noted that when the crying was ignored it became almost non-existent within ten days. At this stage crying behaviour was again rewarded (with attention from the child's teachers) and it increased rapidly. Finally, the therapeutic contingencies (namely ignoring the child when he cried) were reapplied and the crying again decreased, and remained thereafter at a very low level. But this view can be carried too far. Some neophytes to behaviour therapy may give too much attention to very careful and precise strategies at the expense of compassion and sincerity; such behaviourists tend to lose their patients (at least out-patients) prematurely. In the early stages of therapy, acceptance of and empathy with the patient is usually needed. Although this may initially augment the patterns one wishes eventually to discourage, it enables the therapist to establish rapport with the patient.

Krasner: Are you suggesting that the therapist, in the early stages of treatment, is defining a category of behaviour (which may be as simple as responsiveness to the therapist's presence) that he will subsequently reward? I agree with this idea, but would not call such therapy non-contingent.

Lazarus: There is probably nothing that is, literally, non-contingent because some behaviour is always present.

Miller: Another related problem is the satiation effect: an animal or child howls because it is hungry, it stops howling and goes to sleep when one feeds it; this could be either because one is relieving its hunger or rewarding it for howling. We do not know the conditions that determine which of these two opposite effects is the stronger.

Hunt: Response bias can be a problem in the evaluation of the results of psychotherapy. Dr. Leder, your study was so cognitively oriented that this bias might have affected the results. Your patients were taught (and learned) a "proper" vocabulary for dealing with their behaviour problems; to put it bluntly, they learned to say the "right" things about themselves. To what extent did you allow for the effect of this response bias on your results?

Leder: At follow-up these patients were assessed not only on self-report but also on objective changes in their lives. They answered 48 closed-ended questions relating to different areas of activity—their ability to cope with work, family life, sex, interpersonal relationships, symptoms and so on; and three open-ended questions in which they could describe their problems and ways of dealing with them. They were also examined clinically by two independent doctors and in some cases we had additional information from the relatives. Does that answer your question?

Hunt: Only partly. Any assessment depending on self-report—and self-report may enter into a clinical examination—contains the possibility that a response bias learned by the patient during therapy is present. This is a common problem and difficult to deal with.

Leder: But if the patient tells us that, since treatment, he has become able to work or has divorced his wife, he is reporting objective results. The only subjective element is the assessment of, say, his divorce as a positive or negative social change; this type of change had to be assessed individually for each patient. I see the problem but know of no other way in which we could have dealt with it.

Hunt: L. Hersher (1956. Ph.D. dissertation, University of Chicago, unpublished) used the Minnesota Multiphase Personality Inventory as one criterion of improvement after Rogerian therapy. He found that the cases that had improved had developed personality profiles quite similar to those obtained by middle-class subjects who were deliberately attempting to create a favourable impression. Hersher's patients tended to report that all was well by saying good things about themselves, their immediate environment and the world in general. I am not implying that this was the only change in your patients, but I have doubts about what saying good things about oneself, or responding favourably to questionnaires or tests, really means. I wonder what the effects of such unduly favourable self-descriptions will be on the patient's subsequent behaviour. A response bias can itself produce changes in behaviour and some of your good results may have been produced by self-instruction due to the cognitive nature of the therapy. This might be important in mediating generalization of the improvement.

Miller: Do you mean that the patient has been taught to say what the therapist wants him to say, but that this in itself may be therapeutic?

Hunt: Yes. And this seems to be a two-step process: first, the patient learns what to say about himself and, second, saying it changes his behaviour.

Krasner: The early studies on verbal conditioning (Krasner, L. [1962]. In *Research in Psychotherapy*, vol. 2, eds. Strupp, H. H., and Luborsky, L. Washington, D. C.: American Psychological Association), which demonstrated the ease with which positive self-reference and positive emotional words could be conditioned, support this notion.

Miller: It is important to be sure that non-directive therapy really is non-directive. For example, E. J. Murray (1956. *Psychol. Monogr.*, **70**, 1–32) in a study of a case treated with "non-directive Rogerian therapy" found that the therapist tacitly approved certain categories of statements and disapproved others, with the result that the frequency of the former increased and that of the latter decreased, as would be expected from learning theory.

Frank: It is relevant to these comments that every school of therapy maintains that insight and recovery are related. But the real issue may be

that any conceptual structure is better than none rather than that one particular conceptual structure is the best. We may simply be giving people
tools to help them organize their lives, and it is having the means to do this
which reduces their anxiety and increases their ability to cope.

Sandler: Concerning insight, Freud always maintained that patients
recover through insight followed by working through. The Freudian
concept of working through is similar to many of the current desensitizing
procedures. But analysis of children has shown that if they come for
further analysis in adult life, any insight gained has usually been lost
(unpublished data from the Hampstead Child-Therapy Clinic; see also
Freud's classical description of "Little Hans" (Freud, S. [1909]. *Analyse
der Phobie eines Fünfjährigen Knaben*. [1955. *Analysis of a Phobia in a
Five-Year-Old Boy*, in *Standard Edition*, vol. 10, ed. Strachey, J.
London: Hogarth Press]). Probably some hindrance to development
is removed at the time of the child's treatment so that he can make the
next step in development, and reintegrate at a different level. But what has
been learned in the way of insight tends to disappear, or to be no longer
accessible, later. This phenomenon can also be seen in patients who have a
second analysis; when insights remain they are often used defensively.
Thus, although the patients have recovered a full understanding of the
internal and external situations, this only exceptionally remains with them
without modification. Enduring insight does not appear to be a precondi-
tion for recovery even in therapies that lean heavily on the giving of
insight.

I would like to make a general observation about the pitfalls of using
"average" responses in groups of patients. This approach is, of course, valid
in some ways: if we say that a given proportion of patients on a waiting list
for psychotherapy improved before the treatment started, we can form an
idea of what happens to some of the patients. But we may be actually
missing some of the different factors involved (a placebo effect, for example)
and obscuring what happens in the individual patient. A patient who would
be lost in such studies as Dr. Leder's is the man who, out of a sense of guilt,
has to get worse every time he begins to feel better. There are many
patients with such a "negative therapeutic reaction", one of the most
potent resistances to recovery. We lose these subgroups if we only consider
percentages and averages.

Miller: The most useful type of therapist and form of therapy for a
patient may depend greatly on early childhood influences which, in turn,
depend on culture. T. A. Lambo (1964, personal communication), the
Professor of Psychiatry and Vice-Chancellor at Ibadan University, Nigeria,

suggested that the leaders of some of the emerging African nations became intensely anxious because, in industrializing and modernizing their countries, they had to break taboos that had been established in early childhood. The African leaders understood rationally the need to break these taboos but developed severe anxiety when they broke them. Many of these men can be helped more by witch doctors than by psychiatrists, which may be because in the early childhood of these leaders the witch doctors had great prestige; they were the people who originally laid down the taboos so they probably have a special advantage in removing them.

Lebedev: Taboo is not the sole explanation for the development of mental disorders in these cases. In many changing societies individuals who take responsible positions suddenly find themselves in a most difficult situation. They have to learn new facts, a new way of life and bear heavy responsibilities for which their previous experiences have not prepared them. This in itself is a stress situation and is an important factor in the development of mental disorders.

Carstairs: Professor Miller, your hypothesis that the witch doctor is successful with these African patients because he is in touch with the repressive agencies that have contributed to the neuroses may need qualifying. I have seen a similar phenomenon in Ceylon, but I do not agree with your explanation. On the outskirts of Colombo there is a Buddhist temple where the intelligentsia go for the treatment of neurosis. In Colombo, where there is a good medical school, psychiatrists and a mental hospital, it is not socially acceptable to be treated at the hospital, or even at the psychiatric centre, but it *is* socially acceptable to go to the Buddhist temple. The patients at this temple are not particularly devout Buddhists and their neuroses have not been determined by failure to observe Buddhist injunctions or lead the Buddhist life. But the priests there, who use many different techniques, share with their patients the same concepts of illness. And this brings us back to the discussion of insight. Cynics have said that when psychiatrists describe a patient as having achieved insight, this simply means that the patient now agrees with the therapist. It is certainly true that the most potent therapeutic interactions occur when therapist and patient share a common concept of the disease process. A few generations later this shared concept may be seen to have been a shared delusion, but at the time it is a potent delusion. Socially shared opinions are social realities; and this holds for the treatment situation.

BEHAVIOUR THERAPY AND GRADED STRUCTURE

ARNOLD A. LAZARUS

*Department of Behavioral Science, Temple University School of Medicine, Philadelphia,
Pennsylvania*

INTEREST in modifying maladaptive patterns of behaviour has continued
to burgeon over the past decade. Therapeutic methods based on learning
principles have, with varying degrees of success, been applied to clinical
problems ranging from tics to schizophrenia. Conditioning procedures have
successfully shaped, modified, controlled, eliminated and reinstated
innumerable response patterns. A brief perusal of Barnard and Orlando's
(1967) recent bibliography on behaviour modification will underscore the
vast array of deviant behaviours that have been successfully treated by
clinical methods "conceived of within some learning theory framework".

The evidence leaves no doubt that conditioning processes have succeeded
in bringing many deviant and disruptive behaviours under appropriate
stimulus control. Nevertheless, from a scientific standpoint, claims for the
overall therapeutic superiority of conditioning techniques rest almost
entirely on uncontrolled clinical impressions and anecdotal evidence. Of
course it would be foolhardy to bypass or ignore the fact that ingenious
operant training schedules have significantly altered the manifestations of
many psychotic processes (Ayllon and Azrin, 1965) and have offered hope
for mentally retarded subjects, autistic children, and other patients with
formerly intractable disorders (Bijou and Sloane, 1966; Orlando and
Bijou, 1960; Lovaas, 1966; Lovaas, Schaeffer and Simmons, 1965). Encouraging results have been obtained with aversion therapy in certain
sexual deviations (Feldman, 1966; Marks and Gelder, 1967). Conditioning
methods appear to be the treatment of choice in various cases of enuresis
(Lovibond, 1964), encopresis (Neale, 1963), writer's cramp (Beech, 1960;
Liversedge and Sylvester, 1960), and stuttering (Goldiamond, 1965). It
seems that most phobic patients may usually anticipate immediate and
lasting relief after desensitization therapy (Lang, Lazovik and Reynolds,
1965; Paul, 1966).

Thus, therapists who remain impervious to the clinical applications of
learning principles and conditioning techniques undoubtedly decrease the

probability of their own success in certain instances. Yet the overall therapeutic value and reliance that may be placed upon specific learning principles and conditioning techniques in, say, an adult out-patient setting, pose interesting practical and theoretical problems.

CONDITIONING TECHNIQUES IN CLINICAL PRACTICE

Wolpe (1958, 1964) argues that behaviour therapy is as effective with complex neurotic syndromes as with unitary or monosymptomatic disorders. According to his system, adequate identification of the problem can usually reduce vague and complex (even existential) complaints to discrete areas of anxiety and hypersensitivity. Thus, a person who complains of amorphous misery and unhappiness coupled with chronic anxiety and guilt, will often, after a systematic behaviour analysis, be found to have several phobias and undue sensitivities. For example, he may have extreme fears of injury and death, plus exaggerated concern about criticism and rejection. He may also be inhibited and unassertive in crucial areas, perhaps sexually deficient, and somewhat ruminative. His guilts, miseries, and other presenting complaints are then presumed to emanate from, and rest upon, these specific areas of unadaptive behaviour, each being a consequence of inimical learning.

Treatment for a case like this would probably call for a barrage of systematic desensitization, assertive training, and graded sexual assignments. Some adjunctive techniques like faradic stimulation with or without "thought stopping", and perhaps inhalations of carbon dioxide–oxygen mixtures may also be applied. At the end of some thirty sessions, one would expect the patient to be significantly less hypersensitive, less inhibited, and more adequate sexually. These gains may have generalized to the presenting complaints. Thus, *joie de vivre* may exist in place of misery and despair, while anxiety and guilt may have given way to self-assertion, confidence, and a fitting indifference to disapproval from meaningless individuals.

There is persuasive clinical evidence (but as yet no controlled data) that the above approach, which I have termed "broad spectrum behaviour therapy" (Lazarus, 1966), achieves more favourable outcomes than nondirective and interpretative procedures (Wolpe and Lazarus, 1966). However, the routine application of relaxation-training, desensitization, aversion-relief and so forth, is extremely tedious and laborious. Further, these procedures alone are often therapeutically insufficient. Many cases require didactic intervention and emotional re-education over and above specific conditioning procedures. In addition to (and often in place of) laboratory-derived techniques like systematic desensitization, I tend to focus considerable attention on relationship variables; the patient's system of values, attitudes and beliefs; aspects of high and low self-esteem; practical considerations such as leisure and recreational pursuits; dyadic transactions; and various group processes. One may practise this "technical eclecticism" (Lazarus, 1967) within a learning theory framework, but one's allegiance to laboratory studies and laboratory procedures may become extremely tenuous when attempting to decrease the vagaries of emotional suffering, as opposed to eliminating avoidance responses evoked by harmless snakes and spiders. I must plead guilty to the charge of having functioned as a clinician who employed broad spectrum behaviour therapy, and then attributed his results solely to strict behaviour therapy (see, for example, Lazarus, 1963).

CLINICAL AND ACADEMIC ASPECTS OF THE DESENSITIZATION PROCESS

While controlled studies (for example, Davison, 1966, 1968) have indicated that systematic desensitization is indeed a counterconditioning process and not merely a product of suggestion, relaxation, attention and so forth, it is not so easy to distil the essence of broad spectrum behaviour therapy. In clinical practice, one is more or less honour-bound not to withhold any seemingly effective manoeuvre, but "in the interests of science" it may often be considered ethical to do so. An effective clinician endeavours to maximize the placebo effect, and, if necessary, combines suggestion with the full force of his own personality to influence the patient to engage in less deviant and more constructive behaviours. Desensitization techniques are therefore customarily preceded by a brief explanation of the theoretical rationale and an exposition of the impressive experimental and clinical findings.

Despite some experimental indications that subjects who were desensitized without the usual verbal preliminaries responded favourably to desensitization procedures (Lazarus, 1960), I have remained curious about the impact of the typical pre-desensitization address. Consequently, eight clinical cases who needed desensitization therapy were recently treated without the usual elaborate explanations. Many of the patients questioned the value of desensitization, complaining that they felt foolish and could not see how the procedure would help them. After ten sessions, four patients reported a diminution of anxiety, while the remaining four patients showed no improvement.

Of six similar subjects who were given an elaborate pre-treatment address about the value of desensitization, the results after ten sessions were that only one case derived no apparent benefit. While these clinical impressions are riddled with bias and error of every conceivable kind, they are in line with the findings of a more rigorous experimental study by Leitenberg and co-workers (1968), who concluded that "the effects of systematic desensitization cannot be attributed solely to the variables of a graded hierarchy plus relaxation."

If the variables responsible for the efficacy of specific counterconditioning techniques such as desensitization are more numerous and complex than experimental analogues would suggest, it is obvious that when combinations of techniques are applied to intricate clinical problems, academic and experimental precision becomes a catchword rather than a reality. As Rosenthal's (1966) important account of experimenter and observer effects seems to indicate, the relationship between experimenter and subject is always genuinely dyadic—even when subhuman organisms are involved. Those experimentalists and academics drawn to behaviour therapy by its apparent simplicity should be reminded that "to select desensitization hierarchies, to find effective reinforcers, or to isolate target behaviours requires not only technical skill but the qualities of a *Menschenkenner* who is sensitive to human behaviour beyond his academic knowledge" (Kanfer and Phillips, 1966, p. 126).

THE EFFECTS OF GRADED STRUCTURE

When results run counter to an experimenter's expectations, it is possible that forces more powerful than experimenter bias may be responsible. Descriptively, one of the most obvious features of behaviour therapy is that it is highly structured. As Goldstein, Heller and Sechrest (1966, p. 246) point out, the favourable results reported for desensitization therapy are probably a partial reflection of "the advantages that may be obtained by providing better structure". Behaviour therapists usually give their patients a concise outline of the way in which their problems were acquired, how they are probably being maintained, and how learning principles can be used to replace their maladaptive habits with propitious responses. Clear-cut methods and objectives are established. "Your fear of ambulances and hospitals will require desensitization; your social reticence seems to call for role-playing and behaviour rehearsal; and your poor study habits will probably respond best to some form of operant retraining." The patient can appraise his own progress step by step. He is an active participant. He helps to construct anxiety hierarchies; he learns to relax more deeply; he imagines and rehearses numerous scenes and events; and he applies a self-administered schedule of rewards (for example, "Each hour of study entitles you to smoke two cigarettes."). My findings are very much in keeping with Phillips and Wiener's (1966) evidence that a prearranged time limit adds to the overall effectiveness of these procedures.

On the assumption that graded structure as such would play a very *minor* role in accounting for behaviour change, I carried out the following experiment:

Thirty adult patients with chronic behaviour problems were selected for three forms of treatment limited to twelve sessions each. Acutely anxious cases requiring immediate or very brief management were excluded, as were persons who seemed extremely agitated or depressed, or persons diagnosed as psychotic and therefore in need of drugs or hospitalization.

The selected patients were assigned to one of three treatment groups: (*a*) time-limited behaviour therapy; (*b*) time-limited psychotherapy; and (*c*) time-limited graded structure.

The sample consisted of 6 white South African patients and 24 white American patients. They were reasonably homogeneous regarding socio-economic background and education; 23 of the 30 patients were university graduates. As with most time-limited programmes, no patients dropped out of treatment.

Each patient received an intake interview, as well as the Willoughby Questionnaire (1934) and a sentence completion test. Before the next interview, the patient was required to take home and complete a detailed life-history form and a fear check-list (Wolpe and Lazarus, 1966). Cases received either behaviour therapy, or psychotherapy, or graded structure in that order. Thus every third case received graded structure. I must repeat that the therapist (myself) expected both the psychotherapy and the graded-structure procedures to yield results significantly inferior to those obtained with behaviour therapy. Tables I and II indicate that the three groups were comparable for sex, age, and pre-therapy Willoughby scores.

The patients undergoing *behaviour therapy* were told that they would have twelve treatment sessions with me and they would be referred elsewhere if they felt they needed further therapy after this. These patients received whatever combination of behavioural methods their problems seemed to warrant—usually desensitization, assertive training, general advice, and some form of behaviour rehearsal.

The patients receiving *psychotherapy* were similarly informed that I would be available for twelve sessions only and that additional therapy, if necessary, would be available elsewhere. The psychotherapy patients were encouraged to seek the historical origins of their current problems. Various areas of conflict were explored and the symbolic significance of their symptoms was examined.

TABLE I

SEX AND AGE DIFFERENCES OF PATIENTS IN TRIAL

Treatment	Number	Males	Females	Mean age (years)	Range (years)
Behaviour therapy	10	4	6	32·8	19–43
Psychotherapy	10	3	7	38·5	24–51
Graded structure	10	4	6	31·0	21–48

TABLE II

PRE-THERAPY AND POST-THERAPY WILLOUGHBY SCORES

Treatment	Pre-therapy Willoughby scores		Post-therapy Willoughby scores	
	Means	Range	Means	Range
Behaviour therapy	54·7	26–62	22·7	14–42
Psychotherapy	58·9	22–68	38·5	16–60
Graded structure	52·3	30–71	29·0	12–62

The *graded structure* procedure was conducted as follows. Patients were informed that therapy would be limited to twelve sessions, after which referrals would be arranged if necessary. They were told that therapy would be divided up into four equal but separate phases. Each phase would consist of three sessions. Graduation from one phase to another would be contingent on passing a brief test in each instance.

Phase one consisted of three sessions devoted to an examination of the patient's salient life experiences. He was asked to divide his life up into five-year blocks and to enumerate the most significant events during each five-year interval. Most patients had no difficulty in supplying three hours' worth of information but, in a few cases, the therapist had to elicit more information by questioning the patient in some detail. The first quiz, which was administered at the beginning of the fourth session, required the patient to elucidate possible connexions between seemingly disparate events in his history. After some ten or fifteen minutes, he was congratulated on having qualified for phase two.

Phase two consisted of questioning and discussing the meaning and significance of some of the seemingly more interesting responses to the incomplete sentence test. This continued until the beginning of the seventh session when the patient was given a second quiz in which he was asked to describe possible links between particular sentence completions and past experiences. He would then be allowed to enter phase three. Patients were led to believe that they could fail these tests and thus retard their progress. They were thus given a sense of achievement when passing from one phase to another.

Phase three consisted of reading aloud and discussing the concept of self-actualization (Maslow, 1954). This material was selected for its interest value and clinical relevance. Yet it is not a form of bibliotherapy in the sense of offering specific help or in terms of numerous do-it-yourself tips that can be gleaned from texts on behaviour therapy. At the start of the tenth interview, the patient was "tested" to determine whether he had "qualified" for the fourth and final phase.

The three interviews comprising *phase four* were divided up into *visual training*, *auditory training*, and *awareness training*. Patients were told that these exercises would strengthen and enhance their concentration, self-confidence, alertness and serenity. During *visual training*, patients were required to picture the numbers 1 to 10 on a blackboard and to erase them mentally. The image was repeated using different coloured chalk. They were given the homework assignment of subjectively picturing pleasant scenery at least twenty times a day at suitable moments. *Auditory training* had patients imagining various sounds: their favourite singer or other music, ocean surf, church bells, wind in trees and so on. The homework assignment was to try to combine pleasant auditory and visual associations. Thus, a person who found the image of a sandy beach especially pleasing was to picture the scene vividly while also "hearing" the breakers. Finally, *awareness training* had the patient examine, in ardent detail, any common object—a cigarette, a pen, a sheet of paper, anything available. He was asked to note how many new details emerged and how even a common object acquires new dimensions when closely studied. The patient was asked to concentrate intensely in turn upon the size, shape, weight, texture, temperature and colour of the object. At the end of the session he was advised to study deliberately, and thus increase his awareness of, everyday events. "Pay particular attention to what people say, how they say it, to their movements, attire, gait, and posture. Make notes about all new observations."

A post-treatment assessment interview was held approximately a week later. Thus, patients in all treatment conditions were seen a total of 14 times (one intake interview, twelve treatment sessions, and one post-treatment assessment).

Assessment of results

The assessment interview began with the patient completing a post-therapy Willoughby test. He was then asked, in general terms, whether he had derived benefit from therapy and whether he would rate himself as "improved". All cases answered in the affirmative, which yielded a 100 per cent "improvement rate", if one pays attention to these kinds of data! When patients were specifically asked whether the actual problems which led them to seek therapy had been resolved, many subjective improvements turned out to be objective failures. When further evidence of actual behaviour change was required, the "spectacular" 100 per cent improvement rate was reduced to a meagre 50 per cent, as shown in Table III. Similarly, all groups showed improvement according to the post-therapy Willoughby

TABLE III

THERAPEUTIC OUTCOMES BASED ON EVIDENCE OF
CONSTRUCTIVE BEHAVIOUR CHANGE

Treatment	Cases showing behaviour change
Behaviour therapy	7 out of 10
Psychotherapy	2 out of 10
Graded structure	6 out of 10

scores, but no significant differences among groups were found although the behaviour therapy procedure appeared to yield better results than the two other forms of treatment.

Because I do not wish to be the sort of clinician who draws far-reaching conclusions from shaky data, I shall make only one tentative inference, which is more in the nature of posing one speculative question: why did six out of ten relatively sophisticated people who underwent the fatuous graded structure procedure (originally conceived as a pseudotherapy control) report constructive gains which rivalled the clearly-focused, problem-centred, behaviour therapy approach?

In addition to factors like chance and bias, many other opinions and suggestions could be offered. Various pseudoscientific cultists would labour the point that many of the "inert variables" employed are the very essence of meaningful psychic change—for instance, concentrated exercises in visualization and the awareness training. All sorts of arguments may be advanced, but it is hoped that all would agree that these preliminary results warrant a re-run under more controlled conditions.

In contrast to my original expectations, I now hypothesize that *graded structure*—with a succession of definite therapeutic stages through which a patient can advance—is perhaps one of the most important ingredients in behavioural therapeutic successes. By deliberately adding further structure to the usual behaviour therapy framework, the therapeutic potency of this approach could well be enhanced.

Recently, for instance, patients undergoing relaxation therapy were required to practise a particular sequence of tension and relaxation exercises for one week, after which a slightly different regime was prescribed for the second week. They were then given a third and final variation. Patients who were told that the three relaxation programmes constituted an elementary, intermediate and advanced progression tended to practise the exercises more conscientiously and appeared to derive greater benefit than those who were simply told that it was helpful to master several relaxation sequences.

To conclude with an interesting aside, each patient, after treatment, was asked to underline words on a check-list of adjectives which he felt best described the therapist's personality. The psychotherapy patients tended to find the therapist "flexible, spontaneous, gentle, interested and shy", compared to the behaviour therapy patients who found him "warm, sympathetic, open, sensitive and systematic". The patients who received graded structure gravitated to the words "rigid, critical, formal, honest and aloof".

SUMMARY

The vast range of clinical problems to which learning principles and conditioning techniques have been applied extends from unitary tics and phobias to long-term psychoses, mental retardation and delinquency. Yet claims for the overall therapeutic superiority of behaviour therapy are based on clinical impressions rather than on controlled data. Those who believe that nearly all complex neurotic disorders can be reduced to phobic clusters and accordingly deconditioned are simplistic and naïve. Even a specific procedure like systematic desensitization contains more variables than a simple counterconditioning paradigm can provide.

In opposition to expectations, a clinical experiment has yielded tentative evidence that *structure* may be one of the most potent aspects of behaviour therapy. The application of specific techniques lends structure in and of itself, but when patients are enabled to experience a sense of achievement at graduating from one therapeutic phase to another, constructive outcomes seem greatly facilitated. The deliberate addition of *graded structure* to the usual behaviour therapy framework may well advance the therapeutic potency of this approach.

ACKNOWLEDGEMENT

Dr. Neil J. Yorkston read the first draft of this paper and made several helpful suggestions and constructive criticisms.

REFERENCES

AYLLON, T., and AZRIN, N. H. (1965). *J. exp. Analysis Behav.*, **8**, 357–383.

BARNARD, J.W., and ORLANDO, R. (1967). *Behavior Modification: A Bibliography.* Nashville: Institute of Mental Retardation and Intellectual Development's Papers and Reports, IV, 3.

BEECH, H. R. (1960). In *Behaviour Therapy and the Neuroses*, pp. 349–372, ed. Eysenck, H. J. Oxford: Pergamon.

BIJOU, S. W., and SLOANE, H. N. (1966). In *An Introduction to Clinical Psychology*, 3rd edn., pp. 652–684, eds. Pennington, L. A., and Berg, I. A. New York: Ronald.

DAVISON, G. C. (1966). *Diss. Abstr.*, **26**, 61–65.

DAVISON, G. C. (1968). *J. abnorm. Psychol.*, **73**, 91–99.

FELDMAN, M. P. (1966). *Psychol. Bull.*, **65**, 65–79.

GOLDIAMOND, I. (1965). In *Research in Behavior Modification*, pp. 106–156, eds. Krasner, L., and Ullmann, L. P. New York: Holt, Rinehart & Winston.

GOLDSTEIN, A. P., HELLER, K., and SECHREST, L. B. (1966). *Psychotherapy and the Psychology of Behavior Change.* New York: Wiley.

KANFER, F. H., and PHILLIPS, J. S. (1966). *Archs gen. Psychiat.*, **15**, 114–128.

LANG, P. J., LAZOVIK, A. D., and REYNOLDS, D. J. (1965). *J. abnorm. Psychol.*, **70**, 395–402.

LAZARUS, A. A. (1960). *New Group Techniques in the Treatment of Phobic Conditions.* Ph.D. Thesis, University of the Witwatersrand, South Africa, Faculty of Arts.

LAZARUS, A. A. (1963). *Behav. Res. Ther.*, **1**, 69–79.

LAZARUS, A. A. (1966). *Behav. Res. Ther.*, **4**, 95–97.

LAZARUS, A. A. (1967). *Psychol. Rep.*, **21**, 415–416.

LEITENBERG, H., AGRAS, W. S., BARLOW, D. H., and OLIVEAU, D. C. (1968). *J. abnorm. Psychol.*, **73**, in press.

LIVERSEDGE, L. A., and SYLVESTER, J. D. (1960). In *Behaviour Therapy and the Neuroses*, pp. 327–333, ed. Eysenck, H. J. Oxford: Pergamon.

LOVAAS, O. I. (1966). In *Childhood Autism*, pp. 115–144, ed. Wing, J. K. Oxford: Pergamon.

LOVAAS, O. I., SCHAEFFER, B., and SIMMONS, J. Q. (1965). *J. exp. Stud. Behav.*, **1**, 99–109.

LOVIBOND, S. H. (1964). *Conditioning and Enuresis.* New York: Macmillan.

MARKS, I. M., and GELDER, M. G. (1967). *Br. J. Psychiat.*, **113**, 711–729.

MASLOW, A. H. (1954). *Motivation and Personality.* New York: Harper.

NEALE, D. H. (1963). *Behav. Res. Ther.*, **1**, 139–149.

ORLANDO, R., and BIJOU, S. W. (1960). *J. exp. Analysis Behav.*, **3**, 339–348.

PAUL, G. L. (1966). *Insight vs. Desensitization in Psychotherapy.* Stanford: Stanford University Press.

PHILLIPS, E. L., and WIENER, D. N. (1966). *Short-term Psychotherapy and Structured Behavior Change.* New York: McGraw-Hill.

ROSENTHAL, R. (1966). *Experimenter Effects in Behavioral Research.* New York: Appleton-Century-Crofts.

WILLOUGHBY, R. (1934). *J. soc. Psychol.*, **5**, 91–95.

WOLPE, J. (1958). *Psychotherapy by Reciprocal Inhibition.* Stanford: Stanford University Press.

WOLPE, J. (1964). *Br. J. Psychiat.*, **110**, 28–34.

WOLPE, J., and LAZARUS, A. A. (1966). *Behaviour Therapy Techniques: A Guide to the Treatment of Neuroses.* Oxford: Pergamon.

DISCUSSION

Sackett: I am interested in the use of the imagining of objects and situations in some of these procedures. In other experiments, for example psychological testing, what people say they do and what they actually do are often completely different. But with these conditioning techniques the patient is asked to imagine the frightening object and then provided with reinforcement—relaxation, say. What is the evidence that permanent behavioural changes follow conditioning an outcome to an imagined rather than to an actual object?

Lazarus: In the early conditioning studies, the actual object was used: a person who feared cats would be shown photographs of cats, and then furry toy cats, and finally live cats, at varying distances. The original counterconditioning paradigm (Jones, M.C. [1924]. *J. exp. Psychol.*, **7**, 382) consisted of presenting the real object of the phobia while the child was engaging in a competing response—eating. In this situation the actual object was gradually brought closer to the contented child. But in some situations it is obviously impossible to present the phobic object itself and, fortunately, such elaborate measures are not necessary because the same neurones are probably involved whether one looks at an object or closes one's eyes and pictures it. Thus, imagery can be effectively used for deconditioning. The rationale for this is that when a situation is presented to an individual, phantasies are built up in connexion not only with this situation but also with a wide range of associated notions. Thus a broader range of eidetic images may be covered during desensitization in imagination than on confrontation with actual objects or situations.

Sackett: How does one promote relaxation in a patient with a snake phobia when he is thinking of snakes?

Lazarus: The sequence is the other way round: when the patient is already relaxed we present the feared image, just below the threatening level, so as not to disrupt the relaxation, and the strength of the image is then gradually increased.

Sackett: These ideas do not correspond with Held's visuomotor model (see Held, R., and Rekoth, F. [1963]. *Science*, **141**, 722-723). Held studied adjustment to perceptual distortion with passive or active learning in man, and found that if the subject learned passively (as with imagining) transfer of training almost never occurred. I am bothered that the "as if" situation in the conditioning procedures may have a parallel in Held's passive learning.

Miller: The notion of the therapeutic effect of counterconditioning while imagining the phobic situation is supported by experimental evidence

showing a large amount of transfer from conditioning to overt environ-
ment-produced cues to covert response-produced cues and *vice versa*. For
example, in an experiment on conditioning to verbal cues (Miller, N. E.
[1951]. In *Handbook of Experimental Psychology*, p. 464, Fig. 8, ed. Stevens,
S. S. New York: Wiley), a subject was presented with trials during which
exposure of the letter *T* on a memory drum was always followed by
electric shock, while exposure of the figure 4 was never followed by a shock.
The subject named each symbol when he saw it. After a discrimination
had been established, the subject was presented with a series of dots, without
any electric shocks, and instructed to think 4 when he saw the first dot, *T*
when he saw the second, 4 when he saw the third, and so on. The record of
the galvanic skin response gave unequivocal evidence that the discrimination had transferred from seeing the symbols and pronouncing them
aloud to merely thinking about them.

In a later experiment in my laboratory, R. F. Grose (1952. *A Comparison
of Vocal and Subvocal Conditioning of the Galvanic Skin Response*. Ph.D.
dissertation, Yale University Library) performed a beautifully balanced
experiment in which one half of his subjects learned a similar discrimination
while pronouncing the symbols *T* or 4 and the other half learned it while
merely thinking the symbols. Then one-half of each of these groups was
tested without shocks while pronouncing, and the other half while thinking, the symbols. So much transfer occurred from the condition of
pronouncing and hearing to that of merely thinking, and also from the
condition of thinking to that of pronouncing and hearing, that there was
no apparent difference between the groups trained and tested under the
different conditions and those trained and tested under the same conditions.

G. Razran, in his own studies on semantic and phonetographic generalizations of salivary conditioning to verbal stimuli (1949. *J. exp. Psychol.*, **39**,
642-652), and in studies from the Soviet Union that he has summarized
(Razran, G. [1961]. *The Observable Unconscious and the Inferable Conscious in
Current Soviet Psychophysiology: Interceptive Conditioning, Semantic Conditioning and the Orienting Reflex. Psychol. Rev.*, **68**, 81-147) has emphasized
the role of verbal responses and meaning in the generalization of conditioned
responses.

The results of all these studies support Professor Lazarus' conclusion that
considerable therapeutic transfer can occur from thinking about and
imagining a situation to actually being in that situation. But the laws
governing such transfer can and should be determined more exactly by
additional research.

Gelder: There is evidence from the actual treatment situation that a subject *is* imagining what he says he is. Dr. Matthews and I have studied this (Gelder, M. G., and Matthews, A. [1969]. *Br. J. Psychiat.*, in press) by asking patients to grade imagined stimuli according to their anxiety content and then to imagine them one by one, together with another situation which needs as much attention but does not induce anxiety. We have objectively demonstrated significant differences in arousal between neutral scenes and those that patients grade as evoking high and low anxiety; we used changes in forearm blood flow as our objective measurement in this particular experiment. In this way there is some check that the patient is really experiencing anxiety when he says he is.

Kubie: I am surprised that the amount of conditioning is so small, so brief, and needs so little reinforcement, in all these experiments.

Sackett: All these results conflict with my experiences in verbal conditioning, of nouns and of the rate of voicing opinions, with thousands of students enrolled in introductory psychology courses at the University of Wisconsin. I have found only minimal evidence of positive verbal conditioning in these subjects.

Miller: Was it always a student conditioning another student in these experiments, or were faculty members ever the experimenters?

Sackett: We used students and students, and also faculty members and students.

Miller: W. S. Verplanck (1956. *Psychol. Bull.*, **53**, 70-83) reported that when the experimenter was another student but not a close friend (that is, when prestige was not involved) conditioning could not be produced, but when the experimenter was someone whom the student wanted to please, such as a faculty member or a close friend, considerable learning was produced by the experimenter merely saying "Aha" after the type of statement he wanted to reinforce.

Sackett: The most important variable in our studies was sex; the extent of conditioning differed significantly according to whether the experimenter was male and the subject female or *vice versa*.

Hunt: In some informal and unpublished experiments on myself I found that I could change my blood pressure and peripheral skin resistance by deliberately manipulating my thoughts.

Kubie: J. T. Marsh and F. G. Worden (1956. *Psychiat. Res. Rep.*, No. 6, pp. 171-177) and others have shown that preconscious input can also alter such autonomic parameters as pulse rate, respiration, skin temperature and resistance, and blood pressure. Marsh and Worden used word association tests in their investigation. Lists of words, which included a few emotionally loaded words, loaded specifically for each individual under study, were exposed on a tachistoscope. With brief (subliminal) exposures, too brief for the words to be read, some of the patients showed changes in autonomic responses to the loaded words only. Some of these patients also showed remarkable affective as well as autonomic changes. This raises the question of whether there are inherent differences in thresholds for autonomic overflow from preconscious input.

Lazarus: These differences in the success of conditioning may be explained by the psychic differences between objects and words. Words are almost always available, and innumerable responses may become linked to a single word or concept. What a person fears in reality he also usually fears in imagination, which is why his real fear can be dealt with through imaginal scenes.

Hunt: Instructional control can be very influential in verbal conditioning. For example, if one tells human subjects to notice plural nouns, and respond to them or to give plural nouns in association, one can elicit fair quantities of this behaviour just by asking for it. Similarly, in Miller's study (1951. *loc. cit.*) instructional control was given: the subjects were told what to do when they saw the two symbols and this affected the results of the experiment.

Carstairs: But were the subjects in this experiment *conditioned* or did they *learn*?

Hunt: Aren't conditioning and learning synonymous in this situation? It might be better to say that the subjects *performed*.

Gelder: Verbal conditioning can be produced in neurotic patients without instruction. However, the first meeting of the subject with the interviewer is important in quite a different way: a subject's response to subsequent verbal reinforcement depends on the relationship he forms with the interviewer. It has been shown (Gelder, M. G. [1968]. *Br. J. soc. clin. Psychol.*, in press) that when the therapist shows interest and concern in the patient in a brief preliminary interview, verbal conditioning readily occurs when reinforcement is introduced later. When this initial interaction is omitted, but every other aspect of the experiment is unchanged, there is no significant response to verbal reinforcement. Thus, although Professor Hunt is right that instructions can modify verbal conditioning, there are other less specific aspects of the encounter between subject and interviewer which are important. It is these other factors that make verbal conditioning so relevant to the study of psychotherapy.

Freeman: Professor Lazarus, I would like to ask you two questions about behaviour therapists: (*a*) do behaviour therapists sufficiently take into account the fact that changes in the patient may not be due so much to a specific aspect of the technique as to the impact of the therapist on the patient; and (b) are behaviour therapists sufficiently aware of the importance of the psychic reality? I would hypothesize that (at least in brief psychotherapy) improvement is not so much related to a specific technique as to the general approach adopted by the therapist: the most obvious example is hypnosis. The remarkable improvement in your results when you added "graded structure" to your behaviour therapy technique tends to support my hypothesis. Phantasy plays an extremely important role in the therapeutic situation. Why do some patients feel better (or worse) almost immediately after their first visit to the psychiatrist? How do we explain the placebo effect, both negative and positive? The whole of psychoanalytic literature, from Freud onwards, shows that the explanation for those changes that occur early in therapy lies in the expectations (ideas, fears, imaginings and so on) of the patient. Recognition of the part played in therapy by psychic reality gives an explanation for the observation that intelligent, educated patients can assimilate and utilize such naïve techniques as behaviour therapy. Man's intellectual capacity is but little related to his potential for phantasy and affective reactions.

Lazarus: I cannot answer for all behaviour therapists, but my own response to your first question is that there is good evidence of a close link between the specific behavioural technique used and the outcome (Paul, G. L. [1966]. *Insight vs. Desensitization in Psychotherapy*. Stanford, Calif.: Stanford University Press). This certainly applies to therapy with autistic children (Davison, G. C. [1964]. *Behav. Res. Ther.*, **2**, 149-159; Ferster, C. B., and De Myer, M. K. [1962]. *Am. J. Orthopsychiat.*, **32**, 89-98; Wolf, M. M., Risley, R., and Mees, H. [1964]. *Behav. Res. Ther.*, **1**, 305-312; Lovaas, O. I., *et al.* [1965]. *J. exp. Child Psychol.*, **2**, 67-84). Reversal studies reported in the literature (Harris, F., *et al.* [1964]. *J. educ. Psychol.*, **55**, 35-41; Hart, B. M., *et al.* [1965]. In *Case Studies in Behavior Modification*, pp. 320-325, eds. Ullmann, L. P., and Krasner, L. New York: Holt, Rinehart & Winston) also support the concept that the actual strategies employed are the active ingredients in therapy. But in the treatment of pervasively distressed adult human beings, riddled with anxiety and guilt, techniques derived from laboratory experiences may not be as important as other variables. Most of these "other variables" can be explained within a learning theory framework, and none are mystical, but I agree that some behaviour therapists may not be aware of the importance of the patient-therapist interaction. For example, I recently observed the treatment, by Joseph Wolpe, of an intellectually under-achieving intelligent boy. Wolpe administered mildly aversive electric shocks to the patient when he reported that he had not been studying. The boy soon began studying more frequently and diligently and his improvement was attributed entirely to this aversive conditioning. But Wolpe paid no attention to the important relationship between himself and the patient, who showed a very strong positive regard for Wolpe and wanted to please him. The boy's compliance was probably a much more important factor than the aversive conditioning in effecting his improvement. This notion was confirmed when we subsequently found that the conditioning was probably not even aversive—the shock-producing apparatus was not working properly.

Dr. Freeman, could you please define psychic reality again? I am not used to this expression.

Freeman: The thinking of every human being, particularly in the first five years of life, is dominated by imagining; in other words, phantasy is much more important than reality. The fact that young children are frightened of the "wrong" things is good evidence of this. Children may be terrified of a shadow on the wall at night but unafraid of running into a busy street. Their mental functioning is dominated by a type of cognition that is not adapted to reality. Objects have meanings other than their real meanings. This type of thinking persists in the adult but is mainly repressed. We see it in psychotics.

Sandler: The frightening content of a phobia is the element that psychologists used to call the "apperceptive mass" in the individual's perception of the phobic situation; in other words, this content consists of unconscious elements which still retain a psychic reality. And it is this element that is important when the subject imagines the phobic situation.

Gelder: Phobic patients often say that what goes on in their minds before they enter a feared situation is much more frightening than the situation itself.

Foss: Professor Lazarus, will you describe the Willoughby Questionnaire?

Lazarus: This questionnaire consists of 25 items, which include questions about such factors as stage fright, various aspects of insecurity, hypersensitivity, being watched while working, fear of heights, and certain social anxieties. The subject rates each answer from 0 to 4, according to intensity. Thus the total scores range from 0 to 100.

Sandler: My own experience (unpublished), using the Tavistock Self-Assessment Inventory (Sandler, J. [1954]. *Br. J. med. Psychol.*, **27**, 142-145), is relevant to the use of symptom-fear check-lists and similar questionnaires, and the extension of these sorts of procedures to the psychiatric interview. The striking finding in two studies using such inventories was that patients who had had a lot of treatment *rated* many more fears after treatment than before it. Similarly, many psychoanalysts who have had a long training analysis and are now functioning well may comment that they still have to cope with many anxieties. But this may be because they are aware of anxiety at deeper levels than subjects who have had a shorter analysis. Different thresholds for awareness of anxiety may exist which may not be related to behaviour; thus a subject with insight may report, or record on a questionnaire, more anxiety than a subject without insight, even if in fact the anxiety of the former subject is less than that of the latter. In any form of psychotherapy results assessed by scales and inventories may be adversely influenced by the amount of insight gained. An example of this is seen in the poor figures when the results of analytic psychotherapy are assessed in this way.

Marks: The transfer of learning from the treatment situation to real life is a difficult clinical problem. W. S. Agras (1967. *Behav. Res. Ther.*, **5**, 193-199) and S. Rachman (1966. *Behav. Res. Ther.*, **4**, 1-6) have shown that transfer can occur after imaginal deconditioning. But some patients who improve in the treatment situation fail to carry this improvement through into real life; or they may improve in life but not in the relationship with their therapist. Another problem in the treatment of phobias is that patients may not experience anxiety when they imagine a phobic situation. Dissociation between image and reality must exist in these patients, which makes desensitization very difficult.

Lazarus: The inability of some patients to reproduce their anxiety by imaginal stimuli can sometimes be overcome if they verbalize the images. It may also help if scenes are described very vividly. Or subjects can be trained to evoke affective imagery by practising with pleasant images and by describing, on demand, phantasies that they have created.

Marks: How useful are the data obtained by this mixing-up of techniques, and of patients with many different problems? What sorts of problems did your patients have?

Lazarus: I agree that it is confusing to amalgamate many different types of neuroses rather than dividing the material up into specific syndromes. My cases were not suffering from unitary phobias, but may be described as being generally anxious.

Marks: How long was the follow-up in your study?

Lazarus: I have no long-term follow-up data yet, but four patients in the group treated by graded structure have maintained their improvement for more than 6 months so far. In general, my findings in follow-up studies have been that relapses do not arise spontaneously but occur in response to inimical events in the life situation, with resultant reconditioning.

Leder: Professor Lazarus, why were you so surprised that the patients in the group treated with the graded structure procedure improved? Surely the fact that the patients believed in this therapy, even though you did not, contributed to the good results?

Lazarus: Exactly. The results were so interesting just because of my disbelief.

Leder: But if you had believed in therapy by graded suggestion and not in behaviour therapy the results might have been reversed. Are you implying that if another therapist used these two forms of therapy, but regarded behaviour therapy as a placebo, he would construe the favourable results with behaviour therapy as being just a placebo effect?

Lazarus: Yes.

Malan: Professor Lazarus' study was a true experiment in that he was controlling for the possibility that the overwhelmingly important factor might be *the therapist's belief in the procedure;* he believed in the effectiveness of one form of therapy and not of the other. We can argue about what the procedure was and whether it was effective but that does not alter the validity of the experimental design.

Foss: My impression is that operant conditioning of verbal behaviour is effective provided the subjects do not know what is happening. This might be relevant to the problem of how one interprets a technique in which some instruction is given before the actual behaviour therapy.

Krasner: The effectiveness of verbal conditioning in subjects who are unaware of what is happening to them is one of the hottest controversies in this field today.

Lazarus: My own clinical study cannot be compared with studies of awareness and non-awareness in operant conditioning; but pretreatment instructions may certainly be expected to effect both psychotherapeutic outcome and the results of operant conditioning (Goldstein, A.P., Heller, K., and Sechrest, L. B. [1966]. *Psychotherapy and the Psychology of Behavior Change.* New York: Wiley.)

Foss: When we discuss the imagining of objects we should try to categorize the imaginal type of the individual. P. L. Short (1953. *Br. J. Psychol.,* **44**, 38-51), following up some of Professor F. Golla's ideas, divided imaginal types into two extremes—"sensory" and "motor". Most people are a mixture of the two. When a person who uses sensory imagery thinks of words he will imagine he is hearing them or seeing them in writing; but a motor type of individual will imagine the actual writing or speaking of the words. Short found that there were objective differences in these two types: the extreme motor type tended to breathe irregularly while solving problems and had a persistent α-wave on the electroencephalogram, whereas the extreme sensory type breathed regularly and his α-wave was suppressed or absent. The validity of this classification could be checked with imaginal therapy techniques, which might affect the two extreme types of persons differently.

Lazarus: That is very interesting. The motor type of subject might respond to written scenes and not to verbal descriptions. This certainly could be put to the test with patients in conventional desensitization therapy.

Krasner: The procedure used by Professor Lazarus in his graded structure group is similar to the control placebo procedure of G. L. Paul (1966, *loc. cit.*) in that Paul, also, had no previous experimental evidence that his technique was psychotherapeutically effective in any way.

Sandler: I was most impressed with your results, Professor Lazarus. Traditional learning theories might suggest that a subject treated by graded structure was being deconditioned against disappointment: he thought he was moving forward as he passed the various steps. This may be relevant to a phenomenon that some psychoanalysts see in some of their colleagues, namely, in psychoanalysts who work only on the basis of positive transference and who do not take up or analyse the negative transference. The results of this approach, particularly in the training of student analysts, are often very good: the candidates change markedly, have a strong positive (often idealized) relationship with their analyst, and so on. But because the hostility to the analyst has not been taken up—at least not at the conscious level—one can see its effects emerging in the personality of the ex-analysand, even though he is functioning well. Something similar, in the form of a pushing of disappointment away from the behavioural tasks, might have occurred in your studies and may have favourably affected your results. In contrast, hostility to the therapist may have been allowed to emerge at the time of treatment and in the follow-up interview; this would also influence the results, but adversely. Another fallacy in experiments on verbal conditioning is that the subject realizes preconsciously what the experimenter is up to. The subject may then respond with *compliance* rather than with conditioning. Although he could not consciously define the situation, his response has been influenced by subliminal, peripheral, preconscious information. An individual can put together and think about this sort of information without being consciously aware of it.

Marks: What differentiates behaviour therapy from any other form of psychotherapy? Once we start to deal with imaginal stimuli in behavioural therapies we are extending the term "behaviour" very widely and including in it the kind of covert behaviour which is also dealt with in dynamic psychotherapy and psychoanalysis. Behaviour therapy as described by you, Professor Lazarus, might equally well be called "active psychotherapy". This would explain the similarities in recovery rate in subjects in your two groups, the one treated with the graded structure procedure and the other with behaviour therapy. What little difference there is between the groups might be due to the amount of interest and directiveness shown by the therapist. A suitable name for treatments using directed behavioural techniques might be active psychotherapy.

Gelder: Active psychotherapy, or desensitization carried out in this particular way, provides a bridge between behaviour therapy and other forms of psychotherapy.

Bandura: We might make greater progress in developing efficacious treatments if ill-defined and partisan labels were retired from use. Much time has been spent fruitlessly in attempts to define what constitutes "behaviour therapy" and "psychotherapy". I am reminded of F. Alexander's (1956. *Psychoanalysis and Psychotherapy.* New York: Norton) extended debate with his psychoanalytic colleagues as to whether or not his method of treatment qualified as psychoanalysis. A more productive approach to the understanding of psychotherapeutic processes is to focus on the basic psychological mechanisms through which behavioural changes are produced. These mechanisms are undoubtedly brought into play to varying degrees by conditions created, either deliberately or unwittingly, by agents of change in treatments arbitrarily designated as behaviour therapy, psychotherapy, counselling and so on.

In recent years a marked proliferation of psychological ventures designed to cure all types of social maladies has occurred. These endeavours include meditation, massage, sensitivity training, and marathon social encounters in which participants from all walks of life are provided with opportunities to analyse each other's interpersonal reactions. When the intended outcomes of treatment remain ambiguous, and improvement is measured in terms of the subjective ratings of the therapists, all methods are likely to yield statistically significant changes. Objective measures of behavioural changes constitute the most stringent criteria of the power of a given method. In evaluating the efficacy of different procedures, the percentage of clients who are completely cured should be our major concern, thus discouraging complacency about methods that produce partial improvements but leave many clients with considerable behavioural incapacity.

Lazarus: I agree that the term "behaviour therapy" has little operational meaning and that we need to define specific changes in behaviour and aim towards precise criteria on outcome, and away from vague and almost mystical categories of "general improvement". This is easily done with relatively concrete behaviour problems (for example children with school phobias); but patients in an out-patient setting complain of nebulous difficulties, and the only available criteria for assessing change may be self-reports. All verbal self-reports are not useless data. A depressed patient who says that he no longer feels depressed is presenting valid scientific information. This is obvious to the practising clinician, but too many academicians subscribe to the notion: "If you can't measure it, it either doesn't exist or, if it does exist, if can't be important."

Kubie: One serious difficulty in assessing the results of psychotherapy is that the therapist's communications are influenced by the balance between empathy and objectivity. A clinician's report on his experience with a patient is inevitably slanted. His is a fallible report of his fallible memories of fallible perceptions—a strange foundation for a science. Yet this fallible report has until recently been accepted in all types of psychology, because of the evanescent nature of the data. Tape recordings of spoken interviews, or better still Videotape recordings of such interactions, are essential tools, opening new doors for research. Experimentalists are just as deeply involved and as emotionally biased in their work as clinicians. It is more useful for workers with different preconceptions and trainings to study one Videotape recording together for two hours than to listen to hundreds of hours of memories.

ASSESSMENT OF TOKEN ECONOMY
PROGRAMMES IN PSYCHIATRIC HOSPITALS

Leonard Krasner

Department of Psychology, State University of New York, Stony Brook, New York

In recent years a new approach to the treatment of problem behaviours has been developed; this is known as behaviour modification. The procedures used, their historical antecedents and their similarities to and differences from traditional procedures have been extensively documented (Krasner and Ullmann, 1965; Ullmann and Krasner, 1965; Eysenck, 1960; Wolpe and Lazarus, 1966; Eysenck and Rachman, 1965). The token economy programme is a programme in which behaviour modification procedures developed in the laboratory and used with individual clinical problems have been extended to large-scale clinical units. Such programmes involve the systematic application of reinforcements contingent upon selected behaviours.

A token economy has three specific characteristics: first, the designation of certain *behaviours* as good or desirable and hence to be reinforced; second, a *medium of exchange*, an object—the token—that "stands for" something else; and third, a way of utilizing the tokens, in other words, the *back-up* reinforcers or the good things in life. These may include food or being allowed to sit peacefully in a chair, and cover a wide range. The economy part of the term appropriately relates to the supply-and-demand aspects of the programmes; these aspects determine changing token values.

The goals of a token programme are to develop behaviours which will lead to social reinforcement from other people, and to enhance the skills the individual needs to take a responsible social role in the institution and, eventually, to live successfully outside the hospital. Basically, the individual learns that he can control his own environment.

ILLUSTRATIVE TOKEN ECONOMY PROGRAMMES

Ayllon and Azrin (1965) reported the results of the first use of a token economy programme in a psychiatric hospital ward. The behaviours selected for reinforcement included such things as serving meals, cleaning floors, sorting laundry, washing dishes and self-grooming. The reinforcement was the opportunity to continue to engage in these activities. Thus the reinforcers selected were part of the normal hospital environment.

Although it is widely believed that few stimuli are effective reinforcers for schizophrenic patients, Ayllon and Azrin (1965) made no *a priori* decisions about what might be an effective reinforcer, but observed the patients' behaviour to discover what they actually did. They applied the general principle expressed by Premack (1959) that any behaviour occurring frequently when freely allowed can be used as a reinforcer. Thus, the reinforcers included such items as: rooms available for rent; selection of people to dine with; passes; a chance to speak to the ward physician, chaplain, or psychologist; opportunities for viewing television; candy; cigarettes; and other amenities of life. Tokens served as acquired reinforcers that bridged the delay between behaviour and an ultimate reinforcement. These investigators placed particular emphasis on the objective definition and quantification of the responses and reinforcers, and upon programming and recording procedures.

Ayllon and Azrin (1965) reported a series of six experiments in each of which they demonstrated that target behaviour changed systematically as a function of the token reinforcement. One experiment is typical of the procedures they developed. The response they were interested in consisted of work assignments off the ward. A patient selected the job he most preferred from a list of available jobs for which he could receive tokens. After ten days he was told that he could continue working on this job but would be given no tokens for it. Of the eight patients observed, seven selected another job immediately, and the eighth patient switched a few days later. In the third phase of the experiment, the contingencies were reversed and the jobs that had been preferred originally again earned tokens. All eight patients immediately switched back to their original jobs.

The results of six experiments described by Ayllon and Azrin demonstrated that the reinforcement procedure was effective in maintaining the desired performance. In each experiment the performance fell to near zero when the established response–reinforcement relation was discontinued. On the other hand, reintroduction of the reinforcement procedure restored performance almost immediately and maintained it at a high level.

The Ayllon and Azrin token economy was used on a ward for long-stay female patients in a mid-western state hospital. Another token economy programme (Atthowe and Krasner, 1968; Krasner, 1965, 1966a) was set up in a Veterans Administration (VA) Hospital in California with male patients (average age = 58 years) having a median time of hospitalization of 24 years. Most of these patients had been labelled as chronic schizophrenics and the rest as having organic cerebral disease. As a group, their behaviour was apathetic and indifferent; the patients showed inactivity, dependency and social isolation. The procedures used were similar to those developed by Ayllon and Azrin except that there was less control by the experimenters in the Atthowe and Krasner programme; this was designed to be used on an *open* ward where patients could come and go—if, of course, they had the right number of tokens for the gate-keeper. The token economy had to compete with the economy, which used dollars and cents, outside the ward. Many kinds of economic problems had to be faced and special procedures were developed—a banking system to foster savings, a monthly discount rate to cut down hoarding, and yellow tokens to prevent stealing—to deal with them.

Before the introduction of tokens most patients refused to take part in any of the available activities and showed little interest in their environment. The patients sat or slept in the ward during the day; this inactivity resulted from years in which compliant and apathetic institutional behaviour had been shaped. Our team decided that these patients could do better than sit and waste their lives away. Among the behaviours selected as valuable were: enacting the role of responsible people who are adept at self-grooming, keeping their living quarters clean, dressing neatly, keeping a job, and interacting with other people. Responsibility in this sense also included responsiveness to normal social reinforcement. Thus giving tokens was always accompanied by social reinforcement, such as "Good", "I'm pleased", "Fine job", and an explicit statement about the contingencies involved, for example, "You received three tokens because you got a good rating from your job supervisor."

This token economy programme was a significant success as measured by changes in specified behaviour, observers' ratings, and reactions of hospital staff. The changes in behaviours, such as attendance at group activities, were a function of the number of tokens (value) given for the activity. Group attendances increased as more tokens were given for them, and decreased when the "pay off" returned to its previous value.

The greatest change was in the appearance and atmosphere of the ward, and in the staff expectations of what the patients were capable of. The morale of the staff increased enormously when they found that their participation in the token economy programme had a therapeutic effect on the behaviour of the patients; it became a matter of prestige throughout the hospital to work on the token ward. Two other wards in the hospital

6*

finally adopted similar token economies because of the apparent therapeutic effect of the programme.

Schaefer and Martin (1966) described the effects of a token economy programme, in a California state hospital, on a specific type of patient-behaviour—apathy. They noted that the overt behavioural pattern of apathy is a manifestation of a *limited* response to the environment. As the environment changes, the patient does not. To measure this lack of response Schaefer and Martin recorded patients' behaviour at half-hourly intervals on three scales: (*a*) mutually exclusive behaviours—walking, running, standing, sitting, lying down; (*b*) concomitant behaviours—talking, singing, playing music, painting, reading, listening to others or to the radio, watching television, group activities; and (*c*) idiosyncratic behaviours —rocking, pacing, chattering. They reviewed the clinical records to designate patients as withdrawn, apathetic, or uninterested and found that the absence of concomitant behaviours was an excellent measure of what is generally called "apathy". Once a behavioural target had been selected, the next step was to determine whether this behaviour could be influenced within the framework of a token economy.

Tokens plus verbal praise and more direct reinforcers (cigarettes) were given by the staff for three major areas of behaviour: personal hygiene; social interactions such as polite "good mornings" and meaningful questions; and adequate working performance such as emptying waste-paper-baskets. All three types of behaviours indicate caring and a positive interest in the environment.

The sample in Schaefer and Martin's study consisted of 40 long-stay schizophrenic patients whose medical records indicated apathy. Half the patients were allocated to the experimental group and half to a control group, which received routine ward treatment procedures, according to the toss of a coin.

The patients were first checked on the three scales (*vide supra*) on five consecutive working days, every half-hour from 6.00 hours until 21.00 hours. The reinforcement procedure was then started, and the patients were again observed, every half-hour during a five-day working week, after one and after two months. Patients in the control group improved slightly, but not significantly, but improvement in the experimental group was statistically significant. That is, the number of observations on which concomitant behaviours were not emitted decreased significantly in the experimental group. Thus the token programme was successful in improving a specific target behaviour.

Other successful token economy programmes with adult psychiatric patients have been reported by Steffy and co-workers (1966), Marks, Schalock and Sonoda (1967), and Gericke (1965). Token economy programmes have been extended to other groups, including mental defectives, delinquents, adolescents, and subjects who had class-room behaviour problems.

TOKEN ECONOMY WITH DELINQUENTS

The treatment of delinquent behaviour by a token economy programme at Camp Butner, North Carolina, has been described by Burchard (1967). He started from the concept of antisocial behaviour as behaviour which is "acquired, maintained and modified by the same principles as other learned behavior" (p. 463). He argued, therefore, that an individual "can learn constructive, socially acceptable behavior by being placed in an environment where the behavioral consequences are programmed according to the principles of operant conditioning. Instead of administering an excess of reinforcement or punishment on an indiscriminate, non-contingent basis, behavior would be punished or reinforced systematically on a response contingent basis" (p. 463). This is an experimental residential programme in behaviour modification for mildly retarded delinquent adolescents. Burchard utilizes techniques based on the principles of "reinforcement, punishment, and programmed instruction". This is a standardized programme, carried out mainly by non-professional people, and has been developed to teach these delinquents the practical skills that are essential for them to adjust adequately to the community, and to eliminate or markedly reduce antisocial behaviour. As in other types of token programmes, the procedures require the definition of the behaviours to be reinforced, the selection of an effective reinforcer, and the programming of the reinforcement contingencies. The behaviours selected for reinforcement are, first, those which produce an identifiable change that can be reliably observed and reinforced in the environment; and, second, those which provide the individual with a behavioural repertoire that will elicit reinforcement in a community environment. Behaviours selected were those that could contribute to keeping a job, staying in school, budgeting with money, buying and caring for clothes, buying food and meals, and cooperating with peers and adults. In order to reduce stealing, which was more of a problem with Burchard's subjects than it is with our psychotics, the reinforcers were aluminium tokens stamped with the resident's number. Thus, the individual could use only those tokens stamped with his own number. The reinforcing items and privileges were those which were also available for all residents in the institution on an infrequent and non-contingent basis.

Most of the token programmes emphasize positive reinforcement and avoid deliberate negative consequences. Atthowe and Krasner (1968) used a system of "fines" for a few undesirable behaviours such as cursing or spitting but this system was not effective. Fines may be defined as a way of making available additional reinforcers for which a patient could pay if he very much wanted to perform an undesirable act. It might be worth five tokens to curse at somebody, or (see Burchard, 1967) to hit someone on the mouth.

Burchard used punishment procedures developed from laboratory operant conditioning work (Azrin and Holz, 1966), his aim being to develop a procedure which could be applied immediately after the response, and could be of short duration yet intense enough to decrease the frequency of the response. In the development of these procedures he followed the same pattern used in developing positive reinforcement procedures, namely defining the behaviours to be punished, selecting effective stimuli, and programming the punishment contingencies. The behaviours selected for punishment were those which typically elicit some form of punishment in a community, such as fighting, lying, stealing, cheating, physical or verbal assault, temper tantrums or property damage. The punishment consisted of the withdrawal of positive reinforcement, that is, tokens. The punishing stimuli consisted of two verbal pronouncements, "time out" and "seclusion", both of which led to the loss of tokens or the opportunity to earn tokens. When a member of staff says, "time out", the resident is charged four tokens and must sit on one side of the day room for three to five minutes until his behaviour becomes appropriate. Seclusion is used for more serious disturbing behaviour such as fights, serious property damage, or refusal to go to the time-out area. When "seclusion" is spoken the resident is charged fifteen tokens and taken to an empty, darkened room where he must stay until he has been quiet for thirty minutes. If the resident behaves well in seclusion, staying the minimum time, he is reinforced with five tokens on his return to the living quarters.

Burchard also makes use of the concept of "response cost" developed by Weiner (1963). If a subject does not pay his debts every day he loses what is called one behaviour credit: this is his response cost. Unless a subject can maintain his maximum number of behaviour credits, all reinforcers cost additional tokens. If he does maintain his maximum number, he automatically has free access to the yard area outside his unit and can purchase a trip to town (90 tokens) or an hour's recreation time (15 tokens) with the female patients.

Within this general token economy context, Burchard has completed a series of specific experiments, one of which is now described. Burchard selected a specific behaviour, for example sitting at a desk during workshop and school time. The design of the experiment was based on the type of analysis in which reinforcement is contingent on the response during the first phase, non-contingent during the second phase, and contingent again during the third phase, each phase lasting for five consecutive days. The subject received five tokens for accumulating time while sitting at his desk and also for doing specific school tasks. In the second phase he received an equivalent amount of token reinforcement but non-contingently. In the third phase the contingent reinforcement was resumed. There was an immediate decline in performance during the non-contingent phase and a reinstatement of performance under reinforcement during the third phase; these results are similar to the results in other token programmes.

The application of behavioural principles to the modification of the behaviour of juvenile delinquents is illustrated by Project CASE (Contingencies Applicable for Special Education) at the National Training School for Boys (Cohen, Filipczak and Bis, 1966). The target behaviour was academic work in the form of programmed instruction. If the student completed a unit of the programme with a score of at least 90 per cent, he became eligible to take an examination which could earn him token reinforcement in the form of points, each worth one cent. These points could be used to buy items such as Coca-Cola, potato chips, or Sears Roebuck material, to gain entrance into a lounge where his friends were, to register for a new programme, rent books, buy time in the library, or rent a private office with a telephone. The points, unlike the tokens in the programmes used by Ayllon and Azrin, and Atthowe and Krasner, were not transferable from one person to another. The only way the student could obtain points was through the desired behaviour, namely studying.

In their study, Cohen, Filipczak and Bis also showed that the systematic contingent application of reinforcement is most effective within an environment in which the likelihood of desirable behaviour is enhanced and that of undesirable behaviour decreased. Thus these investigators built a special environment including class-rooms, study booths, control rooms, library, store and lounge. They gradually incorporated new and more relevant "pay offs" so that the students gradually switched from working for Coca-Cola to the more educationally relevant behaviour of working for library time or new programmes. It is vital gradually to increase the complexity of expected behaviour in token programmes in order to avoid stagnation.

The results reported on the 16 students in the project indicated that the programme was highly successful in generating desirable educational activities. There was also an accompanying change in behaviour. In four and a half months there were no discipline problems; further, the boys did not destroy or deface the facilities in any way; the social behaviour of the delinquent boys matched that of non-delinquents.

TOKEN ECONOMY IN THE CLASS-ROOM

A major recent development with the token programmes has been their extension into the class-room with relatively "normal" students.

O'Leary and Becker (1967) report on the use of tokens in training atten-tiveness in a class where one teacher dealt with 17 youngsters with behaviour problems. The investigators introduced a token reinforcement system to the whole class. Observations were focused on the eight most disruptive children. Two observers recorded behaviours labelled deviant (for example pushing, talking, making a noise and chewing gum) every 30 seconds for an hour and a half on three days in a week. Behaviours manifested during the observation periods were classified as either disruptive or non-disrup-tive. On the first day of training the experimenter put the following words on the blackboard: "In Seat, Face Front, Raise Hand, Working, Pay Attention, Desk Clear". The experimenter then explained that tokens would be given for these behaviours and that the tokens could be exchanged for back-up reinforcers of candy, comics, perfume and so on. The teacher, during several brief class interludes, rated the extent to which each child had met the criteria. For the first three days tokens were exchanged at the end of each period; tokens were then accumulated before being cashed in, first for two days, then for three and finally four, days. The process was designed gradually to fade-out the back-up reinforcer so that the more traditional acquired reinforcers of teacher's praise would take over. In addition, group points (exchanged for ice-cream) were awarded for quietness of the group during the rating period. Further techniques of verbal praise, ignoring (extinction) and time-out-from-reinforcement were used as appropriate. During the baseline observation period the disruptive-deviant behaviour ranged from 66 to 91 per cent of the observations. The daily mean of observed deviant-disruptive behaviour dropped to a range of from 4 to 32 per cent during the period of token training. The authors concluded that "With the introduction of the token reinforcement system a dramatic, abrupt reduction in deviant behavior occurred. . . . The program was equally successful for all children observed, and repeated anecdotal evidence suggested that the children's appropriate behavior generalized to other situations." (O'Leary and Becker, 1967, p. 637).

Baldwin (1967) investigated the effects of various reinforcers on the development of social skills in a group of mentally retarded subjects. He was also interested in whether intelligence quotient (IQ) or chronological age were variables in responsiveness to these reinforcers. His sample consisted of 72 boys and 24 girls from 6 to 12 years of age and with IQs of 30 to 70. All had been institutionalized with a diagnosis of mental retardation. Children with comparable characteristics were chosen from four wards. The four treatment conditions were: a token economy; a social reinforcement group (social reinforcers consisting primarily of verbal and motor indications of approval); immediate food reinforcement; and a control ward receiving no special treatment. The behaviours measured were social skills. The results indicated that the token programme was significantly more effective than the other programmes for older children, whereas food reinforcement was significantly more effective with the youngest children. Baldwin's results are important because they demonstrate the age differential in responsiveness to the concreteness of the reinforcement. As might be expected, a younger child is more amenable to the effect of tangible reinforcers. Some socialization is necessary for the individual to learn that he can delay gratification. In their general responsiveness to reinforcement, mentally retarded children are similar to normal children. It is of interest that in Baldwin's study differences in IQ were irrelevant in the children's responsiveness.

Baldwin (1967) also reported that attendants trained in token economy techniques with retarded children in one ward setting showed significantly more positive patient-oriented responses and less custodial behaviour in other wards than attendants without such training. This is an important element in token economy programmes, as already mentioned.

Wolf, Giles and Hall (1968) reported on a token economy designed to develop and maintain the academic behaviour of children with low scholastic achievement in a community setting. This report described the results of the first year of after-school remedial education for such children from the fifth and sixth grade in a poor, urban area. The remedial programme incorporated standard instructional material, the mastery of which was supported by token reinforcements.

The reinforcement procedure resembled a trading-stamp plan. Each child was given a folder containing groups of four differently coloured pages divided into squares. The different colours signified different sorts of rewards. After a child had completed an assignment correctly he was given points by the teacher who marked the appropriately coloured squares. At first, points were given after each problem that was worked correctly. As the student acquired a more accurate output, the amount, or difficulty, or both, of work needed to obtain points was gradually increased. The number of points to be given to a child for particular work was decided by the teacher. This decision was sometimes determined partially through negotiation with the child—a unique feature of this programme. Filled pages of points were redeemable, according to their colour, for a variety of goods and events including weekly trips to outdoor events or the cinema, food, money, articles that were available in the store, and long-range goals such as clothes, inexpensive watches and second-hand bicycles. The children could earn tokens in each of three areas: regular class-room work; work completed in the remedial class-room; and six-week report-card grades.

With this basic paradigm, Wolf, Giles and Hall (1968) performed several experimental analyses of the token procedures. In the overall programme they compared the academic achievement of their experimental students during the year with that of a matched control group (15 in each group). The results indicated that the remedial group gained 1·5 years on the Stanford Achievement Test as compared to 0·8 of a year for the control group; these differences are significant at the 0·01 level. There was a similar significant difference in report-card grades. The authors conclude: "... The remedial program's effectiveness in maintaining the children's participation was indicated by the high attendance record, and the fact that whenever the opportunity was given them the children chose to attend class on regular school holidays. . . . The cost of the program, which was substantial, must be contrasted with the longterm cost to society in terms of human as well as economic resources lost by not educating these children adequately. The cost could be reduced significantly by utilizing the potential reinforcers which already exist in almost every educational setting. Properly used, such events as recess, movies, and athletic and social activities could be arranged as consequences for strengthening academic behavior." (Wolf, Giles and Hall, 1968, pp. 63-64).

The results of token economy programmes with a wide range of institutionalized subjects, as illustrated by the above examples, are highly promising. Krasner and Atthowe (1968) recently listed approximately 110 reports of token economy programmes in over 50 different institutions in the United States, Canada and Australia. These included programmes with institutionalized adults, mentally retarded subjects, delinquents, adolescents and emotionally disturbed children.

RESEARCH EVALUATION OF TOKEN ECONOMIES

However, the token economy must also be critically evaluated in a research context. The problems of token economy research are at least as complex as those in any other area of human behavioural change, and probably more so. Institutional research is particularly hard because of the difficulty of controlling relevant variables. Most evidence from research in mental hospitals indicates that some change in the behaviour of patients can be brought about by almost any programme using some form of "total push". The enthusiasm, positive expectation, and increased attention and interest shown by the staff participating in a high prestige research programme all provide massive extra amounts of social reinforcement likely to bring about and maintain new and desirable behaviour in the patient. The goal of the research investigator using a token economy is to demonstrate, first, significant behavioural change, and, second, that the change is due to the specific techniques used in the programme.

Token economy programmes can be divided into the following categories according to the research techniques used:

(a) Programmes that are primarily demonstration projects, in which no attempt is made to control variables. Although change may be observed, it cannot with certainty be attributed to the tokens *per se*.

(b) Programmes using the subjects before the programme is introduced as a baseline, that is, as their own controls (for example Ayllon and Azrin, 1965; Atthowe and Krasner, 1968). Operant measurement is taken of the patients' behaviour for a specific period of time. The token programme is introduced and the same behaviours continue to be measured. The token contingencies may be removed and again the behaviour continues to be measured. Then the token contingencies are reintroduced.

(c) The effectiveness of the token economy procedure can be tested by the use of control groups which receive either no specific treatment or a different treatment. Marks, Schalock and Sonoda (1967), for example, worked with 22 chronic schizophrenic males divided into 11 pairs matched on the basis of a rating of their adjustment to the hospital environment. One member of each pair was assigned to group *A*, called "reinforcement therapy", and the other to group *B*, called "relationship therapy". In group *A* each patient received tokens (poker chips) for individual specified behaviours, and the cost of a meal was ten tokens. Initially the reinforced behaviours were selected by the staff. Later the goals were frequently set by the patients themselves. Selected behaviours were tailored to the individual and his progress. One man might be rewarded for simply receiving and paying tokens, another for improving his appearance, another for discussing discharge plans with a social worker, another for expressing feelings. The relationship therapy (for patients in group B) was designed to enlarge and deepen the patients' self-understanding and self-acceptance through daily psychotherapy meetings. The nine therapists taking part avoided giving social reinforcement when specific behaviours appeared. Each subject received both forms of treatment for approximately ten weeks on each. Eighteen measures, mostly connected with work and social and conceptual performance, were assessed before and after the treatments. The authors concluded that both therapies were effective in improving the behaviour of chronic hospitalized patients, but that reinforcement therapy was more economical of staff time. They concluded also that "reinforcement can be used in a 'psychodynamic' way. It can be used to shape self-assertive, critical, and dominating behaviors as well as the more conforming ones. Under both therapies there are more evidences of changes in behavioral efficiency than of changes in self-regard or personality structure." (Marks, Shalock and Sonoda, 1967, p. 238).

(d) Programmes in which performance in the token economy is related to performance in another learning task. Panek (1966) worked with 32 chronic schizophrenics (from the Atthowe-Krasner ward). He conditioned common word associations (from the Kent-Rosanoff and Russell-Jenkins lists) with positive and negative contingencies of verbal and token reinforcement, and then compared success in associated learning with the total number of ward/token transactions. This latter figure was taken as a measure of the responsivity to reinforcement; that is, the patient who *earned* most tokens and *spent* most tokens was considered most *responsive* to the token programme. The results showed a significant increase of common word associations under either positive (saying "right" and giving a fractional ward token) or negative (saying "wrong" and taking away a fractional ward token) reinforcement, but no significant differences under the two contingencies. Most important, rankings of the rate of learning were significantly correlated with rankings of the total use of tokens. This is one of the few studies which have demonstrated that the individual who is responsive in one conditioning task (such as a token economy) is also responsive in an individual verbal conditioning task. This suggests that the conditioning task could be used as a predictor of the response to token programmes. It also relates to a previous series of studies (Krasner, Ullmann and Fisher, 1964; Krasner, Knowles and Ullmann, 1965) which demonstrated that verbal conditioning of attitudes in one task was significantly correlated to performance in another task requiring motor performance.

Three additional features of token economy programmes warrant attention: the preliminary training procedures needed for the staff; the social and ethical implications; and the potential development of the programmes for broader social use (Krasner, 1962a, 1966b, 1968).

TRAINING FOR PARTICIPATION IN TOKEN ECONOMY PROGRAMMES

In an institution in which behavioural techniques have not been extensively used time must be spent in training the personnel who will operate the token economy procedures. It is the universal experience that staff training is the most important element in the success of the token economy programme. Initially there is usually strong resistance to any programme which apparently threatens the stability of life on the ward, and token programmes in particular often necessitate a radical change in the philosophy of treatment. The patient is approached as a responsible individual who is being helped to a position of full control over his behaviour. He is trained to learn new habits of behaviour. He is not to be viewed as a sick person suffering from a mental illness and therefore incapable of responsible behaviour. The view that the patient in a mental hospital is an individual with problems in living rather than a sufferer from illness is just beginning to gain some acceptance (Szasz, 1961; Ullmann and Krasner, 1969). But this is not a new concept and goes back at least to the period of moral treatment which has been recently so favourably re-evaluated (Bockoven, 1963; Dain, 1964). Thus a basic element in the training procedure is to change the staff's concept of the role of the patients.

Equally important is the necessary change in concept of the role of the staff, especially of the aide and the nurse. Implicit in the token economy programme is the switch of the nurse from a custodial role, or from a mental health role with its aura of tender loving care, to that of a hard nosed scientifically oriented "behavioural engineer"—a term aptly introduced by Ayllon and Michael (1959).

Contingency reinforcement by nurses and aides on hospital wards is not, of course, a new procedure. Hospital patients are usually given rewards in the form of approval, cigarettes and extra privileges for behaviour that the staff want. A kind of continuous shaping programme finally turns the patient into a fully institutionalized individual, apathetic and withdrawn. Token economy programmes are different because they apply behavioural principles in a controlled, planned, systematic and contingent manner so as to modify behaviour deliberately in a socially desirable direction.

SOCIAL IMPLICATIONS OF THE TOKEN ECONOMY APPROACH

The social implications of token programmes can be approached from another viewpoint. Token economy programmes, because of the issues they arouse, may be compared to Utopian planning. It may seem curious to equate a treatment programme for hospital patients with the setting up of an ideal society, but I suggest that the ideal place to initiate Utopias is the mental hospital. Although Utopia literally means "no place", the "some place" in which planned social living programmes can be carried out and tested for effectiveness is the mental hospital. The kinds of questions that must be answered when a token economy is set up are similar to those that must be answered in the planning of the "good" society. First, what are the goals of the society, the desired behaviours to be reinforced? Second, what training or educational procedures are necessary to shape or maintain these behaviours in this society? Third, how can the current way of life be modified so that there is a reasonable chance of initiating the new planned programme? Many writers have tried to answer these questions (More, 1551; Butler, 1872; Bellamy, 1888; Skinner, 1948; Huxley, 1962; Parrington, 1964).

Walden Two (Skinner, 1948) is of special interest because in this book a behavioural scientist attempts to foresee and to some extent control the consequences of his scientific endeavours. Further, the principles of token economy and *Walden Two* are both based on the operant conditioning principles developed by Skinner (1938, 1953), which have also permeated the class-room through programmed learning procedures.

In fact *Walden Two* is a token economy. Individuals in the community work for "labor credit"—entries in a ledger. Several of the token programmes use the same technique, avoiding physical tokens. The allocation of specific credits for specific tasks is based on principles suggested by Bellamy (1888). The different credit values for different kinds of work are adjusted from time to time on the basis of demands. This principle is also used in several token economy programmes (for example, Ayllon and Azrin, 1965). Thus pleasant jobs have lower value and must be worked at for long periods to earn tokens, whereas unpleasant jobs (cleaning sewers for example) have high value and hence little work time. In *Walden Two* each member of the community must earn 1,200 labour credits in order to maintain his status in the community. But tokens are not needed for specific good things in life—all goods and services are free. The number of labour credits needed to maintain oneself in the community may be changed according to the needs of the community. The aim of the society is to obtain enough work from its members such that the society may maintain itself "with a slight margin of safety".

Six planners in *Walden Two* are paid 600 credits per year (so they must do additional work to stay in the society) to plan the community, and hence to govern it. These positions are analogous to those of the research team planning a token economy programme. The specialists in charge of divisions and services in *Walden Two* are the managers, whose positions may be compared to those of professional staff of a hospital. Neither the managers nor the planners are elected by the rest of society. The analogy between mental hospital token economy programmes and *Walden Two* breaks down at this point because the research investigators and professional staff of a hospital are not part of the community of patients. The goal in setting up a Utopia in a mental hospital would be to train patients to become planners and managers so that the whole community can be autonomous. It will not be easy for professional people to permit programmes which take the control of behaviour out of their hands and put it in the hands of the patients. But this is not impossible because implicit in a token economy programme is the idea that one is dealing with responsible, not sick, people (*vide supra*).

The concept of a Utopian society based on operant conditioning principles, be it a token economy in a hospital or a *Walden Two*, elicits considerable philosophical opposition. For example, the essayist and social critic, Joseph Wood Krutch, views his humanistic social philosophy as the antithesis of a Skinnerian type of social order. Krutch (1967) conjures up a vision of a "termite society" in which there is no individuality and only one social imperative, "the greatest good of the greatest number". He considers that termites are merely machines in their mindless and efficient manner of operation. Krutch argues that the characteristics of termite society approximate to the ideal of certain Utopias such as *Walden Two*. "There is no selfishness and only the welfare of the community counts. There is no competition, only cooperation; no struggle for individual wealth, superiority or status." (Krutch, 1967, p. 40).

Krutch further takes Skinner to task for arguing that a society should emphasize the behaviours which will make it more probable that the society will survive, for by that test the termite society is very successful. Krutch (1967, p. 45) criticizes *Walden Two* because the citizens are unaware of the extent to which they have been conditioned to automatic "right attitudes"; men behave reasonably "not because they reason but because they do not; because their automatic responses are the right ones—as they are also in a termite colony." Krutch thus places the greatest value on man's ability to choose.

The same arguments are put forward, in various forms and at various levels of sophistication, against what is thought to be the determinism of the token economy society. But token economy programmes are far from deterministic or mechanistic. Systematization does not mean mechanization. In fact the major element in these programmes is flexibility. Unless the programme continually changes by incorporating new behaviours, changing values, and bringing in new "good things", it becomes as static as any traditional programme. When a token programme begins it is impossible to predict contingencies that may be available within a year. This is perhaps the most valid criticism against Utopias which try to offer solutions on an eternal basis. Even *Walden Two* represents a fixed society in which all human problems have been worked out. Change itself must be programmed into the design. The goal of the programme is for an individual to be enabled to make choices in his life. If he has more than one behaviour in his repertoire, an individual is obviously freer than if he has no alternatives.

Token economy programmes incorporate all the principles of behaviour modification, which include most experimental techniques of changing human behaviour that have been recorded (Krasner, 1962b). Learning a new behaviour may be influenced by operant and classical conditioning, modelling, placebo, or expectancy. All these procedures may be objectively described in behavioural terms, measured and controlled. Some of the descriptions of token programmes have used oversimplified reinforcement concepts. Reinforcement is operating, but it is more than just a question of a token reinforcing a behaviour and thus increasing the likelihood of its occurrence. There are many more cues in any one situation. In the Atthowe-Krasner programme, for example, giving the tokens was accompanied by social reinforcements such as saying "I'm pleased", "That's very good", or smiles and head nods. The purpose of these extra reinforcements was to maximize a social influence process and to develop the eventual effectiveness of social reinforcement. The aides and nurses who give these social reinforcements have been trained to expect them to be highly effective in producing change and also to respond positively to minimal change. Whatever cues are involved in high expectancy are maximized to enhance the social influence of the process. Demonstrations of appropriate behaviour are given by aides or by other patients; in other words modelling is used (Bandura, 1965). Whatever variables are involved in the placebo effect (Frank, 1961) are also present in these programmes, as in all behaviour modification. But, as in desensitization studies (Paul, 1966), the evidence is that the specific technique of token reinforcement adds something in addition to all other effects. The hypotheses that have been raised in these discussions require experimental confirmation, and studies designed for this are still in their early stages.

TRANSFER OF EFFECTS FROM TOKEN ECONOMY PROGRAMMES

Behaviour changes only in a social context. The question then is: Does behaviour generalize from one situation to another? Although both laboratory and individual case studies with operant procedures have attempted to approach problems of generalization (for example changing class-room behaviour and then measuring changes in behaviour outside the class-room), most of the token economy programmes have not attempted such measures and approach changes in behaviour outside the programme rather differently. The goal of institutional change is usually to encourage such behaviour as will enable the individual to function well in a situation outside the institution. In order to do this one must first analyse the new external situation to determine what behaviours are necessary for the individual to maximize social reinforcement for himself.

A new token economy programme in progress at the Veterans Administration Hospital, Palo Alto, uses this approach. Rather than trying to change behaviour within the institution and hoping that changes in behaviour outside will develop in consequence it is decided at the outset what behaviours will pay off for the individual in a foster home or living with other patients in a community setting; and these behaviours are reinforced, shaped and developed by tokens. For example, if the patient is to move into a home and live with other ex-patients, the important behaviours to develop include cooking, cleaning in the house, shopping, management of money, and especially gardening and maintenance of the house. This last is extremely important so as to elicit favourable responses from neighbours who will see these efforts as a way of enhancing the value of the property rather than as a potential danger.

CONCLUSIONS

The topic of this symposium is the application of learning to psychotherapy. This paper has argued that token economy programmes are the most advanced type of social engineering currently in use and have developed from the earlier applications of learning to modify the behaviour of disturbed people. I suggest that eventually three types of treatment procedures will be used when people seek help from professional healers. First, what Kanfer (1966) and Schofield (1964) have called "friendship therapy". Second, the specific application of behaviour modification to change specific disturbing behaviours. Third, social engineering as exemplified by a token economy. Token economy procedures need a combination of social and economic planning. When an economist (for example Galbraith, 1967) relates a "general theory of motivation" to the economic structure of society, he is presenting hypotheses that can be tested in small social units, such as hospital wards, by means of a token economy. The research potential of the application of behavioural principles to social affairs is enormous and represents the next stage of development in the application of learning to psychotherapy.

SUMMARY

This paper presents the results of a token economy programme in a psychiatric hospital and a review of other such programmes in the United States, Canada and Australia. A token economy involves the systematic application of reinforcement principles contingent upon desired behaviour. It requires the designation of certain behaviours as desirable, hence to be reinforced; a medium of exchange—the token; and back-up reinforcers— the "good things in life". The origin of such programmes may be traced, on the one hand, to laboratory work based on operant conditioning and, on the other, to hospital procedures involving environmental control, such as the historical moral treatment and the more recent therapeutic community. The author (together with J. M. Atthowe) initiated a token economy programme at the Veterans Administration Hospital, Palo Alto, California, in September 1964. Techniques of training staff, problems in initiating programmes, assessment of change, and experimental designs are discussed. The procedures and results are compared with those of other programmes. A survey of similar programmes indicates that they have been successful in changing the behaviour of adult psychiatric patients, retarded children, delinquents, adolescents, and disturbed children. The token economy represents a link between treatment programmes and social and economic planning. Finally, the social and ethical implications of these programmes are discussed.

ACKNOWLEDGEMENT

Supported in part by U.S. Publie Health Service Grant MH-11938.

REFERENCES

ATTHOWE, J. M., JR., and KRASNER, L. (1968). *J. abnorm. Psychol.*, **73**, 37–43.

AYLLON, T., and AZRIN, N. H. (1965). *J. exp. Analysis Behav.*, **8**, 357–383.

AYLLON, T., and MICHAEL, J. (1959). *J. exp. Analysis Behav.*, **2**, 323–334.

AZRIN, N. H., and HOLZ, W. C. (1966). In *Operant Behavior: Areas of Research and Application*, ed. Honig, W. H., pp. 380–443. New York: Appleton-Century-Crofts.

BALDWIN, V. L. (1967). *Diss. Abstr.*, **27**, (9-A), 2865.

BANDURA, A. (1965). In *Research in Behavior Modification*, pp. 310–340, eds. Krasner, L., and Ullmann, L. P. New York: Holt, Rinehart & Winston.

BELLAMY, E. (1888). *Looking Backward: 2000–1887*. Boston: Ticknor.

BOCKOVEN, J. S. (1963). *Moral Treatment in American Psychiatry*. New York: Springer.

BURCHARD, J. D. (1967). *Psychol. Rec.*, **11**, 461–476.

BUTLER, S. (1872). *Erewhon*. Everyman's 881. New York: Dutton.

COHEN, H. L., FILIPCZAK, J. A., and BIS, J. S. (1966). *Contingencies Applicable to Special Education of Delinquents: Establishing 24-hour Control in an Experimental Cottage.* Silver Spring, Maryland: Institute for Behavioral Research.

DAIN, N. (1964). *Concept of Insanity in the United States, 1789–1865.* New Brunswick, New Jersey: Rutgers University Press.

EYSENCK, H. J. (ed.) (1960). *Behavior Therapy and the Neuroses.* Oxford: Pergamon.

EYSENCK, H. J., and RACHMAN, S. (1965). *The Causes and Cures of Neuroses.* San Diego: Robert Knapp.

FRANK, J. D. (1961). *Persuasion and Healing.* Baltimore: Johns Hopkins Press.

GALBRAITH, J. K. (1967). *The New Industrial State.* Boston: Houghton Mifflin.

GERICKE, O. L. (1965). *Psychiat. Studies Projects*, **3**, No. 5, 1–10.

HUXLEY, A. (1962). *Island.* New York: Harper.

KANFER, Г. H. (1966). *J. consult. Psychol.*, **31**, 171–177.

KRASNER, L. (1962a). *Am. Psychol.*, **17**, 199–204.

KRASNER, L. (1962b). In *Research in Psychotherapy*, vol. 2, eds. Strupp, H. H., and Luborsky, L. Washington, D. C.: American Psychological Association.

KRASNER, L. (1965). *Operant Conditioning Techniques with Adults from the Laboratory to "Real Life" Behavior Modification.* Paper presented to American Psychological Association, in Chicago, 1965. (Unpublished.)

KRASNER, L. (1966a). *The Translation of Operant Conditioning Procedures from the Experimental Laboratory to the Psychotherapeutic Interaction.* Paper presented to the American Psychological Association, in New York, 1966. (Unpublished.)

KRASNER, L. (1966b). *J. soc. Issues*, **21**, 9–30.

KRASNER, L. (1968). In *Assessment and Status of the Behavioral Therapies and Associated Developments*, in press, ed. Franks, C. M. New York: McGraw-Hill.

KRASNER, L., and ATTHOWE, J. M., JR. (1968). *Token Economy Bibliography.* New York: State University of New York, Stony Brook.

KRASNER, L., KNOWLES, J. B., and ULLMANN, L. P. (1965). *J. Pers. soc. Psychol.*, **1**, 407–412.

KRASNER, L., and ULLMANN, L. P. (eds.) (1965). *Research in Behavior Modification.* New York: Holt, Rinehart & Winston.

KRASNER, L., ULLMANN, L. P., and FISHER, D. (1964). *Percept. mot. Skills*, **19**, 811–816.

KRUTCH, J. W. (1967). *And Even if You Do.* New York: Morrow.

MARKS, J., SCHALOCK, R., and SONODA, B. (1967). *Proc. Am. psychol. Ass.*, **75**, 237–238.

MORE, T. (1551). *Utopia.*

O'LEARY, D. K., and BECKER, W. C. (1967). *Exceptional Children*, **5**, 637–642.

PANEK, D. M. (1966). Doctoral thesis, Washington State University, Faculty of Sciences.

PARRINGTON, V. L., JR. (1964). *American Dreams: A Study of American Utopias.* New York: Russell & Russell.

PAUL, G. L. (1966). *Insight vs. Desensitization in Psychotherapy.* Stanford: Stanford University Press.

PREMACK, D. (1959). *Psychol. Rev.*, **66**, 219–233.

SCHAEFER, H. H., and MARTIN, P. L. (1966). *Psychol. Rep.*, **19**, 1147–1158.

SCHOFIELD, W. (1964). *Psychotherapy: the Purchase of Friendship.* New York: Prentice-Hall.

SKINNER, B. F. (1938). *The Behavior of Organisms.* New York: Appleton-Century-Crofts.

SKINNER, B. F. (1948). *Walden Two.* New York: Macmillan.

SKINNER, B. F. (1953). *Science and Human Behavior.* New York: Macmillan.

STEFFY, R. A., TORNEY, D., HART, J., CRAW, M., and MARLETT, N. (1966). *An Application of Learning Techniques to the Management and Rehabilitation of Severely Regressed, Chronically Ill Patients: Preliminary Findings.* Paper presented to Ontario Psychological Association, Lakeshore Psychiatric Hospital, Ottawa, February, 1966. (Unpublished.)

SZASZ, T. S. (1961). *The Myth of Mental Illness.* New York: Hoeber-Harper.

ULLMANN, L. P., and KRASNER, L. (eds.) (1965). *Case Studies in Behavior Modification.* New York: Holt, Rinehart & Winston.

ULLMANN, L. P., and KRASNER, L. (1969). *A Psychological Approach to Abnormal Behavior.* New York: Prentice-Hall.

WEINER, H. (1963). *J. exp. Analysis Behav.*, **6**, 415–421.

WOLF, M. M., GILES, D. K., and HALL, V. R. (1968). *Behav. Res. Ther.*, **6**, 51–64.

WOLPE, J., and LAZARUS, A. A. (1966). *Behaviour Therapy Techniques: A Guide to the Treatment of Neuroses.* Oxford: Pergamon.

DISCUSSION

Carstairs: It might be interesting to try to define the relationship of this particular type of social engineering—token economy—to another much older tradition—money economy. In 1801 P. Pinel (*Traité Médico-philosophique sur l'Aliénation Mentale.* Paris: Richard, Caille and Ravier; cited by Carstairs, G. M. [1959]. In *Congr. Rep. II Int. Congr. Psychiat.*, vol. 1, pp. 99-102, ed. Stoll, W. A. [Zurich 1957]. Zurich: Orell Füssli Arts Graphiques S.A.) described the change in the patients in his ward for the severely disturbed when they engaged in financially productive work supplied by the merchants of Paris. The attention of these disturbed patients was held by the prospect of a modest wage. P. A. Peffer (1953. *Am. J. Psychiat.*, **110**, 84-92), in the Veterans Administration (VA) Organization in the United States, recorded the results of a similar approach; his work was repeated by some colleagues and myself (Carstairs, G. M., O'Connor, N., and Rawnsley, K. [1956]. *Br. J. prev. soc. Med.*, **10**, 136-140). One of Peffer's first papers was entitled "*Money: a Rehabilitation Incentive for Mental Patients*". Peffer devised a system of retraining in the VA hospitals, with money as the token. Nearly all industrial therapy in hospitals has focused on the area of the patients' working lives. Attempts are made to re-engage them in productive activities for reward, with some expectation of generalization to other behaviours. But the difference between these systems and your study is that you have deliberately chosen to reward behaviours unrelated to the external work situation. There is a fundamental contradiction between your Utopian token economy and the money economy of the real world: your programme trains people to respond to the expectation of rewards for good behaviour, and what they have learned must now be transferred so that they respond to the much less tangible rewards of social acceptance and approval. When I visited the VA Hospital, Palo Alto (where you introduced your original programme) in 1966, some of your colleagues explained to me that the society outside actually provided strong financial disincentives to leaving hospital. When a patient is rehabilitated to a certain point he is shrewd enough to calculate that he would need a very well-paid job outside to earn as much as he can earn if he remains as a VA patient. This is the contradiction.

Krasner: The predecessors of the token programmes are not only the systems used by Pinel and his colleagues but the whole moral-treatment approach, which specified that certain "good" behaviours would be rewarded and "bad" ones might be punished.

Carstairs: F. Leuret, a champion of "moral treatment", gave his patients a cold douche every time they reported a delusion, until they learned better (cited by Walk, A. [1954]. *J. ment. Sci.*, **100**, 833–837).

Krasner: Most of the current token programmes emphasize positive reinforcement. When negative reinforcement is used it is as a withdrawal of the opportunity to earn tokens.

Miller: How successful was your programme in terms of the number of patients discharged from hospital?

Krasner: We indicated in advance that we were not aiming for the patient's discharge; the goal in the programme I described was to bring about change within the hospital setting. But we did find that compared with the figures for the previous year more of our patients were discharged during the first experimental year, although the proportion of these that were readmitted was the same as previously. We are now starting another programme at the VA Hospital, Palo Alto, in which the goal is discharge from hospital (see my presentation, p. 171). It is true that many VA hospitals reinforce the likelihood that the patient will remain in hospital.

Marks: There seem to be two possible and different goals of token economy programmes. First, to teach the patient to lead a more active and sociable life in the ward, which incidentally results in a smoothly running ward; and, second, to influence the original reasons (ideas of suicide, for example) for the patient's admission to hospital (the reasons which, presumably, prevented him from living in the community) so that he can learn to maintain himself outside hospital. It is unlikely that one can influence these two goals through the same programme. But if, as you have just described, you change the contingencies that are reinforced, behaviour directed to the second goal may emerge.

What is the cost-effectiveness of these programmes? Do you need to increase the number of staff, compared with the number needed for routine custodial care? And do the number of working hours need to be increased for your programmes?

Krasner: Our experience and the reports of others indicate that an increase in the number of staff is not necessary. In some programmes the number of staff has actually been decreased because their work becomes more effective. The training period of the staff, and whether one can use the personnel already in the hospitals, creates real problems. It may be better to use relatively untrained, younger people who are inexperienced in mental health work because they have much less to unlearn than older assistants.

Kubie: The George Junior Republic is an institution for adolescents in which the "citizens" can use only the token money (*vide infra*) which they earn. This institution was started in the 1890's in upper New York State by a Mr. William George who had been born and brought up on a farm in that area. He made a fortune in New York and, every summer, took destitute children from the streets to his farm. Then he found that he could not bear to send them back to the city streets. He finally sold his business and returned to upper New York State to organize for these children an inter-racial, integrated, coeducational, residential treatment school—the George Junior Republic (Kubie, L. S., and Cluett, J. [1955]. *The George Junior Republic*. Freeville, New York: Franklin Print Shop; [1955]. *The George Junior Republic: An Interpretation*. Freeville, New York: Franklin Print Shop). This institution has a meaningful self-governing system with an elected executive, legislative and judicial board. It has its own currency system. The citizen-students print their own paper money and stamp their own plastic coins. They are paid for everything they do, including study (this counts as white-collar work); and they pay for everything they get. If they go home for a holiday, they change their money for dollars at a rate of exchange which they determine themselves. Thus the school and the national currency systems are interrelated. These boys come from both the poorest and the wealthiest families. If a child from a rich home is sent a present he can accept this provided he has saved enough of his earnings to pay the customs duties. This is a meaningful system, not just a token economy. The citizens run their own bank, and the system plays an important part in the organization of their lives and ego structures.

Krasner: The programmes I have described also involve real economic systems. This applies particularly to the study by H. L. Cohen, J. A. Filipczak and J. S. Bis (1966. *Contingencies Applicable to Special Education of Delinquents: Establishing 24-hour Control in an Experimental Cottage.* Silver Spring, Maryland: Institute for Behavioral Research) at the National Training School.

Kubie: But through the self-governing system at the George Junior Republic the boys can alter the shape of their own lives. They make their own culture. It is not a dictated framework for their living.

Freeman: An important application of the token economy approach might be to increase our understanding of the psychological structure of the chronic schizophrenic patient. There is a tendency, particularly in psychiatric research projects in neuropharmacology, biochemistry, psychology and so on, to regard any collection of chronic schizophrenics (such as the inmates of a chronic ward in a mental hospital) as a homogeneous group. But people who work closely with these patients can see that it is an oversimplification simply to classify them all as chronic katatonics and hebephrenics. The token economy programme might show up important differences between the patients who respond and cooperate with the programme and those who do not.

Krasner: One of our first problems is to find out who is not responsive to the programme. Most of the patients cooperate in playing the game and accepting our rules. But when we find a patient who will have nothing to do with the programme we take the responsibility for this upon ourselves. We do not blame the uncooperative, or punish him by moving him to another ward, but assume that we have not completely worked out all the contingencies in the individual's life and so have not found suitable ways of reinforcing desirable behaviour in him. For example, one patient in our programme would not earn tokens, or take them when he did earn them. We observed that he used to walk in the grounds and feed a cat, with obvious enjoyment. So we told him that he could continue to feed the cat but it would cost him one token. He had to do something to get a token and so he had to join the system. Incidentally, the token economy programme does not preclude individual treatment and we still use individual behaviour therapy for certain patients.

Freeman: I wanted to know whether your data can help us to classify the patients into different groups according to how they respond to the programme. Your study is particularly interesting because of the trouble you have taken to find out why, and to what, patients respond. Such detailed information about chronic schizophrenics is rare.

Krasner: We did not use these data to classify chronic schizophrenics or to categorize the different characteristics of those who were and were not responsive initially, since we assumed that eventually we would find ways of helping almost all patients to respond.

Lebedev: Are there any differences in the attitude of different groups of patients to these techniques? For example, did children and adults, or neurotics and psychotics, respond in different ways? And are there any clinical features which contraindicate the use of your method?

Krasner: Large differences in attitude to token economy programmes in different groups of patients have not been reported. The patients do not resent the programme provided the staff are, and are seen to be, confident of its value. I know of no work using token economies in the neuroses; the use of tokens *per se* might be too simple, even insulting, for the relatively sophisticated neurotic patient. Nonetheless, the principle of trying to change behaviour in order to elicit positive reinforcement from others may be useful in psychotherapy for neurotics. It is too early to make any reasonable statement about contraindications on the basis of our studies. But token economy programmes have been used with alcoholics (Marrol, H. G. [1967]. *Q. Jl Stud. Alcohol,* **28,** 105-115).

Lazarus: Reinforcement techniques have been used with neurotic private patients in an out-patient setting. Therapists have made their fees contingent on changes in the patient's behaviour; instead of a fixed fee per session the therapist fined the patient (that is, he raised the fee) if deviant responses persisted, and lowered the fee if behaviour improved. Self-administered aversive techniques have also been used with variable effects. Dr. James P. Mathie of Michigan (unpublished material) described an alcoholic who agreed to burn five dollars whenever he had a drink. Unfortunately, he became so anxious about the money he was burning that he had to drink more to forget it. With aversive techniques one must find a suitable aversive situation for each individual. Some people would not care about burning money but would find it terribly painful to burn a favourite book. Another example of a self-administered aversive technique was used with an obese woman who agreed not to wear a false front tooth each time she deviated from her diet; she rapidly lost weight (Mathie, J. P., unpublished).

Krasner: Self-shock is another way of giving aversive therapy—the patients (neurotics) have shock boxes to use on themselves.

Lebedev: Patients with certain mental disorders, particularly depression with suicidal tendencies, sometimes try to dissimulate their pathological state: they try to hide their symptoms and conform to normal patterns of behaviour. Although superficially such behaviour seems to indicate an improvement in their condition, in fact the extent of the mental disturbance has not changed. If in such cases the outward improvement in behaviour is rewarded, reinforcement is not being directed to the basic mechanisms underlying the symptoms (which is the aim of any kind of therapy) but to the tendency to dissimulate. Would you comment on this problem, Professor Krasner?

Krasner: This question illustrates the differences between the behavioural and psychodynamic approaches. Behaviour therapists tend to focus on behaviour—observed behaviour and the consequence of behavioural change—and do not utilize the concept of the symptom and the underlying disease it represents. The behaviour-oriented therapist is less likely than the psychoanalyst to worry about whether he has induced basic personality changes in the patient. He argues that even a small change in behaviour may have many ramifications: if a patient behaves differently people react to him differently. Thus a small change in behaviour may give rise to considerable changes in the overall situation.

Leder: How does the token economy system of rewarding affect the relationships between the patients? Is the patient who is "top of the tokens" an object of envy and hate, or of admiration? And what effect does the programme have on the internal life of the hospital community?

Krasner: We had to decide initially what sorts of behaviour we wanted to reinforce and we decided to reward personal interactions (the opposite of apathy). We therefore rewarded such behaviours as talking to or playing a game with another patient. Our programme was not designed to develop leaders, although this could be done by using a system of differential rewards for leadership behaviour, that is, for taking the initiative. Although we did not set out to measure the attitude of the other patients towards those who were successful in earning tokens, my impression is that most patients were not particularly interested in what other patients were earning. But any sort of interest, whether this was expressed as questions about the number of tokens earned, or admiration, or hostility, or even attempts to steal tokens, was reinforced because in this particular programme we were trying to counteract apathy.

Leder: Do your data provide any information about whether the patients developed cognitive awareness about the programme and its aims as their behaviour changed? Were you able to discuss the programme with them at any stage?

Krasner: We explained the programme to the patients several times, both before and after it started, and they were asked to put written suggestions about it in a suggestion box. Our explanations elicited little response (for example, there were no comments on whether the patients liked the programme or not), but we assumed that they were being received. We rewarded every suggestion, whether it was adopted or not, with tokens.

Miller: Did you explain the contingencies to the patients?

Krasner: We simply told them that they were being rewarded according to their behaviour. It was implicit in the programme that we were rewarding behaviour that we approved of because it was good for the patient. But we did not attempt to explain the theoretical rationale.

Leder: The treatment might be more effective if you could do this.

Krasner: I agree; we may attempt this in another programme.

Leder: Does the type of behaviour that is rewarded influence the results? For example, what would happen if you rewarded undesirable (say, disruptive) behaviour with tokens?

Krasner: It has been argued that disruptive behaviour is maintained by the reinforcement of people's reactions to it, that is, by its consequences; and both desirable and undesirable behaviours can be increased by rewarding them. The subject of a token economy programme will (reasonably) assume that the behaviour that is rewarded (whether desirable or undesirable) is one that we are trying to encourage.

Miller: You commented in your presentation that you could increase the incidence of either of two different desirable behaviours by a system of differential rewards; and presumably the same thing would apply to any two behaviours, desirable or undesirable.

Foss: Is it correct that the main difference between the early token economy programmes and your own is that in your study reinforcement is immediately contingent on the behaviour to be encouraged?

Krasner: No. Immediate contingent reinforcement is characteristic of all token programmes.

Foss: I am perplexed by the mechanics of, for example, the study of D. K. O'Leary and W. C. Becker (1967. *Exceptional Children*, **5**, 637-642). These authors worked with 17 children simultaneously. How could any observer give immediate contingent reinforcement to such a large number of subjects?

Krasner: This was also the initial reaction of the observer (a teacher) in this study. O'Leary and Becker first trained the teacher in the general procedures involved. Apparently anyone in front of any audience can, with training, observe what is going on in the whole area. So the teacher was trained to observe all the children in the class-room. At the end of the first hour she rated the "goodness" of the children's behaviour on a scale of 1 to 10; this took her about three minutes per child.

Foss: So reinforcement was not contingent on any specific piece of "good" behaviour, but was governed by an impression of behaviour during one hour; that is a long time for "immediate" contingency.

Krasner: The reinforcement was contingent on behaviour in the preceding 30 minutes or so.

Foss: Children, and probably adults also, behave as though they needed to establish dominance hierarchies; they want to be near the top of some hierarchy and if necessary they invent hierarchies for this purpose. This might be a snag in your programmes, because one of the most common of these invented hierarchies is an antisocial one. I predict that some of your patients will try to be near the top of the hierarchy that consists of individuals who opt out of the programme.

Krasner: This may occur, particularly in the studies on token economy programmes with delinquents, but we have not found it yet. But we did evolve a positive way for opting out of the programme: patients who earned a large number of tokens qualified to join a special group. The members of this group were entitled to all the benefits of the system without having to earn tokens. They remained in the group, and enjoyed the associated prestige, for as long as they continued to practise "good" behaviour.

Carstairs: I am surprised that you did not observe this "dominance in a hostile hierarchy". K. Kesey described exactly this in patients in group therapy (1962. *One Flew over the Cuckoo's Nest.* New York: New American Library).

Krasner: Kesey's book was not written about our token economy programme.

Carstairs: If Kesey were in your team now he might write another book!

Sifneos: I am particularly interested in paranoid people who are suspicious of systems. Explanations will not change this attitude. Were there any such patients in your programmes, Professor Krasner?

Krasner: The patients in our first study were burnt-out schizophrenics, but the sample contained no actively paranoid patients. We did not reward an individual for expressing his delusional systems or paranoid ideas but neither did such behaviour interfere with the programme. But we could devise a programme to counteract active paranoia by reinforcing non-paranoid behaviours. T. Ayllon and J. Michael (1959. *J. exp. Analysis Behav.*, **2**, 323-334) recorded data on one paranoid patient. They defined paranoid and non-paranoid talk for this patient, and devised ways of measuring them. The observers (nurses) were trained to respond to the non-paranoid and ignore the paranoid talk. In a few weeks there was a dramatic decrease in the latter and a corresponding increase in the former.

Sandler: We have not yet discussed one dimension of the psychotherapy of neurotic patients: the negative reaction to reward. One of the major factors contributing to the failure of psychotherapy in neurotics is guilt about success, guilt even at the thought of getting better. A characteristic of the lives of these patients who show a "negative therapeutic reaction" is their repeated ruin by success. Any sign of improvement may create a negative reaction in a patient with strong guilt feelings. This phenomenon emphasizes some of the differences between the psychodynamic and learning theory approaches to psychotherapy. Behavioural techniques might be successful with many neurotics but it is difficult to see how these techniques could be effective with the type of patient for whom success (reward and positive gain) engenders such guilt that he has to engage in self-damaging behaviour. Subjects with work failures and career difficulties are often in this category. How could one determine reinforcement for such patients? One would have to introduce such a paradoxical system of rewards and disincentives that improvement would be indicated by deterioration: as the patient recovered he would inevitably relapse.

Krasner: Whatever technique we use, minute assessment of the life situation of the individual is vital. For a patient who reacts negatively to success, we must decide in advance what behaviours to reinforce in order to help him. This poses an especially complex problem of assessment because quick success may not be the most appropriate behaviour to reinforce. But careful analysis of the life situation will almost always reveal suitable reinforcements for any individual.

Sandler: This may be a more fundamental problem than can be solved by the reconstruction of *internal* processes according to observed *external* behaviour. Even the thought of success (or anything offering the promise of success) may call up the need for punishment and failure. Thus the behaviour we see may be failure brought about by a reaction of guilt towards incipient success.

Miller: In other words, as soon as anything is defined as a reward by this group of patients, it becomes aversive. This would defeat the ability of the therapist to reinforce any behaviour because a reward immediately loses its value and becomes a punishment.

Krasner: In this sort of case we would work with the phantasies reported by the individual—phantasied anticipations about the results of treatment and so on.

Kubie: The phenomenon of the man who goes to pieces when he achieves success is not an isolated occurrence seen only in psychoanalytic practice. It is one of the oldest experiences of man. There is nothing new or rare in the writer who blows his brains out after writing a "best-seller", or the millionaire who jumps out of the window. Psychosomatic and some physical illnesses (myocardial infarction and perforated peptic ulcer for example) may also be seen immediately after a great success has been won, whether material, spiritual or artistic. The essence of the problem of psychotherapy will elude us if we shut our eyes to this common experience.

Foss: But, since these are probably the people for whom disagreement rather than agreement is reinforcing, one can still find rewards for them.

Hunt: A reward must be defined pragmatically, not *a priori:* it is something that rewards. In these patients success does not seem to reward.

Sandler: If we carry this definition of reward to its logical conclusion we should punish these patients to relieve them of their sense of guilt. And this turns the therapeutic systems that use rewards upside down. One would be reinforcing the very behaviour one is trying to reduce.

Kubie: In the George Junior Republic the boys repeat this pattern of behaviour over and over again: they react to success and reward by breaking every rule, even by running away. The boy who is the judge in the court proceedings on one occasion will be the prisoner in the dock three months later, and *vice versa.* The only way to break this repetitive pattern is for the learning and therapeutic processes to converge. This takes many repetitions of such role reversals over a long time. Simulation of good behaviour can be induced in many different ways. I am concerned to find out if short-term psychotherapeutic techniques ever produce significant inner changes, precisely because there is neither opportunity nor time for the many repetitions necessary for learning to occur. This problem is currently accentuated by the idea that we must get people out of hospital quickly.

Hunt: Specific behaviour therapy plans must be shaped to the patient's individual problems; this takes shrewdness, time and patience. A number of successive steps or stages may be needed and one does not have to take all the steps simultaneously (the prolonged and repeated working-through in psychoanalysis is a process related to these stages in behaviour therapy).

Proper behaviour therapy strategy in complex cases resembles peeling an onion.

Miller: That sounds like a description of psychoanalysis.

Hunt: The two are not so different in this regard.

Miller: We are all being shaped by the same realities. I am impressed that the more deeply we probe, the more the different approaches to the problems of psychotherapy converge. Professor Krasner, if you were treating a patient for whom punishment and physical injury seemed to be the reward, would you allow her to redeem her tokens by giving her an electric shock or a knife to cut herself with? This is obviously an extreme example, but if the knife and the shock were what satisfied the patient most, would you use them, empirically, as reinforcers?

Krasner: We always try to use positive reinforcement. G. S. Baroff and B. G. Tate (1966. *On the Understanding and Control of Self-Injurious Behavior.* Paper presented to American Psychological Association, unpublished) reported an interesting study, relevant to negative reinforcement, in self-destructive autistic children. These workers gave a very mild shock to children who were violently damaging themselves by head-banging, and the incidence of the violent behaviour decreased sharply. The aversive therapy in this study was a mild shock that we would expect to be much less painful than the original destructive behaviour. These surprising results may be related to the fact that the shock is given by another person whereas the child is attacking himself.

Miller: These superficially illogical results deserve further investigation. According to Premack's (Premack, D. [1959]. *Psychol. Rev.*, **66**, 219-233) empiric definition of reinforcement, self-destructive behaviour in these children has a high frequency and should in theory be an excellent reinforcer.

Kaufman: The fact that the autistic child hurts himself is a consequence of his behaviour; I know of no evidence that, as you have implied Professor Krasner, this is the child's intention. I submit that the child is looking for stimulation rather than damage through his banging. The effectiveness of the mild shock in reducing the damaging behaviour is therefore less puzzling, because the child is giving up more painful for less painful behaviour.

Krasner: I did not mean to imply that the child intended to hurt himself.

Kaufman: But wasn't that the basis of your argument?

Krasner: No. I have no idea what the motives of the autistic child are. But I am surprised that substituting a less aversive for a more aversive influence should be so effective in extinguishing the more painful (and theoretically, therefore, more aversive) behaviour.

Kiernan: I am interested in the transition from token economies to social reinforcement, and eventually to self-reinforcement. It is clearly very valuable to maintain chronic schizophrenic in-patients on a token economy programme, thus allowing them to function more adequately on the ward. However, the ultimate aim with disturbed children is presumably to allow them to function outside the hospital, where "self-reinforcement" is necessary. Are there any data from your own or other studies on the transition from token to social and finally to internalized self-reinforcement?

Krasner: I cannot answer your question directly. I agree that the aim of all these procedures should be to develop a person who can function efficiently because of internalized reinforcement. But the new adaptive behaviours almost always need continuing external (usually social) reinforcement if they are to be maintained. Consider a child in an institution who is trained in good grooming and who then goes into the outside world and joins a group in which there is not only no reinforcement for grooming but it actually elicits dislike. This behaviour cannot be maintained. Token economy programmes should also aim at developing behaviours that will elicit social reinforcement outside the hospital.

Kiernan: How do you deal with a patient who joins the token economy system but demands his tokens in a very aggressive way? Such a patient is working effectively with the token economy and the problem of his aggression could presumably be solved by reinforcing a positive attitude to the staff. But how would you manoeuvre such a man into a position where social reinforcement could be effective?

Krasner: An important part of all token economy programmes must be some sort of check, or feedback, to find out if the adaptive behaviours are maintained. One way of studying this would be to combine social reinforcement with tokens, and then gradually to withdraw the tokens and continue the social reinforcement. It would be useful to find out if social reinforcement alone can maintain the developed behaviour.

THE LEARNING COMPONENT IN THE DYNAMIC
PSYCHOTHERAPEUTIC SITUATION

THOMAS FREEMAN

Holywell Hospital, Antrim, Northern Ireland

THE purpose of this paper is to assess the role of learning in those psycho-therapies which lay major emphasis on the patient acquiring knowledge about the origins, development and immediate causes of his abnormal mental experiences. I shall approach this problem by undertaking an examination of phenomena which are to be found whenever patients suffering from different categories of psychological disturbance are offered the opportunity of entering and participating in what is described here as the dynamic psychotherapeutic situation.

Learning is an integral aspect of psychoanalysis and the psychothera-peutic methods derived from it. In the course of such treatments attention is primarily directed towards helping the patient to enlarge his awareness of all aspects of his psychological functioning. In psychoanalytic therapy this increased knowledge is brought about primarily by interpretation. Not every intervention made by the psychoanalyst can be regarded as an interpretation. Many of these communications, sometimes described as confrontations and clarifications, are presented as a means of paving the way towards an interpretation. The interpretation has the aim of making conscious " . . . the unconscious meaning, source, history, mode or cause of a given psychic event." (Greenson, 1967).

The task of the psychoanalyst is therefore to help the patient to learn about those wishes, phantasies and emotions that are causally connected with the symptoms, and simultaneously to inform him about behavioural patterns of which he has been unaware. In favourable instances control is imposed over aberrant and maladaptive psychomotor reactions. Con-science is modified and outlets are obtained for affects and for the satisfaction of needs.

Experience has demonstrated that in psychoanalytic treatment the learn-ing process does not take place easily or smoothly, and there are occasions when even the acquisition of knowledge does not lead to an improvement in the symptomatology or in the abnormal behaviour. What is the reason for the difficulty in learning and why is the learning not always effective in dispelling the abnormal mental state? Perhaps some answers to these questions may be obtained by turning our attention to patients who suffer from psychoses, sexual deviations and certain types of neurosis. In each of these clinical categories mental functions have undergone a pathological change. This change results in the patient behaving in a specific fashion whenever he is encouraged to engage in a dynamic therapeutic situation.

CATEGORIES IN WHICH LEARNING IS NOT THERAPEUTIC

The psychoses

A characteristic feature of established cases of schizophrenic and paranoid psychoses is the refractory response which appears whenever attempts are made to demonstrate the irrational and inappropriate nature of the thinking and feeling. How can this disorder of judgment with its implication of a learning defect be explained? Can it be attributed primarily to a cognitive deficit which prevents an accurate evaluation of the environment or is it due to other factors?

It is the experience of psychiatrists and nurses who have spent long periods with established cases of schizophrenia that contact can be established with the non-psychotic, healthy mental function in these patients if certain needs are satisfied. In such cases interest in the doctor and nurse follows the need for food, cigarettes or the knowledge that the patient's psychic preoccupations will be given full attention. Disappointment leads to a withdrawal from the doctor or nurse and sometimes to an outburst of anger. In patients of this type the tie with the world of reality is fragile and tenuous. While it remains intact it is possible to observe changes in the patient's appraisal of the environment in the direction of normalcy. Even if only for a brief period the patient will, for example, recognize that his misidentifications are a product of his imagining. In this way he indicates that he has not lost the capacity to learn—to alter his perception of reality on the basis of real experience. Loss of the object world is accompanied by a return of the delusional perception.

In cases of paranoid psychosis the psychiatrist is sometimes agreeably surprised to observe that the patient responds enthusiastically to the psychotherapeutic approach. Positive feelings predominate and the therapeutic contact does not seem so different from the contact in a neurotic subject. This favourable impression is soon dispelled as the patient inexorably draws his delusional complex into the treatment situation. The psychiatrist soon becomes a major persecutor and treatment is broken off.

In cases where the psychotic disturbance is also characterized by a cognitive disorganization the psychiatrist is misidentified and a kind of merging process occurs. The patient attributes features of his physical and mental self to the psychiatrist and simultaneously identifies with certain aspects of the latter.

In these psychotic states learning of the type necessary to lead to a dissolution of the abnormal manifestations cannot find optimum development. This is due to two factors. First, the patient is incapable of relating to another person other than on the basis of the immediate satisfaction of needs, whether physical or psychological. In such instances lack of interest and concern for the psychiatrist results in the absence of a wish to learn about the nature of the psychotic ideas and percepts. Second, even when a learning process has been initiated it is easily disrupted by the delusional reality making its appearance in the patient-therapist situation. The vivid and compelling nature of this content captures the patient's attention and distracts him from the task of examining his misinterpretations of the environment.

Male homosexuality

The second category of clinical states which helps to throw light on the role which learning plays in the dynamic therapeutic situation is that of male homosexuality. When such individuals undertake psychotherapeutic treatment they present special kinds of behavioural manifestations. Sometimes these patients are withdrawn, silent and aloof. Occasionally they make it clear that they consider themselves quite superior to the therapist in every respect. This grandiosity may be hidden behind a facade of timidity and expressed in finding fault with the therapist. In other cases the patient endows the therapist with an entirely inappropriate omnipotence and omniscience.

Cases of this kind are characterized by a preoccupation with the self. The egotism has a pronounced libidinal component which manifests itself in an exaggerated concern for the body, excess pleasure in bodily processes, and a generalized sexualization of relationships. The impression gained from many of these patients is that they maintain a hazy, indefinite relationship with the external world, which is regarded as disappointing, critical and often destructive. As treatment proceeds the ease with which the patient changes roles with the therapist becomes apparent. For example, the patient complains about the therapist as he does about his mother. Later he behaves towards the therapist as his mother does to him. Identifications are easily resolved into their original pattern of object relation and *vice versa*.

Psychoanalytic work with these patients has shown that the narcissism which characterizes their mental life provides a strong resistance to their learning from the treatment process. Interpretations are not easily accepted and even when they are they do not have much beneficial influence on behaviour. This reaction can be attributed to the fact that the patient has never been capable of a sustained, trusting relationship with another person. He only relates to himself and to those who are representations of his actual or wished-for self. One patient's inability to accept and benefit from interpretation resulted from a fear of the therapist. This male patient regarded the analysis as a kind of forcible exposure of his body—a repetition of actual events in childhood. Once exposed, something would be taken from him against his will. He likened this to circumcision and to the enemas which had so frequently been administered in his early years. These assaults on his body and the constant feelings of helplessness were countered by masturbatory phantasies in which he controlled others and punished at will. These phantasies could be traced to childhood when erection gave him a feeling of power and strength. The penis was personified as an object at the mercy of his commands. In this patient self-love had replaced object-love.

Although homosexual patients are prepared to enter and continue a psychotherapeutic relationship they are frequently prevented from benefiting from it because of the attitudes which they adopt to the therapist. These attitudes can be explained on the basis of fixations which have affected the developing capacity for object relations in childhood. These fixations, which are expressed in abnormal narcissism, find compulsive repetition in the treatment situation. It is difficult to avoid the conclusion that these patients behave in treatment as if they were reliving their unhappy early years. This makes the management of the patient-therapist situation extremely difficult and obstructs the learning process.

Neuroses with marked passive, dependent features

The third category to be described consists of those neurotic patients who, after long periods of analytic treatment, do not make a favourable response. The symptoms which were present at the outset remain. The patient has apparently gained much information about the origin, history and immediate causes of his symptoms but this has not had a therapeutic affect. Learning may thus take place but it is in itself no guarantee of symptomatic relief.

A number of reasons suggest themselves to account for this. First, a real

7*

learning process has not in fact taken place. Second, what has been learned has been based on theoretical ideas of symptom formation. These are erroneous and therefore the symptoms remain intact. Third, what has been learned has remained in the sphere of the intellect and has not led to an alteration in the patient's affective and conative attitudes.

The failure to benefit from treatment in spite of the acquisition of insights can be scrutinized from another standpoint—namely by an examination of the patient's personality structure. These individuals are renowned for their passivity and lack of drive. They are self-concerned but, unlike homosexual patients, their egotism is not manifested in inflated self-regard and over-valuation of the body, except perhaps in hypochondriacal preoccupation. Their aggressive and sexual tendencies are restricted, as are their affective reactions. They show a reluctance to become involved in relationships with others, also including the therapist in the therapeutic situation.

In one such patient an unconscious self-preoccupation dominated all object relationships. Before the illness the patient's parents, siblings and male and female friends were a means of expressing different aspects of his own personality. They were not objects in their own right. In analytic treatment the patient repeated the same behaviour. For at least four years he maintained an idealized phantasy of the therapist. As long as the patient believed the therapist was a kind of invulnerable superman he (the patient) could deny his effect on the therapist and the possible repercussions upon himself. Self-concern protected him against an awareness of what he might be doing to his objects—the therapist, his own wife in the present, his parents and siblings in the past. Narcissism thus served as a defence and as a resistance against the treatment.

DISCUSSION

When a patient embarks on dynamic psychotherapy it is with the expectation that beneficial mental changes will ensue. It is hoped that drives and affects which have led to anxiety and guilt will be modified. This change in the personality of the patient should result in his being less demanding and insistent for satisfaction. A further consequence should be an increased ability to tolerate disappointment and frustration. The demands of conscience should become more appropriate and thus feelings of inadequacy and inferiority diminish. The overall result of such changes should be the loss of symptoms and a better ability to adjust to life. Has a learning process taken place in cases where there is this favourable outcome? Is this process, initiated at a conscious level through interpretation, eventually influencing mental processes which operate outside consciousness? The answer to both these questions must be yes.

The clinical phenomena presented by the three categories of patient described above reveal some of the influences which interfere with the initiation, maintenance and effect of a learning process. In psychosis the patient's lack of interest or the prevalence of the psychotic reality vitiates attempts to stimulate a learning process through confronting the patient with his inappropriate behaviour or by interpretation. His object cathexes, to employ a psychoanalytic concept, are so limited that they cannot sustain a treatment alliance which would contain the affective reactions which must occur within the dynamic therapeutic situation. This does not mean that the clinical encounter is bound to be without effect. In certain cases of schizophrenic psychosis unstable identification processes take place which lead to transient alterations in symptoms and behaviour. This can be regarded as a learning process taking place outside consciousness but, like the identifications, this is rarely permanent. In the treatment of neuroses such identifications also take place unconsciously but in neurotics these identifications are stable.

In homosexual and in neurotic patients a therapeutic alliance is often possible. The first steps towards a learning process which may have a therapeutic effect can thus be taken. The clinical data referred to indicate that this process may be obstructed by a number of influences. The most important is the nature of the relationship which the patient effects with the therapist. The second, intimately related to the first, is the tendency for drive and affective patterns to continue their activity in spite of their being brought to the patient's awareness both inside the treatment situation and in real life. When a narcissistic form of relationship arises in the treatment situation, the effects of interpretation are frequently blocked and learning cannot influence the patient's thinking, affect or behaviour. The constant force which compels the patient to repeat instinctually based phantasies of either a libidinal or destructive type defeats all therapeutic efforts. Freud (1926) named this phenomenon "the resistance of the unconscious".

Quite apart from these obstacles there are other hindrances to learning which occur repeatedly in any dynamic psychotherapy even in the least complicated case of neurosis. These obstructions are the resistances which periodically interfere with the progress of therapy. They disrupt such learning as has occurred in consciousness and often dissipate it entirely. Foremost amongst these resistances are those due to transference. Other causes are repression, an excessive sense of guilt, and secondary gain. With an adequate therapeutic alliance some of these resistances can be overcome.

This is not always possible when the secondary gain from the illness provides important satisfactions for the patient.

In this paper I have merely repeated what has often been said before—that analytic psychotherapy is essentially a learning experience for the patient which proceeds both consciously and unconsciously. But the learning process by itself cannot be regarded as the sole factor leading to symptomatic relief. Learning is not an autonomous activity. It is closely related to and in a sense dependent upon other factors which could be seen in the clinical illustrations presented above. Its fate will rest on the state of the patient's instinctual development as reflected in the nature of his object relations. When the capacity for object relations is limited or has been distorted as a consequence of adverse childhood experiences, learning is obstructed by the compulsive repetition of these early behaviour patterns in the dynamic therapeutic situation.

When the role of the learning component in the dynamic therapeutic situation is being considered it is erroneous and artificial to force object relations and learning into separate categories. The question of which is the most important in the therapeutic process is irrelevant. From earliest infancy learning is inextricably involved with the drives and their representation in object relations. Learning at whatever level implies object relatedness. In the dynamic therapeutic situation we are able to observe, at first hand, the intimate relationships which exist between learning and object relations.

SUMMARY

The role that learning plays in psychoanalysis and psychotherapy is examined. Phenomena which appear when patients suffering from different categories of psychological disorder are offered the opportunity of entering and participating in a dynamic psychotherapeutic situation have been discussed. The clinical categories described are schizophrenia, male homosexuality and neuroses which have failed to respond to analytic psychotherapy.

The phenomena observed point to a number of important influences which interfere with the initiation, maintenance and effect of the learning process in treatment. Although analytic psychotherapy is a learning experience, learning cannot be regarded as the sole factor leading to improvement in the patient's state. The result of treatment is equally dependent on the state of the patient's instinctual development as reflected in the nature of his object relations. Object relations and learning capacity are closely linked in development. Learning at whatever level implies the activity of object relations.

REFERENCES

FREUD, S. (1926). *Hemmung, Symptom und Angst.* Leipzig: Internationaler psychoanalytischer Verlag. (1959. *Inhibitions, Symptoms and Anxiety,* in *Standard Edition,* vol. 20, pp. 77–175, ed. Strachey, J. London: Hogarth Press.)

GREENSON, R. R. (1967). *Technique and Practice of Psychoanalysis.* New York: International Universities Press Inc.

DISCUSSION

Miller: We must define the differences between the various psychotherapeutic approaches as well as pointing-out the similarities. We shall not be able to bridge any gaps unless we see clearly where these gaps are.

Malan: We are using the one word—learning—to mean at least three different things; this is confusing, particularly because we do not know the relationships, if any, between the three meanings. Learning has been used to mean (*a*) education, (*b*) the acquisition of a conditioned response to certain stimuli, and (*c*) the acquisition of emotional insight. Learning meaning education (that is, simply imparting knowledge) was the sense in which Dr. Leder used the word when he described passive learning; when we consider behaviour therapy we talk of learning with the second meaning, as a process connected with conditioned (or deconditioned) responses; and Dr. Freeman has now introduced the acquisition of emotional insight as a third meaning for this ubiquitous word. And still other meanings for the term "learning" may exist. What are the differences and similarities between different types of learning?

Kubie: The word "learning" is taken over from the schooling situation. A child at school is not troubled mainly by *what* he has to learn but by the painful *process* of learning. The extent of this pain varies at different times, in different circumstances, and in different subjects. Merely having to sit still is painful for some children. The extent to which the subject studied has acquired special idiosyncratic symbolic significance for a child may also determine the extent of the pain of learning for him. Learning in the treatment situation is also painful. A preliminary, gradual and continuing process of desensitization must always occur in psychotherapy, to enable the patient to accept help. The communications of the therapist are often resented because they force the patient to put into words topics he has previously avoided talking about. Culture also plays a role in the pain produced by the learning ingredients in therapy. Our western culture

surrounds children with a "conspiracy of silence" (Kubie, L. S. [1937].
Psychoanal. Q., **6**, 388-425; [1959]. *Daedalus, Boston, Mass.*, **88**, 646-668;
[1963]. *Encycl. ment. Health*, **4**, 1346-1353). This means that those topics
which are most important and highly charged for the child (death, destruction, accidents, hate, rage, lust, and all the body apertures and products),
and also most painful, are too taboo to be talked about. Usually these
topics are not even given proper names. What the child does not have
words for he cannot talk about, except indirectly, and gradually he becomes unable even to think about these subjects. Yet the highly charged
feelings persist unattached to anything. Indeed a child may come to feel
that if he does not talk about something it does not exist. In this way
persistent feelings become dissociated from their initiating roots. A patient
may then try to deal with a problem by action, while remaining wholly
unable to verbalize his feelings.

The bases of learning, thinking and remembering are not conscious.
We utilize experience by a continuous preconscious processing of inner
human experience (the "imageless thought" of the Wurzburg School),
using conscious symbolic language to draw samples from this preconscious
stream, which continues whether we are awake or asleep. We use these
samples in many ways: to ruminate, to communicate, and to test reality.
This digestion of experience on another level is a continuous and complex
process, which can be blocked and interrupted in different ways and at
different stages of development. In all psychopathological processes the
inner human experiences are distorted by dissociations between the symbols
and what they are supposed to represent. The learning and psychotherapeutic processes converge here. We must learn to understand one another
more clearly in order to help one another.

Lazarus: Unlike some prominent theorists, including Wolpe, I do not
think that all learning is conditioning; the term "conditioning" should be
restricted to the description of laboratory experiments in which clearly-
defined conditioned and unconditioned stimuli are presented in known
temporal relationships with each other. It would be less confusing to refer
to the known learning principles—transfer of training, intermittent
reinforcement, the importance of temporal contiguity and so on—than to
use the terms "learning" and "learning theories" in this vague, non-specific
way. The notion that anything not innate is acquired, and therefore learned,
is too vague to help the practising psychotherapist.

Sackett: It is confusing to talk about divorcing laboratory concepts of
learning from learning in the therapeutic situation before we define the
types of learning that occur in abnormal individuals during therapy, or

even the basic learning process itself. We are assuming that one of the reasons that an individual is abnormal (in any way) is that the learning process has been disturbed, and that we have only to manipulate the appropriate variables and he will become able to learn. But we have not yet defined what it is that is abnormal. Is it that the learning process itself is not operating normally; or is the abnormal individual capable of learning if we could find an appropriate procedure for producing new responses; or is it possible that learning has nothing to do with the problem? Dr. Kubie, is psychotherapy a learning process or not?

Kubie: Learning occasionally means the acquisition of important new facts. Learning in psychotherapy more often means that the patient receives from the analyst explicit or implicit permission to think about and use facts which he knows already but has never been free to use. This may lead to the establishment of new connexions—the understanding of new relationships between events and people, or between feelings and the realities of the facts and people in his life. This process, of course, is affective as well as factual; it is not learning in the sense of systematic "drill and grill". I am not sure that emphasizing the learning elements in psychotherapy or the analogy to learning clarifies our understanding of the psychotherapeutic process. It may just give us an illusion of greater understanding by emphasizing similarities with something familiar while neglecting critically important dissimilarities. I hesitate to stress the association of learning and psychotherapy because it is often misused to support the elementary *cliché* that falling sick is mislearning and recovery is learning. Nevertheless, the misuse of a fact does not justify our discarding it completely.

Sifneos: One cannot consider the process of learning without thinking about the role played by the emotions in facilitating or blocking it. Psychoanalysts often pay a great deal of attention to the emotional component which interferes with learning; neurologists, on the other hand, maintain that the problems of learning and memory are not connected with emotional blocks. What we think about learning depends very much on where we place our emphasis and on what model we use.

Sackett: We must define our terms. Learning may mean any of the following processes: (a) the acquisition of new responses; (b) the unlearning of old responses; (c) the learning of new responses to old stimuli; (d) the perpetuation of old responses to new stimuli; (e) the extinction of innate responses; and (f) the extinction of maladaptive habits.

Miller: A maladaptive habit may prevent, by conflict, the performance of the adaptive habit; in animal experiments at least, the former must be extinguished before the latter can begin. A rat that huddles at one end of the alley, for example, cannot learn to press a bar at the other end until he has unlearned his habit of huddling.

Lazarus: Dr. Freeman, I understand the rationale for treating psychoanalytically subjects whose adaptive responses are suppressed by maladaptive conflicts. But how do you deal with a patient who has never learned adaptive responses?

Freeman: The psychoanalytic view is that adaptive responses appear spontaneously when the conflicts that blocked these responses during development are resolved; potentially constructive elements are present in most human beings. This satisfactory outcome of analytic psychotherapy is most common in patients whose main problems centre on inhibitions. Such patients either feel restricted in doing what they want or are not conscious of their ability to act in certain ways. This is common clinical psychiatric experience and not peculiar to psychoanalysis.

Lazarus: But you are assuming that adaptive learning has occurred and inhibitions have blocked its expression. Many people have large gaps in their response repertoires—learning has never taken place. When inhibitions are removed in these patients we find only a vacuum.

Malan: You are describing two types of patients. First, those who have learned appropriate responses but something in their later development has induced maladaptive behaviour; and, second, patients in whom the normal learning process has never occurred. Extreme examples of the second group are withdrawn schizophrenics and autistic children, for whom it is not enough simply to remove the blocks. To help these patients is very difficult.

Sifneos: Dr. Freeman, you have drawn attention to a group of fairly well-adjusted patients who, as soon as their inhibitions are removed by analysis, have access to many new ways of behaving. Professor Lazarus, on the other hand, has described patients for whom these adaptive responses are not available. I do not think that these two different views are incompatible, they simply refer to two different groups of patients. Dr. Freeman's patients are healthier, and Professor Lazarus' more disturbed. Paranoid patients, for example, have to be explicitly taught what to do, as Professor Lazarus has suggested. They tend to view their interviewer as the devil, and communicate this to him. They expect that he will react in the same way as everyone else has reacted in a similar situation, namely by denying this role and trying to reassure them. But if the therapist accepts the patients' challenge by saying: "I am the devil, what are you going to do about it?" we may learn a great deal about the patients' defences. Such a response may uncover the feelings of intense confusional anxiety and anger which induce these patients to project these painful emotions on to others (in this case the therapist) and give rise to the paranoid delusions. In this way one may help these paranoid patients to unlearn their use of projection as a defence mechanism, and train them in new ways of dealing with their emotional problems. They can be taught to anticipate situations which provoke such painful emotions and learn to avoid these situations. But we need not waste time with such elaborate training for the healthier neurotics described by Dr. Freeman; these subjects become capable of appropriate behaviour once their conflicts are resolved.

Miller: Another factor in establishing adaptive behaviour is the social environment. If this is favourable, if parents and teachers, say, automatically reinforce appropriate behaviours, a young patient will do well when his inhibitions are removed. But society is not always organized to take care of disturbed children and special arrangements (special schools for example) may have to be made for them.

Lazarus: We see these response deficits not only in autism and advanced schizophrenia but in many neurotics. A basic weakness of psychoanalysis may be that it does not groom the patient to face the everyday situations that he has never learned to face. Many patients need didactic training for adaptive interpersonal skills. For example, when a homosexual's anxieties about women have been eliminated he may still be unable to engage in ordinary social interactions with them. He may have to be taught how to approach women (by behaviour rehearsal or modelling) before he can progress to full heterosexual courtship and intimacy. These apparently trivial responses, second nature to most people, often need to be laboriously taught to these patients. Such responses range from how to respond to an introduction at a social gathering to such major activities as making love or dealing verbally with an antagonist.

Freeman: Psychoanalytic therapy can help some homosexuals. It may even, after only a few weeks, induce a form of acting-out in which the patient shows extreme heterosexual promiscuity; he seems to have over-learned, although some of this behaviour may be due to a retreat from the terror of the treatment. One can easily find examples of both too much and too little previous learning.

Krasner: One of the differences between behavioural and dynamic techniques is the goal of the therapist. The psychoanalytic therapist focuses on removing blocks and inhibitions, the behaviour therapist focuses on behaviour deficits.

Sandler: Dynamic psychotherapy is not just the equivalent of the surgical removal of inhibitions followed by discharge of the patient, who is left to fend for himself. Repeated working-through and contrasting (explicitly or implicitly) an alternative solution to that used by the patient are also important, which is why analysis takes so long. One of the criteria for terminating analysis is that the patient is using new behaviours, and functioning well and feeling happy as a result, in his life outside.

Frank: Could you define "working-through"?

Sandler: Working-through is used with two different meanings. It can mean testing in real life the new experiences gained in analysis. It can also mean repeatedly working over, in the analytic sessions, the ramifications of the analysand's basic conflicts as they have affected different aspects of his life.

Frank: Can working-through be defined as behavioural or cognitive according to these two meanings?

Sandler: Roughly, but the distinction between the two is not absolutely clear-cut.

Miller: But would that be a reasonable way of expressing the differences between the most extreme examples?

Sandler: Yes.

Freeman: Working-through is connected with handling the patient's resistances which is why psychoanalysis is such a lengthy process. What happens to the resistances of patients in behaviour therapy?

Miller: Are resistances a product of psychoanalysis or do they exist in other contexts? And can they be ignored in behaviour therapy?

Lazarus: Resistances exist outside analysis but are probably not as widespread as psychoanalysts maintain. But patients who derive secondary gains from their symptoms (in behavioural terminology, patients whose deviant behaviour is maintained by many operant consequences) are not easily helped unless reinforcers are directly manipulated. For example, if a patient's neurosis tends to elicit increased love and attention from significant others, it is unlikely that constructive change will occur without alteration of the neurotic pay off. The behaviour therapy I use is based on technical eclecticism (Lazarus, A. A. [1967]. *Psychol. Rep.*, **21**, 415-416) and does not consist solely of the administration of narrow stimulus-response cues. Resistances are overcome by *active* therapeutic displays of empathy, authenticity, self-disclosure, and acceptance without judgment. In addition, patients learn to carry out specific assignments in graded steps so that threat does not enter prematurely into the treatment situation. If one proceeds too rapidly, one often meets resistance, but this is easily remedied by readjusting the pace of therapy.

Sandler: In clinical psychoanalysis, resistance and defence are two sides of the same coin. In one sense the analytic work is concentrated on the defence mechanisms (denial, projection, displacement and so on) of the patient, and the clinical manifestations of the defences are the resistances. Everybody, including patients after all types of psychotherapy, uses defences. One of the hallmarks of neurosis is that the particular defensive solution arrived at gives pain. In therapies in which the defences are not dealt with the subject may be able to bypass his resistances and important material may be lost.

Krasner: Psychoanalysts view resistances as internal forces which cause the individual to respond in a certain way. Behaviourists view resistances from the outside in terms of their consequences. So it is not surprising that behaviourists and analysts handle resistances differently.

Sandler: Psychoanalysts have often defined the work of analysis as the analysis of resistances. The work of behaviour therapy is not the analysis but rather the bypassing of resistances.

Hunt: Or the use of them.

Gelder: Failure to learn in psychoanalysis may be due to the presence of inhibitions but it may also be connected with the way in which the maladaptive behaviour first arose. This may not have been learned at all, as in schizophrenia; or the maladaptive response may have been learned originally by either a simple process such as conditioning, or through the much more complex processes of social learning. Relevant to this concept is an experiment by W. H. Bridger and I. J. Mandel (1964. *J. psychiat. Res.*, **2**, 31-40) who studied responses learned on the one hand through exposure to electric shocks and, on the other, to *fear* of shock. They showed that different processes of unlearning were necessary to remove the responses learned in the two ways. This is yet another reason why we should specify precisely what sort of learning process we are discussing.

Miller: Some of the learning that occurs in psychoanalysis may be analogous to desensitization in behaviour therapy, although directed towards a different goal. Free association enables the patient in analysis to say frightening words that he would not otherwise be able to say. It is a gradual process. The patient is not forced but paces himself. The analyst receives these anxiety-provoking words calmly—he does not react to them in the punitive way that the patient expects. This situation acts to reduce, by counterconditioning, the fear associated with the frightening words. For example, the patient gradually learns to tolerate words connected with the idea that he hates his analyst, because the analyst does not react in the same way as his mother did to similar hostility.

Freeman: Many factors affect the learning process in psychoanalysis:

insight and interpretation are two such factors. But the essence of the psychoanalytic situation is the opportunity given to the patient to re-experience significant events from his past with a therapist who does not react as others have done. The permissive and reliable atmosphere of the treatment sessions in which these interactions can take place may be more important than specific interpretations, especially when resistances appear. I agree that this experience resembles desensitization.

Sandler: Desensitization in terms of the psychic reality of the patient is very important in psychoanalysis. The psychoanalytic view is that while a memory or phantasy is unconscious it will be regarded as a real perception or a memory of a real event. Thus the phobic patient's picture of and reaction to the phobic situation is *as if* he were perceiving a real threat, even though he may know that his fear is irrational. He cannot consciously distinguish between imagination and perception while the terrifying elements remain unconscious and consequently have *psychic* reality. Similarly, in the analytic situation, the interpretation of unconscious material and consequent release of the feelings attached to it may make conscious a memory or phantasy which had been previously dealt with while it was unconscious. The patient is then able to confront the phantasy with reality, and through this new knowledge of the unreality of his phantasies he could be described as desensitizing himself.

Kubie: Desensitization may also be involved in the disappearance of a child's terror after a nightmare. The fear does not disappear immediately the child wakes. There is a gradual attrition of fear, a slow distancing of the child from his emotion.

MODELLING APPROACHES TO THE MODIFICATION OF PHOBIC DISORDERS

ALBERT BANDURA

Department of Psychology, Stanford University, California

ONE of the fundamental means by which human behaviour is acquired and modified is through modelling or vicarious processes. Research conducted within the broad framework of social learning theory (Bandura, 1965; Bandura and Walters, 1963) provides considerable evidence that virtually all learning phenomena that result from direct experiences can occur vicariously, as a function of observing other people's behaviour and its consequences for them. Thus, for example, persons can acquire complex response patterns through exposure to the performances of exemplary models; emotional responses can be conditioned, through observation, by witnessing the affective reactions of others undergoing painful or pleasurable experiences; fearful and avoidant responsivity can be extinguished vicariously through observing modelled approach behaviour toward feared objects without any adverse consequences happening to the performer; inhibitions can be induced by witnessing the behaviour of others being punished; and, finally, the expression of well-learned responses can be enhanced and socially regulated through the actions of influential models. Modelling procedures are, therefore, ideally suited for effecting diverse changes in psychological functioning.

A comprehensive review of the numerous psychotherapeutic applications of modelling approaches is beyond the scope of this paper. Instead attention will be focused mainly on a series of experiments designed both to establish the efficacy of modelling procedures for treating phobic conditions, and to delineate some of the variables governing the process of vicarious extinction. The findings derived from this programme of research will be discussed at length, followed by some speculations on the probable mechanisms through which vicarious extinction effects are produced.

New therapeutic approaches are traditionally promoted enthusiastically and it is not until after the methods have been applied clinically for some time by a coterie of advocates that objective tests of efficacy are conducted.

Usually the methods are unceremoniously retired by subsequent controlled studies. Workers in psychotherapy have, therefore, come to view any new therapeutic approach as a passing fad. When laboratory tests of efficacy precede clinical application, new methods are subjected to close scrutiny at each stage of development, and those that evolve are likely to produce outcomes sufficiently favourable to weather the test of time.

All the studies reported in this paper employ essentially the same basic experimental design. Subjects are first given an objective test of avoidance behaviour in which they are asked to perform progressively more threatening interactions with a phobic object. Those who are sufficiently fearful to qualify for the project are then assigned, on the basis of the severity of their avoidance behaviour, to various treatment conditions.

Evidence that deviant behaviour can be modified by a particular method is of limited therapeutic significance unless it can be demonstrated that established response patterns generalize to stimuli beyond those encountered in treatment, and that induced changes endure after the formal therapeutic conditions have been discontinued. Therefore the administration of tests for avoidance behaviour toward different phobic objects is repeated after the subjects have completed the treatment programme, to measure transfer effects. The assessment procedures are repeated after one month to determine how well the behavioural changes have been maintained.

Since the absence of anticipated aversive consequences is a requisite for fear extinction, the modelling displays most likely to have strong effects on phobic observers are those in which performances that the observers regard as hazardous are repeatedly shown to be safe in a variety of threatening circumstances. But the presentation of modelled approach responses toward the most aversive situations at the outset is apt to generate in observers high levels of emotional arousal that can impede vicarious extinction. The efficacy of modelling procedures may, therefore, partly depend on the manner in which the modelled performances are presented.

Avoidance responses can be extinguished with minimal distress if subjects are exposed to a graduated sequence of modelling activities beginning with displays that have low arousal value. After emotional reactions to attenuated threats have been extinguished, progressively more aversive modelling cues, which are weakened by generalization of anxiety extinction from preceding displays, are gradually introduced and neutralized. Stimulus graduation is not a necessary condition for vicarious extinction, but it permits greater control over the change process and elicits less anxiety than approaches with repeated exposure to modelling events having high threat value.

VICARIOUS EXTINCTION OF PHOBIC BEHAVIOUR

Our initial study (Bandura, Grusec and Menlove, 1967) was a stringent test of the degree to which strong avoidance behaviour can be extinguished through modelling procedures. We also investigated whether the induction of positive affective responses in observers during exposure to modelling cues that are potentially threatening expedites vicarious extinction.

Young children, who exhibited a strong fear of dogs, were assigned to one of four treatment conditions. One group participated in eight brief sessions during which they observed a fearless peer-model exhibit progressively more fear-arousing interactions with a dog. For these children, the modelled approach behaviour was presented within a highly positive party context designed to counteract anxiety reactions. When the jovial party was well under way, a dauntless four-year-old boy entered the room with a dog in tow, and performed pre-arranged sequences of interactions with the dog for approximately three minutes during each session. The fear-provoking properties of the modelled displays were gradually increased from session to session by varying simultaneously the physical restraints on the dog, the directness and intimacy of the modelled approach responses, and the duration of interaction between the model and the dog.

A second group of children observed the same graduated performances, but in a neutral context. In the two treatment conditions described, the stimulus complex contained both modelling cues and repeated observation of the phobic stimulus. Therefore, in order to evaluate the effects of exposure to a feared animal alone, a third group of children observed the dog in the positive context but without the model. A fourth group participated in the positive activities but was never exposed to either the dog or the modelled displays.

Children's phobic behaviour toward two different dogs was measured separately, after the treatment programme and again a month later. The avoidance test consisted of a graded sequence of interactions with the dog. The children were asked, for example, to approach and pet the dog, to release it from a playpen, remove its leash, feed it with dog biscuits, and spend a fixed period of time alone in the room with the animal. The final and most difficult set of tasks required the children to climb into the playpen with the dog and, after having locked the gate, to pet it and remain alone with it under these confining fear-arousing conditions.

As shown in Fig. 1, the modelling treatment produced stable and generalized reduction in avoidance behaviour. The two groups of children who had observed the peer-model interact without anxiety with the dog displayed significantly greater approach behaviour toward both the experimental and an unfamiliar animal than children in the third and fourth groups (exposure to the dog alone and control conditions with neither dog nor model), who did not differ from each other. The positive context, however,

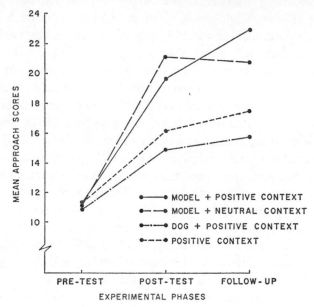

FIG. 1. Mean approach scores achieved by children with dog phobias in each of the treatment conditions on three different periods of assessment. (From Bandura, Grusec and Menlove, 1967; by permission of the American Psychological Association.)

did not contribute much to the favourable outcomes obtained. A more stringent criterion of therapeutic efficacy is the percentage of participants who could manage the final set of tasks. That is, the majority (67 per cent) of children receiving the modelling treatment were eventually able to remain alone in the room and confined with the dog in the playpen; in contrast, this terminal task was attained by relatively few children in the two control conditions.

VICARIOUS EXTINCTION AS A FUNCTION OF MULTIPLE MODELLING

One would expect, from knowledge of generalization processes, that vicarious extinction would be partly governed by the variety of modelling stimulus elements that are neutralized. That is, exposure to multiple models who exhibit fearless behaviour toward variant forms of the phobic object should produce relatively thorough extinction of arousal reactions, and hence, extensive reduction in avoidance behaviour. On the other hand, observers whose emotional responsiveness to a restricted set of aversive modelling elements is extinguished tend to achieve weaker extinction effects. This proposition was tested in a second experiment (Bandura and Menlove, 1968) employing the same assessment methodology with children who displayed severe avoidance behaviour to dogs. In this project the modelled performances were presented in a series of brief cine-films in order to test the efficacy of symbolic modelling techniques, which lend themselves readily to psychotherapeutic applications.

One group of children, who participated in a single modelling treatment, observed a fearless male model display the same progressively more fear-arousing interactions with a dog as in the preceding experiment. The second group of children, receiving multiple modelling treatments, observed several different girls and boys of varying ages interacting positively with various breeds of dogs of different sizes. The size and fearsomeness of the dogs were progressively increased from small dogs that were not threatening in appearance to massive animals that were. Children assigned to a control group were shown cine-films without dogs.

As in the previous experiment, children who observed approach behaviour modelled without any adverse consequences to the performer displayed enduring and generalized reduction in avoidance behaviour, whereas the controls did not show such changes (Fig. 2). Comparison of the performance of the most difficult terminal tasks by children presented with the single modelling display and those who witnessed the multiple modelling, showed that the latter treatment is more effective in completely eliminating phobic behaviour. As a further test of the therapeutic value of symbolic modelling, the control group of children were given the multiple modelling treatment after the main experiment had been completed. These children, whose avoidance behaviour remained unchanged in several tests conducted during the control period, displayed, after the treatment, a sharp increase in their ability to approach dogs.

Comparison of the results of the two experiments suggests that symbolic modelling is less powerful than live demonstrations of essentially the same behaviour. Although the single modelling treatment effected significant reductions in children's avoidance responses, it did not sufficiently weaken their fears to enable them to carry out the most frightening terminal approach behaviour (being confined with the dog in the playpen). But the diminished efficacy of symbolic modelling can be offset by a broader sampling of models and aversive stimulus objects. Children who received this diverse modelling treatment not only showed continued improvement in approach behaviour between post-test and follow-up periods, but also achieved terminal performances at rates comparable to equally severely phobic children who, in the previous experiment, had observed fearless behaviour by a single real-life model.

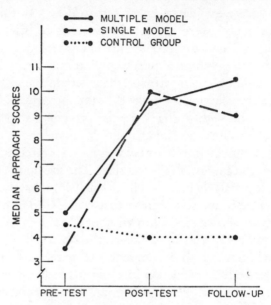

Fig. 2. Median approach scores obtained by children with dog phobias in each of three conditions at different phases of the experiment. (From Bandura and Menlove, 1968; by permission of the American Psychological Association.)

The potency of modelling influences in the transmission of anxiety responses is widely acknowledged, but the therapeutic value of these influences has sometimes been questioned (Jersild and Holmes, 1935) on the grounds that fears persist even though modelling frequently occurs under ordinary conditions of life. The effectiveness of any principle of learning depends not only on its validity but also on the manner in which it is implemented. Inconsistent, haphazard and inadequately sequenced learning experiences will produce disappointing results regardless of the cogency of the principle supposedly guiding the treatment programme.

In many instances weak fears are undoubtedly extinguished, or substantially reduced, through fortuitous naturalistic modelling. But carefully planned modelling experiences are essential for the modification of more tenacious phobias. There is some evidence (Bandura and Menlove, 1968) that parents of children who exhibit severe fearfulness make no attempts to overcome their children's fears because they (the parents) suffer from similar fears. Consequently they seldom model fearlessness and, on the rare occasion when they do so, the modelling endeavours do not consist of the carefully graded presentation of threatening stimuli without which this method is not only likely to be ineffective, but may actually exacerbate anxiety reactions. A not uncommon domestic modelling scene, for example, is one in which a parent is busily petting a dog that is jumping about, while simultaneously bidding the child, who is clinging fearfully, to touch the bounding animal. By contrast, the modelling treatments, in addition to utilizing the principle of graduation to reduce anxiety arousal, involved concentrated exposures to modelling displays under protected observation conditions, and extensive variations of the characteristics of the model, the intimacy of approach behaviour, and the aversive properties of the feared object. Had the modelling sequences been presented in a widely dispersed and haphazard fashion, and restricted to the more reserved petting responses by adults (whom children are likely to discriminate as better able to protect themselves), the vicarious extinction outcomes might have been relatively weak and unpredictable.

In addition to exposure variables, qualitative aspects of the modelled behaviour are likely to exercise some degree of control over vicarious extinction outcomes. It has been shown in studies of vicarious emotional conditioning (Bandura and Rosenthal, 1966; Berger, 1962) that negative affective expressions by models can serve as powerful arousal cues for observers. One would expect modelled approach responses accompanied by positive affective expressions to engender less anxiety arousal and, hence, faster extinction than if the model showed fearful reactions while performing the same behaviour. Parental modelling efforts intended to overcome children's fears are frequently nullified when parents suffer similar apprehensions and force themselves into tense contact with the feared objects. In the present experiments the models frequently expressed pleasant emotional reactions as they performed approach responses in a relaxed manner.

COMPARATIVE EFFICACY OF MODELLING AND DESENSITIZATION
TREATMENT APPROACHES

Our third project (Bandura, Blanchard and Ritter, 1968) used an elaborate experimental design that assessed the comparative efficacy of modelling and desensitization treatment approaches for producing affective, behavioural and attitudinal changes. The participants were adolescents and adults with snake phobias that unnecessarily restricted their psychological functioning in various ways. This type of behaviour disorder was selected for study partly because snake phobias have been frequently employed in evaluating the potency of different forms of behavioural therapy and substantial data have been accumulated on the results (Davison, 1968; Lang, Lazovik and Reynolds, 1965; Schubot, 1966). Apart from the comparative data, this paradigm is well suited for laboratory investigations of extinction processes because avoidance behaviour can be effectively measured and extra-experimental encounters with snakes that might confound the effects of treatment rarely occur or can be easily controlled.

In the initial phase of the experiment the participants were given a behavioural test that measured the strength of their avoidance of snakes. They also completed a comprehensive fear inventory to determine whether the elimination of anxieties about snakes is associated with concomitant changes in other areas of anxiety. Attitudinal ratings on several scales describing various encounters with snakes, and on evaluative dimensions of the semantic differential technique, were also obtained. The latter measures were included to furnish data on the inadequately explored attitudinal effects of behavioural changes induced through social-learning methods. The attitude scales were always given before and after the snake-avoidance test to permit evaluation of the reciprocal interaction between attitudinal and behavioural changes.

The cases were individually matched according to their avoidance behaviour, and assigned to one of four conditions. One group participated in a self-regulated symbolic modelling treatment in which the clients observed a graduated film depicting young children, adolescents and adults engaging in progressively more fear-provoking interactions with a large king snake. To increase the therapeutic power of this method two other features were added. First, clients were taught to induce and to maintain anxiety-inhibiting relaxation throughout the period of exposure. A self-managed modelling treatment should permit greater control over extinction outcomes than one in which a person is exposed to a sequence of aversive modelling cues without regard to his anxiety reactions. Therefore the rate of presentation of the modelling stimuli was regulated by the client through a projector equipped with remote-control starting and reversing devices. Clients were instructed to stop the film whenever a particular modelled performance proved anxiety-provoking, to reverse the film to the beginning of the aversive sequence, and to reinduce deep relaxation.

They then re-viewed the threatening scene repeatedly in this manner until it was completely neutralized before proceeding to the next item in the graduated sequence. After the clients became skilled in the stimulus presentation and self-induction of relaxation, the therapist absented himself from the situation so that the clients themselves conducted their own treatment until their anxieties to the depicted scene were thoroughly extinguished.

The second group of clients received a live-modelling-guided participation form of treatment in which, after observing intimate snake-interaction behaviour repeatedly modelled by the therapist, they were aided, through demonstration, to perform progressively more approach responses toward a snake. At each step the therapist himself performed fearless behaviour, and gradually led the clients into touching, stroking, and then holding the middle of the snake's body with gloved and then bare hands, while he held the snake by the head and tail. When clients no longer felt any apprehension about touching the snake under these secure conditions, anxieties about contact with the snake's head area and entwining tail were extinguished. The therapist again performed the tasks fearlessly, and then he and the client performed the responses jointly; as clients became less fearful the therapist gradually reduced his participation and control over the snake until eventually the clients were able to hold the snake in their laps without assistance, to let the snake loose in the room and retrieve it, and to let it crawl freely over their bodies. Progress through the graded approach tasks was paced according to the clients' apprehensiveness. When they reported being able to perform one activity with little or no fear, they were eased into a more difficult interaction.

Clients assigned to the third group received the standard form of counter-conditioning therapy devised by Wolpe (1958). In this procedure deep relaxation was successively paired with imaginal representations of snake scenes arranged in order of increasing aversiveness. As in the other conditions, treatment was continued until the clients' anxiety reactions were totally extinguished or the maximum time (6 hours) allotted for treatment (not counting relaxation training) was completed. The maximum contact with snakes, either live or in symbolic form, was thus equated across treatments.

Clients assigned to the control group participated in the behavioural and attitudinal assessments without receiving any intervening treatment. This group was included primarily to furnish a control for changes resulting from repeated measurements. A relationship pseudotherapy was not used because several previous investigations have shown that snake avoidance behaviour is unaffected by such experiences. In addition, the controls were subsequently used to test a variation of the symbolic modelling treatment. To evaluate the reliability of treatment outcomes the procedures were administered by two therapists, one female and the other male, with different personality characteristics.

After the treatment series was completed the assessment procedures were readministered to all subjects. The behavioural test, using two snakes of strikingly different colours, consisted of series of tasks requiring subjects to approach, look at, touch and hold a snake with gloved and bare hands; to remove the snake from its cage, let it loose in the room, and then replace it in the cage; to hold it within five inches of their faces; and, finally, to tolerate the snake in their laps while they held their hands passively at their sides. Immediately before and during the performance of each task clients rated the intensity of their fear on a ten-interval scale to provide a measure of affective changes associated with the different methods of treatment.

Behavioural changes

The results of the behavioural test, summarized graphically in Fig. 3, show that the control subjects are essentially unchanged in avoidance behaviour; symbolic modelling and desensitization treatments substantially reduced phobic behaviour; while live modelling combined with guided participation proved to be an unusually powerful treatment and eliminated snake phobias in virtually all subjects (92 per cent).

Affective changes

The modelling procedures not only extinguished strong, long-standing avoidance behaviour, but also effectively neutralized the anxiety-arousing properties of the phobic stimuli. Both of the modelling treatments achieved marked decrements in anticipatory and performance anxiety. Although subjects who had received desensitization treatment also experienced less emotional arousal while approaching the snakes in the various ways described, their fear was significantly less reduced than the fear shown by subjects in the modelling conditions.

Attitudinal changes

Because cognitive and attitudinal changes have rarely been systematically assessed in applications of behavioural therapies, it has been generally assumed that these types of approaches alter behaviours only. One can distinguish between three basic strategies of attitude change. The *information-oriented* approach attempts to modify the subjects' attitudes by altering their beliefs about the attitude object through various forms of persuasive interpretation. This method produces changes in attitudes but generally has little effect on overt actions (Festinger, 1964; Fleishmann, Harris and Burtt, 1955; Levitt, 1965; Maccoby *et al.*, 1962). A second general strategy involves an *affect-oriented* approach wherein both evaluations of, and

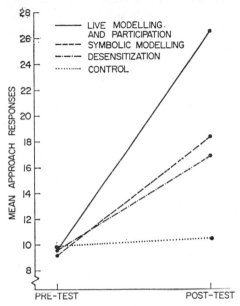

FIG. 3. Mean number of approach responses performed by clients with snake phobias, who received either systematic desensitization, symbolic modelling, live modelling combined with guided performance, or no treatment. Each of the groups contains 12 subjects. (From Bandura, Blanchard and Ritter, 1968.)

behaviour toward, particular attitude objects are modified by altering their affective properties, usually through vicarious or direct conditioning procedures. The third approach, which is often used in social learning (Bandura, 1968) and in experimental social psychology (Brehm and Cohen, 1962; Festinger, 1957), relies upon a *behaviour-oriented* strategy. The results of this procedure have provided considerable evidence that enduring attitudinal changes can be induced most effectively by getting a person to engage in new behaviour in relation to the attitude object without untoward consequences. The relative superiority of the behavioural approach probably stems from the fact that a basic change in behaviour and the resultant experiential feedback provide an objective and genuine basis for new evaluations.

The results of the present experiment show that applications of social learning therapies have important attitudinal consequences. Both symbolic modelling and desensitization, which primarily involve extinction of the negative affect aroused by aversive stimuli, produced favourable changes in attitudes toward snakes. Consistent with theoretical expectation, the treatment condition that reduced the anxiety-arousing properties of snakes and enabled subjects to engage in intimate interactions with snakes effected the greatest attitudinal changes.

Positive transfer of anxiety decrements

The difference between psychodynamic and social-learning approaches to psychotherapy is often misconstrued as the difference between treatment of causes and of symptoms. But one cannot eliminate behaviour as such, except perhaps through direct removal of the requisite neurophysiological systems. Response patterns can be modified only by altering the conditions that regulate their occurrence. Psychodynamic and social-learning therapies are, therefore, equally concerned with modifying the "causes" of deviant behaviour; however, these theories differ (often radically) in what they regard these determinants to be—a crucial difference which, in turn, influences the types of psychological events favoured in the respective treatments. It would be more accurate and advantageous to redefine the cause-symptom treatment controversy as being primarily concerned with the question of whether a particular form of therapy chooses to modify conditions that, in reality, exercise strong, weak, or no significant control over the behaviour in question. One would predict from this point of view that favourable changes induced in one area of behaviour will tend to set in motion beneficial changes in related areas of psychological functioning.

Analysis of the fear inventory scores in our studies does indeed reveal some degree of reduction of fear towards situations beyond the specifically treated phobia, the decrements being roughly proportional to the potency of the treatments employed. Untreated controls showed no changes in either the number or intensity of their fears; desensitization produced a decrease only in the severity of fears towards other animals; and symbolic modelling was accompanied by a reduction in the number of animal fears and a general diminution in the intensity of anxiety in several other areas of functioning. Live modelling combined with participation, on the other hand, effected widespread reductions of fear in relation to a variety of threats involving both interpersonal and non-social events.

The positive transfer obtained in this study probably reflects the operation of at least two somewhat different processes. The first involves generalization of extinction effects from treated stimuli to related sources of anxiety. The second entails positive reinforcement of a sense of capability through success, which mitigates emotional responses to potentially threatening situations. In a follow-up questionnaire most of the clients reported that, having successfully overcome a phobia that had plagued them for most of their lives, they felt increased confidence that they could cope effectively with other fear-provoking events.

Under conditions where a given treatment procedure exercises weak behavioural control, many other variables (such as the personality characteristics of the therapists, attributes of the clients and minor technical variations) will emerge as influential determinants of change. But if a method is sufficiently powerful it should be able to override such influences. To demonstrate that in the cases that showed only partial improvement the major deficits resided in the method rather than in the client, all subjects who failed to achieve terminal performances, including the controls, were subsequently treated with the live modelling and guided participation techniques. Snake phobia was thoroughly extinguished in all these subjects, within a few brief sessions, regardless of their age, sex, anxiety proneness and the severity of the avoidance behaviour. Moreover, this supplementary treatment produced further reductions in fearfulness toward both the phobic stimuli and other types of threats, and additional attitudinal changes.

A one-month follow-up assessment revealed that the beneficial changes produced in behaviour, attitudes and emotional responsiveness were effectively maintained. The clients also gave evidence that the behavioural improvements had generalized to real-life situations. They were able to participate in recreational activities such as camping, hiking and gardening which they formerly avoided because of their dread of snakes; they no longer experienced marked distress when unexpectedly confronted with snakes in the course of their social or occupational activities; and they were able to handle harmless snakes, and a few even served as model therapists for their own children and faint-hearted friends. These favourable outcomes illustrate the need for new psychological facilities that offer brief and highly efficacious treatments for specific types of behavioural dysfunction. Vast numbers of people, who otherwise endure unnecessary restrictions in certain areas of their lives, could benefit from such services.

Ritter (1968) has achieved a uniform degree of success with group modelling procedures in children with snake phobias. Groups of children participated in two 35-minute sessions in which they either merely observed several fearless children exhibit intimate interactions with a snake, or received a modelling-guided participation form of treatment during which the therapist displayed positive responses toward the snake and then gradually eased the children into performing the feared behaviour. Snake phobias were completely extinguished in 53 per cent of the children by modelling alone and in 80 per cent of the children after modelling combined with guided participation. The results of these projects indicate that a powerful form of therapy is one in which therapeutic agents themselves model the desired behaviour and arrange optimum conditions for clients to engage in similar activities until they can perform the behaviour skilfully and fearlessly. The therapeutic outcomes associated with this approach are sufficiently promising to warrant its further extension to other types of anxieties and phobias.

In a recently completed experiment O'Connor (1968) employed symbolic modelling in treating pre-school children who showed extreme social withdrawal, a behaviour disorder that reflects both deficits in social skills and fear of close interpersonal contacts. One-half of this group of children were shown a control film, while a matched group of isolates observed a talkie depicting timid children initially watching ongoing social activities at a distance but eventually joining and interacting with the children, with evident positive consequences. In a behavioural assessment conducted immediately after the treatment session the controls remained markedly withdrawn, whereas children who had received the symbolic modelling showed a fivefold increase in social interaction.

Within the modelling-guided participation treatment there are three processes operative that might contribute in varying degrees to such striking psychological changes. These are observation of fearless behaviour being modelled without any unfavourable consequences, incidental information received regarding the feared objects, and direct personal interactions with threatening objects without adverse effects. In an experiment aimed at isolating the relative influence of these component variables, Blanchard (1968) matched subjects in terms of their snake-avoidance behaviour and assigned them to one of four conditions. One subject in each quartet received the standard procedure, which includes the benefits of modelling, incidental information and guided interaction with a snake. A second subject simultaneously observed the modelling sessions and listened to the verbal interchanges thus being exposed to both modelling and information influences. The third subject received only the modelling component, while the fourth, who merely participated in the testing procedures, experienced none of the constituent influences. Modelling accounted for a major part of the psychological changes, and guided participation also contributed a significant increment, particularly to approach behaviour and fear reduction. On the other hand, informational influences had no effects on either attitudes, emotional arousal or approach behaviour.

MECHANISMS UNDERLYING VICARIOUS EXTINCTION

Research is also needed to clarify the mechanisms through which modelling combined with guided participation achieves such uniformly powerful extinction effects. The findings of the studies described, particularly those based on a paradigm of non-response extinction, can perhaps be best explained in terms of a dual-process theory of avoidance behaviour (Rescorla and Solomon, 1967). According to this view, conditioned aversive stimuli evoke emotional arousal which has both autonomic and central components. It is further assumed that these arousal processes, especially those involving central systems, exert some degree of mediating control over instrumental avoidance responses. The influential role of arousal mediators is most clearly demonstrated by experiments in which avoidance responses to a given stimulus are established through prior classical pairings of that stimulus with aversive experiences. The skeletal muscles of the experimental animals are immobilized by curare to prevent avoidance responses from being conditioned directly to the external stimuli (Rescorla and Solomon, 1967; Solomon and Turner, 1962).

It follows from the dual-process theory that if the arousal capacity of a phobic stimulus is extinguished, then both the motivation and one set of controlling stimuli for avoidance behaviour are removed. Neutralization of an aversive stimulus through classical extinction procedures alone markedly facilitates subsequent elimination of avoidance behaviour (Black, 1958). It has been further shown (Bandura, Blanchard and Ritter, 1968) that emotional arousal can be effectively extinguished on a vicarious basis when observers merely witness models exhibiting approach responses toward feared objects without experiencing any adverse consequences. The more thoroughly emotional arousal to threatening stimuli is vicariously extinguished the greater is the reduction in avoidance behaviour (Blanchard, 1968). In accordance with these findings, the process of change associated with the powerful procedure involving modelling combined with guided participation may be conceptualized as follows. Repeated modelling of approach responses decreases the arousal potential of aversive stimuli below the threshold for activating avoidance responses, thus enabling subjects to engage, albeit somewhat anxiously, in approach behaviour. The favourable outcomes resulting from direct contact with threatening events further extinguish any residual anxiety and avoidance tendencies. Without the benefit of previous vicarious extinction the reinstatement of severely inhibited behaviour generally requires a tedious and protracted treatment programme. After approach behaviour towards formerly avoided objects has been fully restored the resultant new experiences give rise to substantial reorganization of attitudes.

SUMMARY

This paper is principally concerned with modelling processes whereby phobic behaviour is successfully extinguished through observation of modelled approach behaviour without adverse consequences accruing to the fearless performers. Results of several laboratory investigations reveal that live modelling combined with guided participation is an unusually powerful treatment that effects stable and generalized extinction of phobic behaviour in virtually all cases. Moreover, modelling procedures, both singly and in combination with guided performance, produce a marked reduction in emotional responsivity, substantial attitudinal changes, and anxiety decrements in areas of functioning beyond the specifically treated phobia.

A major factor in modelling procedures that expedites behavioural changes is assumed to be vicarious extinction of arousal reactions to aversive stimuli below the level for activating avoidance responses; this extinction thus enables the clients to approach the phobic objects. Direct contact with threats that are no longer objectively justified provides a variety of new experiences which, if favourable, further extinguish residual anxiety and augment attitudinal changes.

Laboratory findings suggest that a powerful form of therapy is one in which therapeutic agents themselves model the desired behaviour and arrange optimal conditions for clients to engage in similar activities until they can perform the behaviour skilfully and fearlessly.

ACKNOWLEDGEMENTS

I am indebted to my collaborators, Joan Grusec, Frances Menlove, Brunhilde Ritter and Edward Blanchard, for their valuable contributions to the investigations summarized in this paper.

This research was supported by U.S. Public Health Research Grant M-5162 from the National Institute of Mental Health.

REFERENCES

BANDURA, A. (1965). In *Advances in Experimental Social Psychology*, pp. 1–55, ed. Berkowitz, L. New York: Academic Press.

BANDURA, A. (1968). *Principles of Behavioral Modification*. New York: Holt, Rinehart and Winston.

BANDURA, A., BLANCHARD, E. B., and RITTER, B. J. (1968). *The Relative Efficacy of Desensitization and Modelling Therapeutic Approaches for Inducing Behavioral, Affective and Attitudinal Changes*. Unpublished manuscript, Stanford University.

BANDURA, A., GRUSEC, J. E., and MENLOVE, F. L. (1967). *J. Pers. soc. Psychol.*, **5**, 16–23.

BANDURA, A., and MENLOVE, F. L. (1968). *J. Pers. soc. Psychol.*, **8**, 99–108.

BANDURA, A., and ROSENTHAL, T. L. (1966). *J. Pers. soc. Psychol.*, **3**, 54–62.

BANDURA, A., and WALTERS, R. H. (1963). *Social Learning and Personality Development*. New York: Holt, Rinehart and Winston.

BERGER, S. M. (1962). *Psychol. Rev.*, **69**, 450–466.

BLACK, A. H. (1958). *J. comp. physiol. Psychol.*, **51**, 519–524.

BLANCHARD, E. B. (1968). Doctoral thesis, Stanford University, Faculty of Arts and Science.

BREHM, J. W., and COHEN, A. R. (1962). *Explorations in Cognitive Dissonance*. New York: Wiley.

DAVISON, G. C. (1968). *J. abnorm. Psychol.*, **73**, 91–99.

FESTINGER, L. (1957). *A Theory of Cognitive Dissonance*. Evanston, Ill.: Row and Peterson.

FESTINGER, L. (1964). *Publ. Opin. Quart.*, **28**, 404–417.

FLEISHMANN, E., HARRIS, E., and BURTT, H. (1955). *Leadership and Supervision in Industry*. Columbus, Ohio: Ohio State University Bureau of Educational Research.

JERSILD, A. T., and HOLMES, F. B. (1935). *J. Psychol.*, **1**, 75–104.

LANG, P. J., LAZOVIK, A. D., and REYNOLDS, D. J. (1965). *J. abnorm. Psychol.*, **70**, 395–402.

LEVITT, T. (1965). *Industrial Purchasing Behavior*. Cambridge, Mass.: Harvard University Press.

MACCOBY, N., ROMNEY, A. K., ADAMS, J. S., and MACCOBY, E. E. (1962). *"Critical Periods" in Seeking and Accepting Information*. Stanford: Stanford University Institute for Communication Research.

O'CONNOR, R. D. (1968). *Modification of Social Withdrawal through Symbolic Modelling*. Unpublished manuscript, Stanford University.

RESCORLA, R. A., and SOLOMON, R. L. (1967). *Psychol. Rev.*, **74**, 151–182.

RITTER, B. J. (1968). *Behav. Res. Ther.*, **6**, 1–6.

SCHUBOT, E. D. (1966). Doctoral thesis, Stanford University, Faculty of Arts and Science.

SOLOMON, R. L., and TURNER, L. H. (1962). *Psychol. Rev.*, **69**, 202–219.

WOLPE, J. (1958). *Psychotherapy by Reciprocal Inhibition*. Stanford: Stanford University Press.

DISCUSSION

Lazarus: Were measurements of the effectiveness of your technique derived from verbal self-reports—inventories and semantic differentials and so on?

Bandura: Yes. Self-reports provided measures of affective and attitudinal changes; behavioural changes were the major criteria for evaluating the relative efficacy of the different procedures.

Lazarus: Dr. Peter Lang (1967, personal communication) noted that, with desensitization techniques, behavioural and autonomic changes and the content of verbal reports may be unrelated. Subjects may *say* they are not frightened but act as if they are; or they may behave quite confidently but say that they are afraid; or they may act and speak calmly while showing anxiety responses on a polygraph. Lang also described a lag between the end of desensitization and the execution of approach behaviour, the suggested explanation for this being that it takes time for the elimination of the autonomic maladaptive response to generalize to speech and behaviour. Live modelling and participation might be expected to induce rapid verbal reports of improvement and positive approach responses, without concurrent autonomic decrements. Did you use any physiological measures that might yield information about this, Professor Bandura?

Bandura: No. The anxiety ratings show that symbolic modelling, and live modelling combined with guided participation, produced more thorough extinction of anxiety than desensitization did. I would interpret discrepancies between autonomic and behavioural changes in desensitization therapy as reflecting incomplete extinction rather than delayed generalization. In the standard desensitization procedure a person's emotional responses to symbolic representations of anxiety-provoking situations are extinguished, and a relatively limited set of aversive stimuli are usually neutralized. Under these conditions, extinction effects must generalize from symbolic events to real-life events containing many aversive elements that were never desensitized. The more that the imagined stimuli differ from their actual counterparts, the less is the likelihood of transfer. The extent to which a subject will engage in approach behaviour, although with some residual anxiety, depends on the extent that desensitization therapy reduces the arousal of anxiety below the threshold which would activate avoidance responses. If subsequent encounters with the actual feared objects do not result in adverse consequences any remaining autonomic overactivity will eventually be extinguished. The major advantage of live modelling supplemented with participation is that anxiety reactions toward actual threats rather than attenuated symbolic counterparts are extinguished, thereby ensuring optimum transfer of changes to different situations and response systems.

Lazarus: Your excellent results would be even more strongly confirmed if physiological measures showed that generalization to autonomic responses had occurred.

Hinde: Will you comment on the effect on your results of the emotional expression of the models when they approach the snakes?

Bandura: The affective expressions of models can, of course, have a profound emotional effect upon observers. Laboratory studies of vicarious classical conditioning in man (Bandura, A., and Rosenthal, T. L. [1966]. *J. Pers. soc. Psychol.*, **3**, 54-62; Berger, S. M. [1962]. *Psychol. Rev.*, **69**, 450-466; Craig, K. D., and Weinstein, M. S. [1965]. *Psychol. Rep.*, **17**, 955-963) have shown that the observation of a performer undergoing painful experiences produces vicarious emotional arousal that becomes conditioned to previously neutral environmental stimuli. J. L. Crooks (1968. *J. Pers. soc. Psychol.*, in press) has shown that strong suppression of behaviour can be established in monkeys solely on the basis of what they observe. The animals in Crooks' study were first tested to determine the extent to which they handled play objects. The animals then participated in a vicarious fear-conditioning experiment in which distress vocalizations were played on a tape recorder whenever a model monkey touched a particular object. Later the monkeys also received a control conditioning procedure in which they witnessed the model's contacts with a different object paired with the distress signals played backwards, thus obliterating the affective negative valence of the sounds. In a subsequent test the observing animals played freely with the control items but actively avoided objects that had accompanied supposedly painful experiences for another animal.

Hinde: If we can compare these studies in monkeys with studies on birds, these techniques would be even more effective if the monkeys were rewarded when they touched the objects not connected to the distress signals (Klopfer, P. H. [1959]. *Behaviour*, **14**, 282-299).

Marks: Professor Bandura, you have used the intensity of fear at contact (or attempted contact) with the feared object as the criterion of the severity of the phobia. But the response to desensitization is not determined by this but by the extent of the patient's anxiety at rest (when he is away from the feared object)—the free-floating anxiety. I would predict that live modelling will provide a dramatic way of speeding up treatment where desensitization has already been shown to be effective, but in patients in whom desensitization is not effective these techniques will not be effective either. In severely anxious subjects with severe agoraphobia and multiple panic attacks, for example, live modelling will probably not be useful.

Bandura: The identification of predictors is important when a given treatment has variable results. But if a therapeutic procedure is sufficiently powerful to effect major changes in all subjects to whom it is administered, then the only value of predictors is to determine the rate at which changes will occur in different sorts of patients.

Gelder: I am surprised that the method you use is so successful because the models (who were children) were so unlike the subjects you treated (who were adult plumbers and such); it must have been very difficult for the subject to identify with the model. I would have anticipated that identification would have been crucial for a successful outcome. I would suggest that if these techniques are used in phobic patients, especially agoraphobics, they will only work if the model is someone with whom the patient can identify. Would you comment on the effect of identification in modelling techniques in general, and especially on its effect on the extinction of fears?

Bandura: The consequences of the model's response are generally a more important influence than his characteristics on the observer's capacity to identify with him. Thus witnessing a similar model being bitten by a snake will probably increase snake-avoidance in the observer, whereas seeing a dissimilar model handle a snake without untoward consequences will produce vicarious extinction of avoidance responses. We included young children as models on the assumption that their lack of fear while performing responses that adult observers regarded as hazardous would provide the most dramatic argument against the anticipated aversive consequences.

Kubie: These techniques and your excellent results pose many conundrums. The best way for us to derive scientifically useful information from our studies of patients is to study the failures. Clinicopathological conferences are urgently needed in psychiatry.

Phobias are not uniform or simple, but complex, multivalent products of complex but varied problems. If phobias were as simple as your results suggest they would soon spontaneously cease to exist. If agoraphobia could be cured by simple corrective experiences it would not exist at all, since agoraphobics see people walking in safety in the streets, and walk safely in the streets themselves, often making heroic and Herculean efforts at self-healing. A phobic patient may succeed in diminishing the restrictive and imprisoning influence of his specific phobia by these efforts, but this never cures the underlying neurotic illness; it produces other phobias in place of the first. Many phobic patients force themselves into the phobic situation and conquer it over and over again, yet with complete lack of relief. For example, an exceptionally attractive young girl was so terrified before she went to a dance that she vomited when she received an invitation; she always forced herself to go, and always had a wonderful time, but the anticipatory panics recurred unabated on every subsequent occasion. Finally she was trapped between two depressions—one over the failure of her heroism and the other if no invitation came. Another example was a young man with severe hydrophobia. He forced himself to learn to swim, and did this so well that he represented his university in its water polo team. But the cost of this heroic action was the development of an array of totally different neurotic symptoms out of the same unresolved problems. Only the surface manifestations of his illness had been relieved. And many superb public speakers or virtuoso performers face every speech or concert with terror although they have never failed to give a brilliant performance. I have also seen a big-game hunter, famous for his skill and courage, who was never afraid of a dangerous wild animal but was petrified of insects. He made a collection of insects, forcing himself to catch them alive, and to prepare and mount them. This had no effect on his phobia. Your excellent results, Professor Bandura, challenge us to try to analyse the subjects of phobias more minutely. Are they all alike? Or does the phobia have multiple alternative roots, thus resembling the units in a dream?

Bandura: The existence of powerful treatment procedures and objective measures of change permit empiric tests of different theoretical formulations regarding the conditions governing deviant behaviour. Psychodynamic formulations assume that anxieties are internally generated by the arousal of unconscious impulses which are then displaced and projected on to events and objects in the environment. External phobic objects are therefore regarded as pseudo-evocative stimuli. According to this theory, the neutralization of reactions to phobic stimuli should have little lasting effect. But successful neutralization of emotional responses to phobic objects through desensitization or modelling not only produces stable decreases in avoidance behaviour without the emergence of new deviant responses, but is often accompanied by reductions in anxiety about other functions. O. Fenichel (1945. *The Psychoanalytic Theory of Neurosis.* New York: Norton) has suggested that snake phobias reflect phallic anxieties. On the basis of his interpretation it would be instructive to compare the extent to which snake phobias are extinguished when treatment is directed toward either the phobic stimuli themselves or to the hypothetical phallic threats. Of course the crucial determinants of phobic behaviour are not always inferrable from the content of the deviant responses. In many cases anxiety-generated behaviour is under the control of multiple stimuli and some of the evocative events, because of a peculiar social-learning history, may be thematically remote.

Miller: Your experiment is fascinating both methodologically and because of the good results: recovery in 100 per cent of cases is a most satisfying outcome for any therapy. Dr. Kubie, would you outline the sort of information you would need in the follow-up studies on these patients to show convincingly that the results are as good as they seem?

8*

Kubie: I cannot accept this challenge without correcting the phrasing of the question. The words carry several unjustified implications. First, the assumption that these patients are all suffering from similar or identical disease processes: there is no evidence for this. A single symptom or symptom cluster does not make a disease entity in either psychological or somatic disorders. The consequences of paralysis of a limb may be identical but the processes by which the paralysis occurs vary enormously. Prevention or cure depends more on the process than on the final condition. The same is true of depression, elation, phobias, compulsions or any other manifestations in the whole range of psychopathological phenomenology. Second, Professor Miller's question contains an assumption that the alteration of symptoms is necessarily and always good in itself. All changes are interesting and one can learn from them, but the amelioration of a symptom may be a disaster from the point of view of the progress of an illness. The patient may escape from his symptoms with a sense of relief only to dive deeper into his illness. Some symptoms are in themselves so destructive to a patient's life, and have such seriously damaging consequences, that their relief provides an opportunity to reconstruct a life, at least partially, after which one can work on the process which produced the symptom. But many other symptoms protect the patient from disaster and their relief, without alteration of the underlying process, can be calamitous. Nor is this phenomenon peculiar to psychological medicine. It is equally true for such somatic illnesses as fever and heart disease, the alleviation of which may sometimes be life-saving and sometimes lethal. I am shocked that this old lesson has been so widely forgotten in psychiatry and experimental clinical psychology. We would be wise to rediscover it, and to understand and apply it.

I shall therefore rephrase the question and break it down into four parts. (1) How do we establish, before our attempts to compare them, that a group of patients represents either a single disease process or a group of contrasting disease processes?

(2) What criteria of change in this underlying process can we use? And what evidence can we have for the direction of change towards either improvement or deterioration?

(3) How do we gather evidence about the relationship of symptomatic change to process change? Symptomatic changes often lead merely to the substitution of new and more skilfully hidden symptoms. We should be constantly on our guard against being fooled by an initial disappearance of symptoms. The disappearance of depression, for example, may lead directly to suicide.

(4) How long a follow-up is necessary and how can follow-up studies be conducted so that we are not misled by using weighted samples? In other words, how can one keep track of patients who do not want to cooperate in this, and without whose cooperation statistics are valueless?

This is some of the information we need if we are going to evaluate our studies of change. We must also try to understand the meaning of change —a difficult task.

THE PSYCHOTHERAPEUTIC INGREDIENT IN THE LEARNING PROCESS

LAWRENCE S. KUBIE

*Department of Psychiatry, University of Maryland School of Medicine, Baltimore**

TITLES of conferences, books and articles are often as revelatory as are the faces with which we meet the world. The title of this conference seems to me to condense many fallacious assumptions about both the learning process and psychotherapy, and also to express that need for oversimplification which besets both fields. The idea that illness is due to mal-education and, consequently, that good education will prevent or correct illness rests on a series of hopeful misconceptions. How can we educate somebody *out* of illness when we do not really know how to educate at all? This is why I could not present a paper focused on the topic of this conference, but chose instead to talk about the role of psychotherapy in the educational process. Having said this much, I have made my most important point. Therefore I should now imitate that old French savant about whom the late David Rapaport used to tell a story. The savant moved slowly and thoughtfully to the podium of the French Academy, looked about the crowded hall, shook his head sadly, said "I have changed my mind", and went home. But I do not quite want to do this. Instead, with your indulgence, I want to expand further on the role of psychotherapy in the educational process. If we once understood this, then we would be in a better position to talk about the obverse relationship.

I am sure that everyone in this room has a different way of characterizing education as a discipline, as a process, and as an achieved state. I am equally sure that no one here would claim that he knows how to measure the state and degree of education, or the ups and downs of the process, or its rate of change and progress. Nor would anyone be sure that he could always say when education has succeeded or when it has failed, since all of us know savants who are full of erudition but who become sillier with each accretion of external knowledge. And certainly everyone who has had experience in education at any level has also had the experience of seeming

* Present address: Wheeler Lane, Sparks, Maryland.

to fail with a student, only to discover years later that the exposure to education which had seemed to fail had played a determining role in the growth of that student and in his ultimate mastery of some discipline. This confronts all of us with the puzzling facts that we do not always know when we succeed and when we fail to educate, and that no one has as yet found out how to measure these variables with precision. This is not a satisfactory state of affairs; but if we face it, the effort to remedy it will start education on its long journey towards becoming a behavioural science (Kubie, 1968). In the meantime, however, no one will deny the existence of education as both a discipline and a process, or that there are varying kinds, states and degrees of educatedness.

Yet this is exactly the position taken by many fulminating critics of psychotherapy: namely, that if you cannot measure it with precision there is no such thing. I too would like to be able to make qualitative and, ultimately, quantitative measurements of the movement, the rate of change, the direction of change, and the ultimate state of change produced by the educational process and, equally, by the psychotherapeutic process, or for that matter by any therapeutic manoeuvre in psychiatry, whether with drugs, surgery, shock, or any combination of these with or without psychotherapy. Further, I anticipate with confidence that precision in the description and measurement of psycho-education and of psychotherapy will be achieved together, precisely because the two are inextricably intertwined. But in the meantime, to attempt to persuade human beings who are in need that there is no such thing as psychotherapy in psychiatry is an expression of personal bias which is hard to forgive. If nothing else that I say here is remembered I hope that this will be (Kubie, 1964).

I must also emphasize the importance of self-knowledge in depth as an ingredient in all learning (Kubie, 1954b). "... What is the effective value of a knowledge of externals if we lack an equally deep personal insight? Can there be wisdom even about the objective world around us, in the absence of wisdom about the world within? Can there be any mature understanding of others without self-knowledge?" Much has already been written on this subject (Kubie, 1957, pp. 12–13). "Education without self-knowledge can never mean wisdom and maturity; but self-knowledge in depth is a process which, like education itself, is never finished. It is a point on a continuous and never-ending journey. It is relative and not absolute. It is a process which goes on throughout life, demanding constant vigilance and a continuous struggle; because active forces are at work in all of us which tend repeatedly to confuse and obscure our images of ourselves. Without self-knowledge man looks out upon a world which he strives to understand through glasses which are colored by the quality of his own unconscious problems. The greater the role in the educational process which is played by the unconscious components of symbolic thought, the wider must be the ancient and dishonorable gap between erudition and wisdom ...

"A scholar may be erudite on conscious and preconscious levels, yet so obtuse about the play of unconscious forces in his own life that he cannot know when he is using realistically and creatively the subject of which he is the master, or when he is using it like the ink blots on a Rorschach card. Education for wisdom must close this gap, by providing insight which penetrates into those areas of human life in which in the past unconscious forces played the preponderant role ...

"Without self-knowledge in depth we can have dreams but not art; we can have the neurotic raw material of literature but not mature literature. Without it we can have no adults but only aging children armed with words, paint, clay and atomic weapons, none of which they understand. It is this which makes a mockery of the more pretentious claims of education, of religion, of the arts, and of science. Self-knowledge is the forgotten man of our entire educational system and indeed of human culture in general. Without self-knowledge it is possible to be erudite but never wise. The challenge to all of us is to have the humility to face this failure and the determination to do something effective about it.

"This position should not be exaggerated. Self-knowledge is not all there is to wisdom. It is an essential ingredient which makes maturity possible. Yet it is the one ingredient which is totally neglected ..." (Kubie, 1954b).

Illness in the learning process

Not infrequently the learning process is interrupted by psychological upsets of varying severity, kinds and durations. These may occur early in the educational process (indeed I have known this interruption of the learning process to occur on the first day at kindergarten). Or it may occur at any later point during the educational orbit, including the final phase as a brilliant individual is nearing the end of an exceptionally successful career as an academic or professional student. Unhappily this may occur among highly successful students as well as among students who fail. It may develop slowly and insidiously or as sudden episodes of explosive disorganization. Such upsets are neither exceptional nor the rule: nor are they the central focus of my thesis. Their relevance to what I have to say derives from the mere fact that they occur at all; because this is evidence that the learning process, even when successful, is not always a psychologically strengthening or healing experience. This should not surprise us when we consider how often even the most "successful" artists, writers, musicians, businessmen, lawyers, preachers, teachers, doctors, scientists, shoemakers, workmen and artisans break down and even commit suicide.

Further, educators in many fields, but especially in the engineering and physical sciences, are fully aware of an even subtler but equally dismaying fact: that is, that even when no frank upsets occur, the student's success as a student may cost him his ability to use his hard-won knowledge subsequently in independent, creative research, in teaching, or even for practical application. The survival of the corpus of the student to the end of the educational tunnel is no guarantee that the freedom of his creative spirit will survive as well (Kubie, 1953, 1954a, 1965). His successful pursuit of academic success may imprison him in neurotic shackles. This provides further evidence that education can no longer blind itself to the importance of concurrent psychonoxious influences. And wherever psychonoxious influences occur, it becomes our responsibility to introduce countervailing therapeutic measures for preventive purposes.

I have pointed out repeatedly that the neurotic process is an endless chain of reverberating consequences of fission among various dissociated components in the psychology of man (Kubie, 1958). The subsequent fusion of what has been fissioned is a slow and laborious task, especially if it is not undertaken until after the fission has already produced long series of complex reverberating consequences, each with its own new superimposed fissions. If, on the other hand, the original fission can be prevented (which is the essential task of prevention in psychiatry: Kubie, 1959b), or if refusion can be achieved before the series of secondary and tertiary consequences of the fission have distorted an entire life, then techniques learned from psychotherapy can be adapted to the educational scene for early preventive purposes. This must become an integral part of education (Kubie, 1963, 1964).

The impact of concealed neurotogenic processes

(See Kubie, 1967, pp. 96–97.)

The child buries pain every day; and the accumulation of buried pain gradually isolates him from both his elders and his age-peers, and makes him afraid to allow his mental processes to flow freely. He becomes in varying degrees constricted. This destructive process could be held in check and reversed if what the child buries were to be exhumed day by day as he is burying it. Thus the early introduction into the educational process of techniques borrowed from but not identical with psychotherapy could unlock the doors which imprison us in our masked neuroses. If we are to act in this way we will have to abandon the conspiracy of silence in which schools and parents alike shroud the painfully charged experiences which are important in human development. We process all experience preconsciously without words; but that of which we *cannot* speak we finally lose words for; and that for which we have no words we finally cannot correct. Thus the conspiracy of silence is one primary source of the tendency to dissociation and repression which is one of the roots of the neurotic process. To limit and reverse, as it occurs, this splintering of experience into unrelated, dissociated, inaccessible, and repressed fragments would be far more economical than is any later attempt to reunite those parts of psychic life that have already been set apart and buried. Some fission is inescapable; but prompt refusion can prevent its becoming permanent, especially if the fusing were done not once but repeatedly in each school year, and in every year throughout the successive stages of a child's development, and on into the years of higher education. Any such programme will need the joint efforts of educators, experimental and clinical psychologists, plus psychiatrists and psychoanalysts who are trained and experienced in working with children, adolescents and adults. This is an awesome prospect; yet nothing less will even have a chance to create an educational process that will no longer intensify neurotogenic dissociative processes, but will lessen and limit and reverse them instead. Many previous studies have pointed out the subtle ways in which traditional educational procedures, with their emphasis on repetitive drill and repetitive grill, become interwoven with the automatic, uncontrollable, obligatory repetitions which are at the heart of the neurotic process.

How then can we equip our children, our students, our patients with the tools that they will need in life without destroying that free play of preconscious processing and of the derived creative imagination which they will need if they are ever to be able to use the tools which they acquire? We have learned that input-overload and the excessive use of drill and grill can tumble the learner into a paralysing rigidity that ends in ignorance. Out of this rigidity emerges either the neurotically inhibited ignoramus, or that special form of the idiot-savant who is a scholar in one field, frozen into laboured uncreativity, but deficient in every other aspect of human wisdom. At the opposite end of the spectrum, excessive permissiveness can do similar harm. We are familiar with the uncluttered mind, master of nothing, free of any burden of facts, yet equally under the domination of neurotic processes. Between the neurotic ignoramus and the neurotic scholar there is not very much to choose, except that the neurotic ignoramus is almost always more fun, or at least less objectionable, because he is less pretentious.

Psychonoxious influences of education

Obviously the psychonoxious influences of education must be considered in relation to its goals. We might say that the goal of education is to enable a man to assemble many items of information on planes of equal accessibility while retaining the ability to take them apart and put them together in new combinations. Or we might say that the goal of education is to enrich a person by making available to him a progressively enlarging apperceptive mass, while protecting his capacity to use this mass freely and creatively. From still another angle the goal might be said to be to help the student to incorporate into himself a capacity for both empathy and objectivity. These are only three of many alternative and complementary ways of characterizing educational goals, some of which come in pairs which are in part contradictory or even incompatible. Actually each step and each phase of the learning process has goals and directional signals of opposite sign. We can pretend to have approximated these objectives only when the student retains his freedom to juggle uncounted items while picking, choosing, rejecting, selecting, and sorting among them, rearranging and comparing them, appraising and measuring, spotting true and false analogies, and recognizing the familiar and the unfamiliar; all the while coding and formulating hypotheses and guesses, testing these, reaching tentative conclusions about them, and confirming or correcting these tentative hypotheses against perceivable bits of internal and external information (Kubie, 1966b). This process is enormously complex and swift. We can readily list its components consciously, but does anyone think for a moment that we carry out any single step of the process consciously? On the contrary, we do it all preconsciously and constantly, even when asleep. In fact such preconscious processing flows smoothly and freely only when it operates in the absence of interference of any kind—better when we are asleep than when we are awake. Free preconscious processing requires that we avoid interfering with it. Yet it encounters at least two ubiquitous and universal blocks—braking and interfering processes. One such block is the superimposition of conscious sampling, whenever this is forced prematurely. Therefore any repetitive conscious drilling and testing and sampling of the predominantly preconscious process of learning should be introduced not in early class-room exercises, as is customary, but as late as possible, that is, after the preconscious learning phases have been carried through (Kubie, 1967). It is at this point that we can safely use conscious symbolic samples to test against reality our understanding and our conclusions, to remind ourselves of items acquired in the past, to gather them together for use, and to communicate them to others. When these conscious processes are reserved until late in the preconscious processing of new information, they will not interfere with the learning process. If introduced early they block the establishing of conditioned associative pathways on the bases of similarity, dissimilarity, true and false analogies, comparisons and contrasts, and figurative allegories (Kubie, 1959c). Premature emphasis on reality cuts off all of these preconscious ingredients in free learning, remembering and creating (Kubie, 1962, 1963, 1964, 1967).

The conscious processes of reminding, remembering, ruminating and communicating are important; but they are not learning. They are automatic and almost instantaneous ingredients which feed back bits of orienting data. Although necessary they are restrictive and limiting; indeed they actually interfere with learning. Yet the fact remains that the coding of data, and tagging them with the symbols of language, begins spontaneously in infancy. The learning of language is never achieved consciously. It is a process of imitation through preconscious conditioning and identification. It is known that, in the absence of organic brain deficits, this proceeds smoothly unless early neurotic illness blocks it.

Yet this interference is also a two-way relationship. The first steps in acquiring the coding and signalling tool which we call language (or symbolic speech) imprison and slow up the incessant stream of preconscious (or "imageless") processing of data, which is at the core of all learning, remembering and thinking. Therefore, in so far as traditional educational procedures introduce too early the conscious symbolic sampling of the preconscious stream, their initial effect is not to add to learning, but to subtract from it; not to free it, but to imprison it. Further, the unfortunate dependence of formal education upon repetitive drill and grill makes use of two of the psychonoxious components of the neurotic process itself. Consequently their use re-enforces the universal tendency to distort the relationship between the symbol and its referent, and even to sever it, thus intensifying the opposing role of repressive dissociation in what we euphemistically call the learning process. In this way our educational methods, while seeking to produce informed men who are not intellectually muscle-bound, tend instead to burden students with dead pieces of knowledge which they carry around thereafter much as the hod-carriers of the past carried sand and cobblestones on their shoulders (Kubie, 1958). Without actually realizing what we are doing, we use conscious symbolic processes to protect ourselves from many neurotogenic fears and compulsions, unfortunately not by solving them, but by hiding from them. Like screen memories, words themselves become devices for masking, screening, distorting and burying information.

In discussing this problem Stuart Chase writes, "The other primary tool is an understanding of ... how language can corrupt understanding as well as further it" (Chase, 1968, p. 172). To this we would add that the earlier in life a small child gains command of language, the greater is the danger that his symbols will lack content. The cost of symbolic precocity is that corruption of understanding against which Stuart Chase warns us. A similar position is taken by Bower (1967) and by Sanford (1967).

Consequently true learning can occur only when the freedom for preconscious processing is preserved. This forces us to the difficult conclusion that subtle forms of group and individual psychotherapy will have to be introduced into our concepts of learning and consequently into our educational organization and practices.

I cannot discuss in detail all of the psychonoxious effluvia of the educational process, but it may be worth listing a few of them: (a) the impact of the acquisition of symbols (both letters and numbers), already mentioned; (b) the rewarding of knowing without doing, which leads to empty erudition without experience; (c) the effects of substituting fiction (to a child, history is fiction) for direct contact with human suffering and without suggesting that the child has any responsibility for its relief; and (d) the effects of the progressive prolongation of the adolescent's life-on-a-dole-from-the-adult-world, as the educational process becomes longer (Kubie, 1959a, 1966a).

If we would take these dangers as points of departure from which to explore different ways, we would seek methods for using living experiences as a preparation for education instead of deluding ourselves that education prepares for living. Most particularly we would struggle to achieve educational sophistication without emotional immaturity and stunting (Kubie, 1956, 1957).

There are still other psychonoxious factors in education. Not even the simplest objects of study are objective facts. If our field is petrology, we project many highly personal and varied meanings (conscious, preconscious and unconscious) on to each specimen. The specimens become equivalent to unstandardized Rorschach images in mobile and irregular forms, or to Zondi or TAT (Thematic Apperception Test) cards. Therefore out of our unconscious conflicts we project on to everything that we study many idiosyncratic and disguised images, feelings and impulses. What we finally "learn" is an imperfect recall of a weighted sample of distorted percepts. Nietzsche warned us against "the Doctrine of Immaculate Perception". It is not to be wondered at that an educational process which has never recognized and therefore has never studied its own psychonoxious and distorting ingredients has produced so much illness and so much self-defeat.

SUMMARY

The role of preventive psychotherapy

What role then can psychotherapy play in education? My working hypotheses are that residues from unconscious conflicts constantly distort the educational process, and that therapy is a continuous struggle to achieve greater freedom for the preconscious processing of new and old data, that is, freedom from domination by rigid, stereotyped, repetitive, unconscious processes. It follows from this that education as a process can proceed freely and the state of being educated can be reached only if the learning experience is interwoven with continuous corrective influences from processes derived from formal psychotherapy but not identical with it. An approach to this goal will also have to include a reassessment of what constitutes *educability* in a human being, emphasizing his emotional maturation as well as his intellectual capabilities to learn. We will have to recognize that emotional health and maturity are at least as essential for education as is the intelligence quotient, and that the idiot-savant and the absent-minded scholar provide evidence that the achievement of erudition does not bring affective maturity, which must be achieved in other ways. Any school system which understood these issues would regularly assess the child's emotional readiness for education, before formal schooling starts, in earliest childhood. It would reassess this every autumn, and possibly at least once during the course of each school year, so that the need for therapeutic experiences, group and/or individual, and for their maturing and freeing influences could be evaluated and introduced into the educational picture as needed.

ACKNOWLEDGEMENT

This study has been made possible through the generosity of the Foundations Fund for Research in Psychiatry of New Haven, Conn.

REFERENCES

BOWER, E. M. (1967). In *Behavioral Science Frontiers in Education*, pp. 3–73, eds. Bower, E. M., and Hollister, W. G. New York: Wiley.
CHASE, S. (1968). *The Most Probable World*. New York: Harper and Row.

KUBIE, L. S. (1953). *Am. Scient.*, **41**, 596–613.
KUBIE, L. S. (1954a). *Am. Scient.*, **42**, 104–112.
KUBIE, L. S. (1954b). *Harv. Alumni Bull.*, **56**, 349–353.
KUBIE, L. S. (1956). *Bull. Menninger Clin.*, **20**, 281–297.
KUBIE, L. S. (1957). In *Today's Children are Tomorrow's World*, pp. 7–18. New York: Associates of Bank Street College of Education Fifth Annual Conference.
KUBIE, L. S. (1958). In *Neurotic Distortion of the Creative Process*, Porter Lectures, Series 22, pp. 104–136, 151. Lawrence, Kansas: University of Kansas Press.
KUBIE, L. S. (1959a). *J. natn Ednc. Ass.*, **48**, 58–63.
KUBIE, L. S. (1959b). *J. Am. Acad. Arts Sci.*, **88**, 646–668.
KUBIE, L. S. (1959c). *Trans. Am. neurol. Ass.*, **84**, 187–188.
KUBIE, L. S. (1962). In *The Unsolved Problem in Education* (Maryland Conference on Elementary Education), pp. 36–44. Maryland: State Department of Education, Baltimore.
KUBIE, L. S. (1963). *Need for a National Institute for Basic Research on the Educational Process.* Hickory Hill Seminar (Unpublished).
KUBIE, L. S. (1964). *Research in Protecting Preconscious Functions in Education.* In *Trans. VII Curriculum res. Inst.*, pp. 28–42. Washington, D. C.: Association for Supervision and Curriculum Development.
KUBIE, L. S. (1965). *Daedalus, Boston, Mass.*, **94**, 564–587.
KUBIE, L. S. (1966a). *J. nerv. ment. Dis.*, **141**, 395–402.
KUBIE, L. S. (1966b). *Psychoanal. Q.*, **35**, 191–198.
KUBIE, L. S. (1967). In *Behavioral Science Frontiers in Education*, pp. 90–109, eds. Bower, E. M., and Hollister, W. G. New York: Wiley.
KUBIE, L. S. (1968). In preparation.
SANFORD, N. (1967). In *Behavioral Science Frontiers in Education*, pp. 73–89, eds. Bower, E. M., and Hollister, W. G. New York: Wiley.

DISCUSSION

Foss: Learning can be discussed, as it has been by Dr. Kubie and Professor Dalla Volta, in terms of schooling and academic study. As an educationalist, I was extremely interested in your presentation, Dr. Kubie. In the United Kingdom today there is dissatisfaction about the idea of a "therapeutic community", and educationalists are caught in the middle of the conflict; some hold that teachers should be quasi-therapists, but others think that teachers should teach. What are the implications for the training of teachers in the material you have presented?

Kubie: Everything I said about the child or adult student applies equally to the teacher. The study of Videotape recordings enables both teachers and students to learn more about themselves than does any other available technique of self-observation. Such study starts a moment of emancipation from neurotic rigidity, and enables us to apply therapeutic principles to the training of teachers. This sort of self-observation, with or without other observers, is both a painful and a moving experience. It is a remarkably illuminating experience to face a television monitor and to associate freely to your own image.

Foss: Shaving is nearly as bad.

Kubie: Surprisingly, to look in a mirror (with or without talking) does not have the same impact. It is the combination of visual and auditory images that is so important. This means that for the first time we have methods which give depth to the old Greek advice to know ourselves.

Frank: You have presented us with the introduction to a book! Your description of the "drill and grill" educational process as restrictive because it is aversive implies that we are controlling learning by punishment. The teaching-machine might be a useful tool in promoting a less restrictive sort of learning, because a teaching-machine avoids failure. The student sets his own pace, he is never punished, and he acquires information in a setting in which he is free to choose his own route rather than being pushed down preordained tracks. But the teaching-machine could not provide another of the positive influences for non-restrictive learning: the emotional interplay between teacher and student. One of the most important factors for encouraging learning is the absence of fear; children should not fear school but look forward to it. And freedom from this fear depends on the attitude of the teachers.

Kubie: The teaching-machine touches only a fragment of the learning process because it emphasizes the too-early mastery of the symbol alone. To study and compare successes and failures in teaching-machine programmes would be useful.

Frank: Creating a situation in which the subject experiences success may be an important factor in both education and psychotherapy, and a link between educational learning and learning in the therapeutic setting. A common denominator between students who fail and patients who do not learn (or recover) may be that they are undermined by repeated failures. The therapeutic value of success was vividly illustrated by the unexpectedly satisfactory results in the patients Professor Lazarus treated by graded suggestion, and in the token economy programmes in which the patients undoubtedly feel successful every time they earn a token.

Krasner: It might be helpful to use the educational model in our thinking about mentally ill subjects; in other words, to regard deviant behaviours not as sick behaviours but as problems in living for which the subject needs re-education rather than treatment. You have suggested, Dr. Kubie, that the help that mentally sick individuals need is to learn to control their own behaviour through experiencing positive responses. This approach would make the goals of psychotherapists and educators very similar. Interesting results might follow this change in our concept of mental illness. For example, the word "patient" might be abolished. Once an individual is labelled "patient" he is pushed into the role of someone who is "ill". It might be easier for him to change maladaptive behaviours if he regarded himself as a student.

Kubie: We should not be ashamed of the word "patient". To be a patient is to play a proud and courageous role. A patient is one who is proud and honest and humble enough to view himself as someone who can profit by changing. Anyone can want to be free from pain; but to want to change, to become a different kind of person, is another and far more difficult matter. An impotent man said: "Cure my impotence; but don't change *me*." The wish to become different requires a humility difficult to achieve. Sometimes a religious conversion induces such humility: sometimes it has precisely the opposite effect and entrenches spiritual arrogance.

An educational process that leaves its students trapped within rigid boundaries merely limits their capacity to change. Additional *facts* may be acquired within a rigid personality framework; but these become only a burden. The goal of both education and therapy is to increase man's freedom for continuing and evolving change.

Krasner: That is exactly what I mean.

Kubie: Unfortunately our loss of the freedom to change starts in early childhood, with the acquisition of symbolic speech (Chase, S. [1968]. In *The Most Probable World*, p. 172. New York: Harper and Row). Here is an extraordinary educational paradox: that man's greatest tool should also become his gaoler.

Sandler: We may find common ground between education and psychotherapy if we consider that people operate through the use of structures created on the basis of the interaction between internal and environmental forces. One dimension of variation would be the extent and complexity of these psychological structures, which have been compared to programmes in a computer. The ability to change may depend on how much an individual can allow himself the use of phantasy and other primitive structures. Symptoms also have an underlying and persisting structural organization. The key point in encouraging free learning in a child may be to develop an internal feeling of security in him. If he has this inner security he can experiment mentally with the different internal structures at his disposal and can create new structures and patterns of behaviour without unbearable pain, or threat of attack, or panic in the course of this inner experimentation. The child who dreads the pain of abandoning the use of certain fixed structures becomes the sort of rigid person Dr. Kubie described. The aims of education and psychotherapy converge when we use this model. Analytic psychotherapy aims to create new structures, to modify old ones, and to allow freedom of choice in testing out the different types of structures in different situations. And these are also the aims of education.

Dalla Volta: In psychotherapy we aim to give the patient new tools to help him to solve his problems; in education we try to stimulate the child's intellectual curiosity. The constructive frustration in psychotherapy and the search for information in education have the same basic goal: the encouragement of the individual's capacity for learning to learn. Dr. Sandler, how would you define the learning that occurs in psychoanalysis? Could it be called the inhibition of maladaptive habits?

Sandler: Yes. The old habits or structures are not lost but, rather, inhibited by the acquisition of new structures which enable needs to be more comfortably discharged. The psychoanalytic approach to learning can be formulated in terms of building up structural changes on the basis of experience. This building-up is common to education, psychotherapy and life experience in general.

Kaufman: There is a difference in the direction of the learning process (learning to learn) in psychotherapy and education. We know that the external world is partly an externalization of our inner feelings, and we ourselves are the precipitate of experiences with the outside world. Nevertheless, whatever it is that is acquired in psychotherapy is related to the operation of the self (that is, it is directed inward), whereas in education the purpose of learning is to form a relationship with the world outside. This directional difference may clarify our attempts to compare learning in education and in psychotherapy.

Kubie: Another direct connexion between learning in education and in psychotherapy involves the anxiety and terror of not remembering—the idea that if one stops for a second one will never start again. The pressure to assimilate facts in the schooling process produces the scientist who is so afraid he will never do another experiment that he follows experiment with experiment, not daring to lie fallow; or the artist who cannot let the paint dry on the canvas before starting a new picture; or the writer who never stops writing because he fears that every book is his last. These people cannot give themselves time to digest their inner experiences. And this terror must be lived through and undone over and over again both during the schooling process and in psychotherapy.

Miller: Factual knowledge is increasing exponentially. Because there is so much to be learned one tends to turn the crank faster and faster. One result of this for school children is that they have no leisure to explore, following their intellectual curiosity, subjects that interest them: they are too busy keeping up with the treadmill. And yet the development of intellectual curiosity is more important today than ever before because most of the facts, especially in science, that children are taught will be out of date in twenty years. The purpose of education should be to teach children how to learn new things, and to develop in them the wish to continue learning throughout their lives. Instead we may be achieving the opposite result; too rapid forced-feeding spoils the appetite for the intellectual feast.

Foss: "Discovery methods" have been used in junior schools in the United Kingdom for many years, but their effectiveness is uncertain. In a study in the United States, B. Y. Kersh (1962. *J. educ. Psychol.*, **53**, 65–71) compared teaching by guided discovery, by conventional modern methods, and learning by rote. To his surprise the children who learned by rote assimilated the principles of what they were taught better than the children in the other two groups. Guided discovery may induce strong motivation for learning, and is undoubtedly easier for the teacher, but it has not yet been proved to be more effective than other methods.

Miller: Rote learning is usually unpleasant for children, but my main objection is not to rote learning *per se* but to having it pushed too fast and to the exclusion of other activities.

Sackett: What is the evidence in the United States that teaching by rote produces students with rigid thinking patterns and minds cluttered with facts?

Kubie: Deans and Presidents of some of our greatest engineering, scientific and technological schools have told me they are convinced that they are destroying the creative ability in some of the best young students in the United States, and that this destruction of good minds occurs not only among undergraduate and graduate students but among research fellows and faculty members. Men of great promise become totally unproductive. The leaders in education accept the need to study this problem as crucial. They have asked that plans for such studies be designed, but in the end they shy away from the problem. This, too, is an interesting and humorous sociological phenomenon.

Hunt: There may be a way of escaping the horrors of literate idiots and illiterate sages. Different sorts of subject matter may be suitable for different learning techniques. The cranial nerves and the multiplication tables, for example, must surely be learned by rote, but subjects that involve wisdom and judgment are best taught by more flexible methods. What subject matter was investigated in the study by Kersh, Professor Foss?

Foss: The children were learning some algebraic principles and how to apply them.

Kubie: Data from experiments with hypnosis (Gill, M. M., and Brenman, M. [1959]. *Hypnosis and Related States.* New York: International University Press; Erickson, M. H. [1967]. In *Selected Papers on Advanced Techniques of Hypnosis and Therapy*, pp. 286–309, ed. Haley, J. New York: Grune & Stratton) suggest that facts can be imprinted without repetition. This challenges the long-established conviction that repetition aids the learning process and suggests that, on the contrary, repetition is a measure of the failure of this process.

Hunt: Why should repetition be necessary in order to learn something? Very complex stimulus situations, such as a scene observed when an individual is passing by on a bus, can be recognized again after one exposure. This remarkable facility for recognition should be one basis for further study.

Foss: At least seven main categories of school learning exist and each should be studied separately to elucidate the most efficient method of learning for each of them. Different types of learning may need, say, feedback, or practice (as with learning a skill or technique). In learning classifications—names and facts—repetition seems to be indispensable but in learning concepts repetition probably matters very little.

Hunt: The form in which information is stored is important in determining its accessibility. A scholar of the "long foot-note" variety has many enumerative data stored, but these may be packaged more for display than for creative purposes.

Hinde: This is just why your two examples of material that has to be learned by rote (the cranial nerves and the multiplication tables) are inappropriate. The people who can do instant complicated mathematical calculations are not necessarily people who have learned their multiplication tables by rote. One such "genius" was the son of a gamekeeper. This boy spent much time in his childhood arranging lead shot in patterns on the ground. He learned to multiply from these patterns and became an infant prodigy for arithmetic calculations. My own experience with the cranial nerves was that I was unable to remember them when taught by rote, but when I could visualize them as a series of segmental nerves I had no difficulty. In both these examples it is the framework of learning that is important.

Sandler: Another approach to the problem would be the study of creative individuals. Creativity in some very gifted people is not conscious; these individuals appear to be relatively free to explore different solutions just below the level of consciousness. The effect of this is that ready-made answers or creations may emerge, apparently spontaneously, into consciousness. In other words, some creative people can allow themselves a degree of license in their thinking that more rigid people cannot tolerate. Some highly creative people are also very neurotic, although neurosis is not a *sine qua non* of creativity. Dr. Kubie, would you comment on the parallels and contrasts between creativity and neurosis?

Kubie: A. Szent-Györgyi, in an informal discussion of creativity (unpublished), said that when he knew too much about a subject he could not think creatively about it. Karl Muck, the conductor of the Boston Symphony Orchestra, felt the same about composing: he knew too much to be able to compose. One aspect of the problem of creativity and education is that one can become overburdened with facts. The relationship between neurosis and creativity is very complex. It has been said that one does not have to have had an unhappy childhood to be creative; but it helps.

Kiernan: It is arguable that the only contribution of learning research to both education and psychotherapy has been in terms of procedures. The theories underlying research in the area of learning have mostly failed to make a lasting impact, and this failure is reflected in the fact that we have been discussing techniques and not theories. Dr. Kubie, would you comment on this?

Kubie: I agree with part of this: procedures are enormously important. A related problem is our careless use of words. A word like "procedure" may be used with different meanings. Or the word "analysis" may cover a large group of basically different procedures. Take, for example, one aspect of the exploratory process known as "free association". When a patient is able to produce free associations, this procedure becomes a tool for sampling all that is happening in his psychological processes at any moment, without weighting the sample. Free associations resemble a Gallup poll. The deliberate introduction of an interpretation into this stream of material gives an opportunity for studying the effect of interpretations on the preconscious stream. We should be much more explicit and precise in our characterization of the procedures we study (Kubie, L. S. [1932]. *Archs Neurol. Psychiat.*, Chicago, **32**, 1137-1142; [1943]. *Bull. Menninger Clin.*, **7**, 172-182; in *Practical and Theoretical Aspects of Psychoanalysis*, chap. 7, pp. 44-57. New York: International University Press; Kubie, L. S., and Margolin, S. G. [1942]. *Trans. Am. neurol. Ass.*, **68**, 136-139).

Gelder: It is salutary to remember that re-educational methods were in vogue in psychiatry at the beginning of this century (Janet, P. [1925]. *Psychological Healing*. London: Allen & Unwin), although they fell out of use later. These early methods were not based on any convincing theory of learning. Since Janet's time our knowledge of the theory behind re-educational or learning techniques has advanced and we now have a seemingly convincing, although complex, theory to explain behaviour therapy. One contribution of our increased theoretical understanding is that it has helped to convince the therapist that what he is doing is worth-while, and therefore has encouraged him to persist enthusiastically. This enthusiasm will be conveyed to the patient and might account for some part of the improvement in results since Janet's day. This is probably not the whole story, but we must not forget this possible explanation for some of our successes and ascribe all our good results to specific learning mechanisms.

Frank: Dr. Kubie, you have discussed the importance of the freeing of the personality of the child through self-knowledge, without which Socrates at least considered life was not worth living. Words may be mis-leading, but how can one convey self-knowledge to a child unless he verbalizes his thoughts, and at what age does verbalization begin to be useful?

Kubie: One of the reasons I am so interested in the newer techniques of self-viewing and self-hearing is because of the associated learning about the self. At a symposium of modern developments in the study of the self-image (1969. *J. nerv. ment. Dis.*, to be published), the participants discussed the importance of experience in techniques concerning the self-image for workers studying the development of the normal child. The effects on the development of the child of exposure to his own image were also discussed. The use of these techniques can correct some of the confusion caused by words.

Frank: Self-knowledge can be pathological, as in the excessive rumina-tion of analysands.

Kubie: Of course one can become obsessional about self-knowledge, as about eating, or drinking water.

Miller: It might be useful if we could teach new, superior techniques for solving social and emotional problems to young children, as has been done for many scientific problems. Calculus, for example, is a problem-solving technique whose use enables the schoolboy of today to solve mathematical problems that had previously baffled the greatest minds. In psychoanalysis one learns the technique of free association. After the analysis is finished, this technique can still help to solve problems in which one's reactions are inappropriate or excessive, and one can detect and deal with defensive mechanisms in oneself. Similarly, a child might be taught that the actual reason for his anger was not the reason he was most aware of. A boy might learn that he was picking on his sister not because she was opposing him but because the rain had ruined his wonderful plans for the afternoon. Could techniques like this be helpful in normal children, Dr. Kubie?

Kubie: Yes; but this raises the question of who is the most appropriate person to make such interpretations to a child—the parent, who is the storm centre of so much conflict, or some adult ally "against" the parent. With such an ally a child might not have to assume so many different roles. The struggle between the generations is more pervasive than we admit. If these inter-generational problems were faced earlier there might be less trouble in adolescence. A similar problem derives from the existence of two different sexes. This difference has been present for so long that we might expect that by now its acceptance would be inherited as part of our genetic pattern. Yet no child ever fully accepts his or her gender-role. Invariably there is some wish to be both male and female, or neither.

Freeman: Psychotherapists may be imprisoned by the techniques they themselves have learned to try to help their patients. Attempts to abandon a psychotherapeutic technique, even though one knows that one may become its prisoner, can create a severe conflict. Any therapist is naturally reluctant to give up a familiar and reasonably successful technique. The only way to resolve this conflict is for analysts, behaviour therapists and psychologists to work together in examining a Videotape record of the therapy sessions.

Sandler: Problems exist in connexion with the disciplined education needed for the acquisition of psychotherapeutic skills, the freedom to use these skills, and the danger of being imprisoned by them. But problems also exist for us in relation to the question of *when* to use our therapeutic skills. Many difficulties arise, for example, from psychoanalytic techniques being applied in inappropriate circumstances. It is vitally important to learn when to use and when not to use a particular technique.

Leder: The T-group laboratory method (Bradford, L. P., Gibb, J. R., and Benne, K. D. (eds.). [1964]. *T-Group Theory and Laboratory Method.* New York: Wiley) might be useful as a technique for studying the learning process in education and psychotherapy because this method contains elements of both education and treatment.

Frank: The expansion of awareness of the self is one aim of the T-group method. Initially this aim was secondary to that of teaching persons about group processes through directly experiencing them. To this end, groups consisting of about 15 members, initially strangers to each other, met daily for several hours with a trainer (hence "T"), whose only function was to clarify what happened during these hours. Group structure, agenda and leadership roles emerged out of the struggles of the members to bring order out of chaos.

Kubie: T-group training is a useful technical aid. Group therapy is another example of a technique in which both learning and therapy occur.

Leder: But the T-group is not set up as a therapeutic exercise; participants do not join these groups for therapy but for education.

Frank: The philosophy of T-groups has changed recently. T-groups are becoming indistinguishable from therapeutic groups because the verbalization of emotions and their expression through action are increasingly emphasized. Powerful forces are thus released, which help some but not all of the members of a T-group. Subjects who enrol for this sort of training are similar to patients in that they are distressed about some aspect of their life although they do not recognize their distress as illness. They may feel dissatisfied, for example, or want to learn more about themselves, or they experience existential anxiety. The dividing line between psychotherapy and T-group training is therefore often faint or non-existent.

Kubie: No patient comes to a therapist to get well. He does not know what these words mean, and nor does the therapist until he and the patient have worked hard together for a long time. At first the patient comes to find relief from pain. Once he understands that getting well means deep and essential changes, he is on the way to health. The therapeutic process, in the sense of a deep change in personality, is closely dependent on the human interactions that occur in psychotherapy. This is one reason why it is impossible at first for the patient to know what he must do and learn. For this reason many discussions on motivation for therapy are so superficial as to be meaningless.

GENERAL DISCUSSION

Malan: The main object of this symposium is for mental cross-fertilization to occur between members of the different schools of psychotherapy. We all hope, for example, that psychoanalysts and behaviour therapists will learn from each other; and that therapists from both these groups will learn from the ethologists, and *vice versa*. One of the great needs in psychotherapy is to be able to distinguish, before starting treatment, between the kinds of disorder than can be cured by relatively simple desensitization techniques and those with associated deep psychopathological roots which need prolonged dynamic therapy. As an analyst, I learned something new from Professor Bandura's discussion of the treatment of snake phobias. For patients with a snake phobia most analysts would prescribe a lengthy course of psychotherapy in which sexual and other anxieties could be resolved. Assuming that Professor Bandura's extraordinarily good results (100 per cent recovery) with a relatively simple technique are maintained at follow-up, psychoanalysts may be shown to have been quite wrong in their prescription. Snake phobias may be shown to have a totally different psychopathology from some other phobias. Simple techniques such as modelling are not effective in patients with severe agoraphobia; agoraphobics, of course, usually show additional features, such as depressive and obsessional traits, as well as the phobia. Thus there may be two (or more) different kinds of phobias, one of which responds to simple desensitization and another that needs extensive reorganization of the personality. The important issue is how to distinguish between these two groups.

Concerning the interchange between ethologists and psychotherapists, Dr. Sackett raised the pertinent problem of aggression in deprived monkeys. We might also discuss the corresponding problem in deprived human beings. Analysts are familiar with the profound inhibition seen in a patient after a break in treatment due to a holiday. In this situation analysts tend to say: "You are angry because you felt abandoned by me during this period", and the patient may respond by releasing violent destructive phantasies. This violent sadistic destructiveness crops up repeatedly during analysis, particularly in patients who experienced much real or imagined deprivation in childhood. But some patients may not respond to this interpretation of their inhibition and depression, and perhaps there is a more physiological, quite different, source for aggression in them. As therapists, we can learn a great deal from the work on aggression in primates.

Dr. Sackett was surprised that a few conditioning experiments in which severely disturbed, deprived monkeys were treated by physical contact with normal, peer monkeys did not influence the maladaptive behaviour. Analysts are, again, familiar with this poor response to treatment in terms of the profound difficulties in treating deprived human beings. Intense destructive behaviour has to be worked through before one can even start to give such patients the experiences they have missed. The patient in analysis has to regress to a state in which he experiences the feelings of a child—the need to be cuddled and fed and so on. If at this stage the analyst can give him real or symbolic experience of what he has missed (in reality or in imagination) then he may recover. If the parallel with monkeys and man is exact, the deprived monkey would have to *regress* before he can be treated successfully. And not only this; the substitute mother would have to persist with her care in the face of the most violent physical attacks—something that no monkey would conceivably put up with.

Miller: These comments are most valuable. We should all by now feel free to criticize each others' work and theories. If we gloss over real differences and disagreements we will never correct them.

Krasner: I suspect that many of the phobias would respond to simple techniques. The psychoanalytic approach may be too profound, and Professor Bandura's simpler technique might be successful in many different phobias.

Malan: But the problem is to predict which phobias can be treated by which methods.

Krasner: The vital issue is not our selection of different groups of patients for different treatments but the formulation of a new concept of the phobic diseases. With such a concept these simple treatments might be applicable to all phobias.

Marks: Early research with any new therapeutic technique can only proceed empirically. One first tries to answer the question: "To what extent is the technique useful and how far can we apply it?" Similarly, we can only proceed empirically as we try to decide whether a particular piece of behaviour should be inhibited or promoted, or if the patient needs to be entirely re-educated. Very different illnesses may present with the same symptom or deviant behaviour, so that different treatments may be needed to cure different patients of what seem to be similar behaviour disorders. Sexual deviations, for example, may respond well to aversive methods alone or in combination with re-education; in some such cases desensitization may be effective and in others dynamic therapy is needed. One cannot make a single golden rule for the use of a specific procedure for a particular symptom. Any new therapuetic technique needs to be tested separately for each category of symptoms because the underlying psychopathology for any symptom varies so widely.

We are also assuming that all behaviour is learned, whereas some behaviours, for example certain fears, have an endogenous or biological substrate. Dr. Sackett clearly demonstrated an innate fear response to threats in his monkeys. Some of the failures in treatment in man may be due not to the fact that the procedure has been given unskilfully but that it is itself inappropriate for the problem concerned.

Miller: To assume the existence of a complete dichotomy between innate and learned responses can be misleading. Behaviour can be innate but subject to modification by learning, or learned but influenced by internal

factors. Innate and learned tendencies interact to produce the final behaviour.

Lazarus: Even in the seemingly simple "barber's chair phobia" (Steven-
son, I., and Hain, J. D. [1967]. *Am. J. Psychiat.*, **124**, 399-403), the problem is
to unearth the fundamental fear-stimulus. Some men avoid a haircut in a
barber's shop because they fear public scrutiny; in others homosexual panic
may be aroused by the nearness of a male attendant (the barber); still other
men become claustrophobic at the barber's, or fear the sharp objects there.
We need to find the relevant and specific phobic component and to treat
that instead of accepting the presenting fears at their face value. Psychodynamic practitioners have said this for many years, but instead of searching
for discrete stimulus configurations they have been overconcerned with
hidden meanings and symbols. In short, a phobia is often simply a specific
irrational fear, but it may be a manifestation of more basic interpersonal
stresses; clinical acumen rather than a knowledge of learning theory is
needed to enable one to differentiate between the two.

Kubie: It is interesting that our discussion has been directed almost
entirely at the phobia, as though it were the paradigm of all psychopathology. The phobia is an interesting manifestation of emotional illness.
Certain hidden elements are common to all phobias but each phobia contains unique components. The nameless dread that we call a phobia is a
trigger response, usually triggered off by a particular stimulus-object or
situation—imagined or real, animate or inanimate. Many trigger responses exist, however, both psychophysiological ("normal") and psychopathological. We may be triggered into sleep or wakefulness, into and out
of a hypnotic state, or into a compulsive obsessional furore. These trigger
responses may have been acquired through conditioning, distorted
symbolic linkages or both. Although a phobia occasionally occurs as an
isolated manifestation of illness, it is always associated with underlying,
interrelated neurotic disturbances. A good example of a complex illness
presenting as a phobia occurred in a patient whose only presenting symptom was a terror of heights. Psychoanalytic investigation disclosed many
profoundly important and related problems in the patient's life. In my view,
to treat this man's phobia alone would have been not only ineffective but
harmful.*

* This case is discussed more fully on pp. 320.

PROSPECTS AND POSSIBILITIES IN THE
DEVELOPMENT OF BEHAVIOUR THERAPY

HOWARD F. HUNT

Department of Psychology, Columbia University, New York

BEHAVIOUR therapy is the deliberate, self-conscious application of the techniques of conditioning and learning, as developed in the laboratory and derived from behavioural learning theory, to the alleviation of human maladjustment. The role of learning in psychotherapy and the contributions of learning theory to therapeutic practice will be most evident in behaviour therapy. As solid clinical data accumulate, and if they continue to support the efficacy of this approach, we can expect two kinds of effects. The more obvious of these will be a spreading adoption of behavioural procedures and ideology in the clinic and consulting room. The second, of more far-reaching significance, will be revisions in theory, and in posture and emphasis in the clinical situation, in both the behavioural and the classical dynamic traditions as they are forced to accommodate to new data. The first type of effect has been well documented (see, for example, Krasner and Ullmann, 1965; Ulrich, Stachnik and Mabry, 1966; Shlien *et al.*, 1968), so this paper will look mostly toward the second.

Given the widespread need for effective psychotherapy, and the technological stasis that seemed to be developing in traditional psychotherapeutic practice, the experimental application of behaviour therapy on a broad scale has been surprisingly delayed. Speculation about this bit of sociology of knowledge is largely irrelevant here, but the great differences in metaphor between behavioural learning theory, which rationalizes behaviour therapy, and dynamic personality theory, which rationalizes traditional psychotherapy, were probably crucial. Personality theories are mentalistic in that they see covert, subjective constructs such as ideas, insights, motives and meanings in the centre of the stage, as mediating mechanisms, while the traditional behavioural approach focuses on habits and reflexes, stimuli and responses, and tends to treat subjective events as epiphenomenal to fundamental stimulus–response processes, even though some of the latter are not well worked out yet.

THE OLD "NEW LOOK"

The polemic literature of the nineteen fifties and early nineteen sixties is striking in the way in which it placed behaviour therapy and learning theory in opposition to dynamic personality theory and traditional therapeutic practice (for example, Wolpe, 1958; Eysenck, 1960). In accordance with this "new look", adjustment problems and psychopathology were seen as undesirable habits or responses, acquired through some sort of "faulty" learning. They could be eliminated in a most straightforward way by appropriate conditioning and extinction procedures, with "improvement" or "cure" defined in terms of attenuation of the undesired behaviour pattern. In contrast, the more traditional view of psychopathology saw the undesired behaviours as symptoms reflecting some underlying pathology—some state, such as a neurotic conflict, within the person—and as representing the best compromise the unaided individual was able to make with the impossible dilemmas into which the vicissitudes of his developmental history had thrust him. To be sure, these symptoms could be manipulated to some extent by reward and punishment, sympathetic understanding or suggestion, but only temporarily. Little permanent benefit could ensue unless the underlying state were somehow changed through new insights and perceptions, motivational maturation and so on. Otherwise, and unless these cognitive and conative changes were brought about, the old symptoms would return or new ones take their place. Given this polarization, one could almost say that it was not entirely clear that the two approaches saw the same problems or had the same goals.

The two approaches were not in fact quite so far apart. For many years, psychoanalysis—the most influential of the personality theories—appears to have been working from a two-factor learning theory in which stimuli could acquire new functional properties by virtue of association with significant events (contiguity or respondent conditioning) and in which behaviour could be controlled by its rewarding or punishing consequences (instrumental or operant conditioning). Some of the stimuli, behaviours and consequences were exotic by laboratory standards, and little of the fine detail had been worked out, but the major outlines were clear (for example, Fenichel, 1945). The theory of psychosexual development and its contribution to formulations about the genesis of pathology further pinpointed the importance of learning by emphasizing that what actually was learned depended upon the individual's developmental status when the learning occurred. The behaviours that the child actually had in its repertoire at the time were the ones strengthened or weakened by reward or punishment; rewards and punishments were expected to focus on the characteristic problems of the developmental stage the child was in; and the nature of the sanctions, including their force and character, would be determined by the way in which the individual perceived the world at that stage in his life. As the metaphor of psychoanalysis held that the various stages of early life differed considerably in all these regards, conditioning and learning were of prime importance in the understanding of personality. Finally, the rising emphasis on conflict-free ego-function and ego-psychology seemed to cry out for the application of learning theory and technology to problems of adaptation.

By the same token, rigorous and explicit behavioural learning theories had been available for the past quarter of a century at least. These theories, derived from laboratory experiments mostly on lower animals, were neither perfect nor complete, and were largely concerned with test situations and behaviours aseptically abstracted from the larger stream of human life, but they certainly were relevant to personality theory and psychotherapy. Many years ago, the pioneering work of Dollard and Miller (1950) and of Mowrer (1950) showed how learning and personality theories could be made to map on each other, and how conventional therapeutic strategies could be interpreted, within the behavioural framework.

The polemic phase probably generated more heat than light, but it had many beneficial effects. Among other things, it legitimized and encouraged planned innovations in procedure (some of them pretty wild, admittedly), stimulated comparative evaluation of therapy, and redirected general attention to therapeutic problems and issues, particularly among experimentally minded psychologists with interest and experience in behavioural analysis. Now that the confrontation has matured somewhat, we are in a better position to appreciate its fruits.

A REVISION OF EMPHASIS

One of the most important changes in emphasis has been the shift away from the remote conditioning history of the patient, and how it produced the unwanted behaviour, to the contemporary factors that maintain it. Thus, an account of the genesis of a behaviour—how or when it was acquired and by what reinforced in its acquisition—is seen as less useful for the purposes of therapy than an account of the rewarding consequences that maintain it here and now, and the stimulus contexts that are the occasion for its occurrence. Though the conditioning history is obviously important for understanding behaviour *in toto*, the events that led to the acquisition of the particular behaviour of interest are important for the immediate purposes of manipulation and control (that is, therapy) only in so far as they currently operate to maintain the behaviour, or to prevent the acquisition of new, desired behaviours. Though such historical factors sometimes do so operate, this new emphasis urges that very often they do not.

This contrasts sharply with the traditional dynamic view of symptoms as recapitulations of past conflicts in modified form, and reduces emphasis on the importance of somehow undoing or reworking the individual's history as a necessary step in therapy. It even contrasts with those behaviour therapy approaches in which treatment procedures are thought to produce their results by extinguishing, or otherwise reversing, the faulty learning that took place long before to produce the symptom as an enduring monument to Pavlovian traumatic conditioning.

The new emphasis arises out of the instrumental conditioning or reward-learning tradition and, more particularly, is Skinnerian in its special concern with the manipulation and control of stabilized, terminal, normal behaviour. The operant conditioning approach (Skinner, 1938, 1953) resembles other behavioural views of learning in stressing that behaviour arises out of a conditioning history in which stimuli acquire reinforcing and discriminative properties and in which responses are selected and strengthened by their consequences. Much of the other experimental literature in learning, however, and most other theories, have focused on the acquisition and loss of conditioned behaviour in acute behavioural situations in the short-term, while operant conditioning has been more attentive to the special problem and possibilities that arise in dealing with well-established behaviour that has gone far beyond the acquisition stage in chronic behavioural situations. Such behaviour often floats quite free of the conditions that led to its acquisition, often passing under the control of quite different contingencies. The operant approach has developed a logic and a technology—behavioural analysis (see Honig, 1966; Millenson, 1967; Goldiamond and Dyrud, 1968) —adapted to dealing with normal behaviour. As most behavioural pathology would seem to be of this terminal, stabilized sort, it should be quite amenable to operant behavioural analysis. Happily, the more important principles of this analysis are robust enough to survive transfer from the "*in vitro*" situation of the laboratory to the "*in vivo*" situations of human existence.

IMPLICATIONS FOR THERAPY

The change has evolutionary, rather than revolutionary significance, however. In accordance with it, one would simply tell the therapist to direct his attention to such an analysis of the case and its context as will reveal the present consequences maintaining the undesired behaviour, and then to alter them; to manipulate circumstances to make alternative, more desirable behaviours possible and more probable; to see that such behaviour is rewarded effectively; and to arrange things (or teach the patient to arrange things) in such a way that the desired behaviour can continue to be supported by the normal contingencies of life that maintain the behaviour of us all, to provide for carry-over into the extra-therapeutic situation. This last provision is particularly important because without it the therapist would just be teaching the patient a few tricks which could be expected to work well only in the consulting room.

Dynamically oriented therapists in the modern tradition, interested in problems of adaptation and relationships, should not find this emphasis uncongenial or shocking. This approach is very much like what such therapists actually do (as I understand it) but described in different words and with a little more stress on systematic plotting and planning by the therapist, and much more definition of specific procedures and goals. Further, this emphasis should be easy to understand, if not to agree with, within the framework of the classical view of psychopathology. The old, familiar concept of secondary gain has simply been elevated from a supporting role to stardom, and generalized to symptoms and situations in which it often might be overlooked as an important factor. Finally, as the bases of primary gain for some symptoms—their neurotic sources—may be either relatively inaccessible or refractory, effective procedures for manipulating symptoms by selective manipulation of secondary gains should be a welcome addition to any therapist's armamentarium, if only to make the sources of the neurosis more accessible. Thus, this new emphasis is not the enemy of all that has gone before. Rather, it should be seen as a development that promises to increase the effectiveness of approaches to therapy already in train.

It needs a high degree of skill, sensitivity and technological sophistication, plus a good "green thumb" for behaviour, to discern what a patient is doing and what he is behaving to get. The contingencies maintaining complex behaviour often cannot be detected by simple observation. The behaviour must be obvious enough to evoke the rewards, of course, but the reinforcement contingencies may be subtle, complexly scheduled, and hard to detect, or so deeply embedded in the ethology of social interactions, family life, or institutional practices that they are difficult to control. Defensive behaviours often have a topography shaped to conceal effectively their functional significance, and some reinforcers have an illicit quality which requires that they be conveyed under suitable cover.

For example, the attention-getting behaviour of children is familiar to us all and, in principle, easy to manage by selective inattention. In practice, the reinforcement is very hard to withhold because the behaviour has been so effectively shaped as to evoke it almost automatically. Consider the situation of a family with a child who has both a school-phobia and limited intellectual ability. Will the parents find it easier to live with a stupid child or with one who is "only" phobic, and will this consideration have an effect on the ease with which the phobia can be relieved? Or consider the family of a chronic alcoholic which often has had years to accommodate its internal power arrangements to the fact of an ineffectual father. If, happily, he has a remission and reassumes the usual paternal role—having opinions, exercising authority and other prerogatives—this economy may be disconcertingly disrupted, and the family, reacting conservatively, may subtly undermine the social support for the new role and thus the support for the remission. Finally, as institutional practices generally are designed to be responsive to pathology, either to care for and cure it or to prevent it from disrupting the operation, they often accidentally support it by subtle reinforcement; and some pathologies, such as overt suicide attempts, have a peremptory quality that few institutions would dare to resist even if they wanted to. (In such settings, one often is tempted to raise the question of who controls whom.)

BEHAVIOURAL ANALYSIS AS DIAGNOSIS

To deal effectively with problems like these demands imaginative and penetrating behavioural analysis, not only of the patient's behaviour but also of its context. Then a powerful repertoire of procedures derived from laboratory experience may be applied selectively, depending upon what the analysis calls for (Honig, 1966; Ulrich, Stachnik and Mabry, 1966; Millenson, 1967; Shlien et al., 1968). These procedures (to name a few) include not only reinforcement and extinction, but also differential and specially scheduled reinforcement, discrimination and chaining procedures, methods for the control of the rate and pacing of response, shaping and fading procedures (differentiation and successive approximation) and so on. The applications themselves may also be complicated and may involve several different procedures in multiple steps to reach the specified end-point. If the procedures fail, this indicates that the analysis was in error or the techniques poorly chosen or badly executed. (The operant approach is optimistic: one delightful thing about it is that it works best only if one assumes that the theory, such as it is, is right and that the only problem is to develop the correct analysis and apply the proper procedures!) Often a great deal of cleverness and sensitivity is needed to find or invent combinations that will work. Used routinely, without prior analysis, and rigidly, without imagination, these behavioural procedures as such are little more than gimmicks. As in most other worth-while activities, behaviour therapy of the best sort requires informed talent.

The focus upon detailed prior analysis of the specific behavioural situation is, thus, another new emphasis. For behaviour therapy, the analysis is equivalent to the traditional diagnosis or case formulation. It implies what should be done and what to expect with regard to specified behaviours that the patient shows in particular situations. It embodies hypotheses about those behaviours and what maintains them, may indicate alternative behaviours that the patient might acquire and how they may be maintained once acquired, and also specifies, by implication, the conditions for validating these hypotheses. In effect, it orders behaviour into functional classes, within a particular patient, instead of ordering patients into diagnostic classes within a nomenclature.

The content of the analysis is determined by what is observed to happen, as interpreted within the framework of reinforcement principles, with preconceptions, personality theory and clinical lore only suggesting where to look, not what to find. Such suggestions, arising out of extensive observations in man, can be very helpful as shrewd and informed guesses, as long as they do not block the therapist from seeing with an open mind what is actually going on. Such open-mindedness can lead to radical redefinition of a behavioural problem. For example, if a patient appears to be unresponsive to the defeats and punishments his neurotic behaviour produces, or if an undesirable behaviour pattern is unaffected by aversive consequences, this is not taken to suggest that punishment does not work, that the individual is incapable of learning by experience like other people, or is seeking pain to assuage guilt, or the like. Rather, the therapist would conclude that the supposedly aversive consequences simply did not have that functional property with respect to that behaviour, and would look carefully elsewhere to find the positively reinforcing consequences that actually maintained it. The functional significance of stimuli is not given *a priori* and by presupposition, but by their actual effects on behaviour.

This approach calls for an attention to detail and a specificity in the formulation of the behavioural situation that is still quite foreign to conventional therapeutic practice and even to some behaviour therapists. Such disciplined attention and detailed scrutiny should be of value in conventional as well as behaviour therapy in illuminating the dark, enigmatic corners that all therapists encounter. And it can pinpoint those aspects of a problem on which the full weight of the therapeutic effort should be directed, to maximize the return on the investment of scarce therapeutic time.

ROLE OF THE THERAPIST

Finally, the behaviour therapist takes an active role, rather like that of an experimenter or teacher. Though he is no more moralistic and evaluative than any other kind of therapist, he is responsible for far more than maintaining a warm, supportive, empathic relationship conducive to self-exploration, new insights and personal growth. He often produces a behavioural effect early in the game, as a demonstration to show the patient how his behaviour is controlled, or informs him about principles of behavioural control in discussion. He works out the analysis which defines the behavioural problem and then decides which of a number of differentially acting procedures to apply. These judgments and decisions are technological and made on the basis of knowledge the patient does not have and is unlikely to discover for himself, at least at first. Thus, though the patient's problem remains the patient's problem, in a curious way it also becomes the therapist's problem, and he becomes deeply and responsibly involved in certain aspects of it. The implications of this feature of behaviour therapy for therapist-specific effects remain to be explored.

SYMPTOM SUBSTITUTION

Though the innovations contributed by behaviour therapy might seem to lie in the introduction of a conditioning and learning technology into psychotherapy, its major effects will be more radical and pervasive. If our unfolding experience shows that pathological behaviour is controlled more by reinforcement in its current context than by its history, and if the symptomatic relief produced by behaviour therapy is followed more by general improvement in the satisfactoriness of life than by the development of substitute symptoms, there would be important repercussions. Personality and psychopathological theory would have to devote more attention to adaptation, including a more explicit and sophisticated approach to learning and behaviour control. Therapists, behavioural or not, would become more active, would analyse the problems confronting them in greater detail, would be more inclined to settle for specific if limited goals, and would be freer in their use of differentiated techniques directed toward

9*

producing specific effects. These would all be natural and reasonable steps to take, regardless of ideology.

Much, then, rests on whether symptom substitution (or return) is, in fact, a problem after behaviour therapy. Because behaviour therapists in general work in a reasonably scientific way, substantial data should be available on this and other matters. With some important exceptions (for example, Paul, 1966), however, what data are available are of disappointingly poor quality. In too many of the case reports and clinical studies, the patients and their symptomatology are incompletely described, and post-therapy follow-up studies are quite inadequate. We do not learn much from these reports about how different kinds of patients responded or what happened long after therapy was finished. Unavoidably, we tend to see only a selected sample of results because failures are not published. In some studies, the behaviour theory is so poor, the analysis so sketchy, and the therapeutic procedures so poorly specified that it is hard to know what happened, or why. Others are ambiguous because of poor control; mechanisms falling outside the usual scope of behavioural scrutiny (such as placebo or transference effects) could be responsible for changes attributed to the behavioural manipulations. Comparisons of effectiveness with other therapies, though generally encouraging (as often happens when new techniques are enthusiastically introduced), are not entirely convincing. We hear too little about the qualifications of the "other" therapists, practically nothing about what they actually did, and often have no way of knowing how comparable the cases and the therapeutic contexts were. Finally, many of the studies that are carefully controlled (for example, Lang, 1968), that clearly specify procedure, and that explicitly investigate symptom substitution, use, as their subjects, college students with such subclinical symptomatology that it is hard to know what are the implications for more severely disturbed clinical cases. The reports, however, are quite consistent in suggesting that symptom substitution has not proved to be the serious problem that the critics of behaviour therapy have predicted. On balance and for the moment we should be inclined to accept this as testimony about a phenomenon, and go on from there.

IMPACT OF BEHAVIOUR THERAPY ON BEHAVIOUR THEORY

The behaviour therapy experience should have an enormous impact on behaviour theory and learning technology. Behavioural psychology has here undertaken to grapple with a vast domain of human experience in which it has made only minor inroads in the past. Problems related to meaning, cognition, language and verbal behaviour arise early in any attempt to deal with the phenomena of therapy, because talking figures so prominently in it, yet behavioural solutions to these problems have met with mixed receptions. And when behaviourists are forced to cope with complex human behaviour "*in vivo*", as they wander off the laboratory reservation, obstacles arising from man's ethology may appear (Hunt and Dyrud, 1968).

In working with animal species not ordinarily used in the laboratory, and in unusual situations, Breland and Breland (1961) encountered a number of curious phenomena in which important segments of behaviour appeared to have slipped out from under powerful controlling contingencies. They had to develop a new conceptual model to accommodate these findings (Breland and Breland, 1966).

Finally, behavioural psychology is not as unified and monolithic as its rhetoric might suggest. Behaviour therapists differ among themselves, in important ways, in handling such matters as drive and motivation or aversive control, which figure so largely in human maladjustment. The head-on confrontation with authenticated phenomena in therapy will inevitably sharpen and mature behaviour theory in many significant ways.

CONTEMPORARY TRENDS

A brief survey cannot hope to touch on all the interesting new developments at this interface, but a few major trends require comment.

Therapeutic milieus

Professor Krasner has already described behaviour modification programmes in specially designed institutional *milieus* (this volume, pp. 155–174; see also Atthowe and Krasner, 1968). These occupy a prominent place in the contemporary scene, and promise not only to reduce frictions in patient management and care, but also to restore to patients some control over their own destinies. Far from being masterpieces of Orwellian horror—1984's in 1968—these programmes can be organized to provide for the acquisition of skills and habits which patients can use to secure for themselves the social and other rewards that sustain the behaviour of all of us both in and out of hospital. More adequate behavioural repertoires open alternative avenues of action and the possibility of choice—the essence of freedom (Goldiamond and Dyrud, 1968; Hunt and Dyrud, 1968).

In an important sense, chronic patients have become trapped in a repertoire that must be giving them something by way of reinforcement.

That something must be very important to them, or why would they go to such lengths (pathological and ridiculous behaviour that places them in the presumably uninviting environment of the chronic wards) to get it? Behavioural modification programmes can produce new repertoires that are effective in securing that reinforcement with much less friction (if one takes the pains to find out what these patients really do want), if the programme also supplements the extinction of pathological behaviour with adequate provision for earning the rewards by appropriate and "normal" behaviour. This is particularly important: it is not enough simply to extinguish the undesirable behaviour by non-reinforcement; legitimate avenues to the rewards the patient needs must be opened to him.

Cohen (1968) has emphasized the importance of careful attention to the design of the *milieu*—the rules and criteria for reinforcement, the physical arrangements conducive to appropriate behaviour and foolproof operation of the system, and the selective use of reinforcers that are really important as well as practically manageable. With rare artistry (and with insightful disregard for conventional wisdom in some instances), Cohen has developed an experimental *milieu* for delinquent boys, directed toward the acquisition of fundamental educational skills and more effective social behaviour by selective reinforcement with such powerful though subtle rewards as access to preferred activities and privacy. With the acquisition of these skills, the boys also acquire options. The ability to read, and write, and cipher opens legitimate channels for achieving money and prestige or self-respect. At the least, some dependable alternative to the sociopathic life-style—a style which may yield immediate tangible rewards but at some hazard—becomes available. The expectation is that some of the boys in such a programme will exercise the option and escape from the endless recycling of their lives between prison and the probation officer.

Also, because of the incorruptibility of this *milieu*, perhaps the first of this kind that these boys have ever known, they may learn not only that such integrity is possible but also that it pays off to behave appropriately. Cohen does not emphasize this possibility, but it could represent a sort of learning with respect to supra-ordinate response and stimulus-classes of great importance in human behaviour. We know little about such classes because they seem to be present only in rudimentary form among the lower animals.

Ideas and insights

People do become persuaded, do see themselves and others differently, do come to view the world in new ways, and so on. These ideas and insights may be thought of as verbal or symbolic responses, however covert, with consequences (referents) that affect overt behaviours over a broad range of topography and apparent theme in a unitary fashion. Once the idea has been acquired, it serves as a discriminative stimulus and changes the probability of a wide range of behaviours quickly and in such circumstances that the change is hard to explain in terms of piecemeal, response-by-response alteration in this repertoire of behaviours through contemporary differential reinforcement of the component elements. In effect, a new strategy appears to have been adopted, with the specific elements of the new behaviour representing tactical implementation of the strategy, as determined oportunistically by the present situation and by previous learning. If the strategy is successful, not only are the component behaviours reinforced but, more important, the strategy—the new idea or insight—is also confirmed, much as the power of a discriminative stimulus is strengthened by differential reinforcement.

Some of the most important new developments in behaviour therapy are related to this formulation. Goldiamond and Dyrud (1968) use this discriminative stimulus metaphor in their behavioural analysis of psychotherapy and symptom formation in relation to instructional control. Salzinger (1968) uses a similar concept in his notion of the conditioning of "rules" in language. The possibilities here go far beyond language, of course, and may provide a behaviouristic metaphor for discussing cognitive mapping, symbolism, internal mediation, and phantasy. In all these new developments we see an analysis that contemplates the creation of classes of discriminative stimuli that have instructional control over a broad range of behaviours which themselves provide tactical implementation of the instruction.

Imitation and modelling

The studies on imitative behaviour and modelling follow a similar thrust. Lovaas (1968), Baer (1968), and Bandura and Walters (1963), for example, see a class of response that represents zero transformation from the behaviour of a model; in other words, the subject learns that the task (response) is to do whatever the model does. Whole repertoires of behaviours thus come under control and can be manipulated conveniently without the experimenter going through the labour of building the repertoires, response by response. Instructional control and modelling are two major steps toward a behavioural account of identification and the acquisition of different roles. These poorly understood but important phenomena have received very little attention in laboratory work on behaviour. Professor

Bandura has increased our knowledge by another large step with his studies of vicarious learning. The phenomenon that people learn by observing other people, and what happens to them, is part of everyday lore, but as lore and as a phenomenon it simply presents a problem. To tie this phenomenon down firmly, determine its scope, and identify important parameters controlling it endows vicarious learning processes with some concrete explanatory power. If instructional control, and modelling, can be acquired vicariously, we shall have made great progress toward understanding in behavioural terms how a role or an identification can lead a person to respond like a model to new situations in which he (the client) has never observed the model and with behaviour he has never practised and which has never been reinforced.

Reinforcements

The confrontation with clinical problems has increased the flexibility and improved the sophistication of reinforcement. Attention and other social reinforcers are widely used (Ayllon and Michael, 1959; Ayllon, 1967; Baer, 1968; Lovaas, 1968), and behaviour therapists are now beginning to know enough about personality to make penetrating guesses about what may be effective as a reward. The reinforcements inherent in everyday life outside the clinic are being used more skilfully and systematically in the design of procedures and plans for the patient. For example, desired behaviours that would normally evoke favourable attention are placed under the control of that reinforcer so that the normal contingencies of life outside—the responses of teachers, parents and peers whom Baer sees as "allies in reinforcement"—will support the behaviour. Improved knowledge of shaping and fading procedures has made it easier to deal with refractory behaviour or unusual situations that are closed to simple and direct intervention (Ulrich, Stachnik and Mabry, 1966; Goldiamond and Dyrud, 1968). In shaping, a crude and approximate form of behaviour may be moulded by gradual steps into the desired form by selectively changing the requirements that must be met for reinforcement. In fading, a response initially under the control of one stimulus may be shifted to the control of another more suitable for long-term support.

The instructional component

Finally, behaviour therapy increasingly includes a large instructional or educational component. Often the therapist gives the patient much direct information about behaviour control, demonstrates principles and techniques, and starts the patient in an active behavioural analysis of his behaviour and situation, both early and later in the treatment. The instructional control rationalizes what is happening and probably facilitates it. In the initial stages a patient who knows where and how to look can aid the analysis. In the later stages, the training plays an important role in fitting the patient to maintain his gains and solve new problems as they arise in his post-therapy life. In some patients the educational-instructional aspect of therapy may conceivably be more important than specific procedures, though little systematic data are available on this yet.

FINAL COMMENTS

Too much of the argument about behaviour therapy has centred on whether the patient is still "sick" after therapy, however symptom-free he may be, when major attention should be focused on the actual behavioural status of patients after therapy. Sometimes so little information is given of the patient's pre-therapy status and history that changes produced by treatment, especially subtle ones, cannot be evaluated for want of firm baselines for comparison. Cases that fail to respond to treatment receive too little attention, even though these are a most fruitful source of information both on the limits of the effectiveness of procedures and on what the procedures actually do. A patient who is a "failure" (by definition, because he has not lost a circumscribed target symptom) may be substantially changed and made more accessible to further treatment along a new line. Similarly, a "success" may be so classified because he lost the symptom that caused other people to refer him for treatment, but the treatment may have been effective primarily in teaching him some less irritating way to pursue his accustomed exploitative ends.

Those who ask whether a patient is still sick after treatment cannot get a clear answer, of course, because what is defined as sickness is somewhat arbitrary and subject to doctrinal influences. Those who ask whether a patient has lost his target symptoms can be given a firm answer, but it will tend to be of limited technical interest because only a circumscribed portion of the patient's behaviour is under scrutiny. But those who ask for details as to how a patient's behaviour has been changed by particular behavioural procedures, whether successful or not, address themselves to a broader topic. They can get firm answers of immediate practical import, of course, but they are also striking out for information of more general significance.

Those who worry about the possible harm that behaviour therapy may do should take some comfort from its pragmatism, and the limits this imposes. According to its own canons, behaviour therapy must demonstrate its own effectiveness. Its own procedures of analysis and verification, properly applied, provide for a test of the hypotheses about specific cases. Further, behaviour therapy assumes that an organism only retains behaviour that is somehow satisfying, favours only that behaviour which maximizes satisfaction, and works persistently and cleverly toward that end (satisfaction) no matter what we do.

SUMMARY

The development of behaviour therapy provides for a growing and productive symbiosis between dynamic personality theory and psychotherapeutic technique, on the one hand, and modern behaviour theory on the other. Despite long-standing concern with basically overlapping problems, and despite earlier attempts at cross-fertilization, the ideological traditions and metaphors of each approach differed so radically that the past interface between them has been unnecessarily opaque, polemic and competitive.

The major effects of this development may well be more pervasive and radical than just the introduction of a conditioning and learning technology into psychotherapy. Assuming that pathological behaviour is controlled more by reinforcement in its current context than by its remote history, and that symptomatic relief produced by behaviour therapy is followed more by general improvement in the satisfactoriness of life than by substitute symptoms, we can expect repercussions in personality and psychopathological theory and in therapeutic practices generally. Theory will devote more attention to adaptation processes and to learning and behaviour control. Therapists will be more active, will analyse the behavioural problems confronting them more closely, be more free with their use of differentiated techniques selected to produce specific effects, and more inclined to settle for, or specify, particular if limited goals.

Similarly, head-on confrontation, in therapy, with authenticated phenomena and unsolved problems will extend, sharpen and mature behaviour theory.

REFERENCES

ATTHOWE, J. M., JR., and KRASNER, L. (1968). *J. abnorm. Psychol.*, **73**, 37–43.
AYLLON, T. (1967). In *Comparative Psychopathology*, pp. 240–248, eds. Zubin, J., and Hunt, H. F. New York: Grune and Stratton.
AYLLON, T., and MICHAEL, J. (1959). *J. exp. Analysis Behav.*, **2**, 323–334.

BAER, D. M. (1968). In *Research in Psychotherapy*, vol. 3, pp. 3–20, eds. Shlien, J. M., Hunt, H. F., Matarazzo, J. D., and Savage, C. Washington, D.C.: American Psychological Association.

BANDURA, A., and WALTERS, R. H. (1963). *Social Learning and Personality Development*. New York: Holt, Rinehart and Winston.

BRELAND, K. B., and BRELAND, M. (1961). *Am. Psychol.*, **16**, 681–684.

BRELAND, K. B., and BRELAND, M. (1966). *Animal Behavior*. New York: Macmillan.

COHEN, H. (1968). In *Research in Psychotherapy*, vol. 3, pp. 21–53, eds. Shlien, J. M., *et al.* Washington, D.C.: American Psychological Association.

DOLLARD, J., and MILLER, N. E. (1950). *Personality and Psychotherapy*. New York: McGraw-Hill.

EYSENCK, H. J. (ed.) (1960). *Behaviour Therapy and the Neuroses*. Oxford: Pergamon.

FENICHEL, O. (1945). *Psychoanalytic Theory of Neurosis*. New York: Norton.

GOLDIAMOND, I., and DYRUD, J. E. (1968). In *Research in Psychotherapy*, vol. 3, pp. 54–89, eds. Shlien, J. M., *et al.* Washington, D.C.: American Psychological Association.

HONIG, W. K. (ed.) (1966). *Operant Behavior: Areas of Research and Application*. New York: Appleton-Century-Crofts.

HUNT, H. F., and DYRUD, J. E. (1968). In *Research in Psychotherapy*, vol. 3, pp. 140–152, eds. Shlien, J. M., *et al.* Washington, D.C.: American Psychological Association.

KRASNER, L., and ULLMANN, L. P. (eds.) (1965). *Research in Behavior Modification*. New York: Holt, Rinehart and Winston.

LANG, P. (1968). In *Research in Psychotherapy*, vol. 3, pp. 90–102, eds. Shlien, J. M., *et al.* Washington, D.C.: American Psychological Association.

LOVAAS, O. I. (1968). In *Research in Psychotherapy*, vol. 3, pp. 103–121, eds. Shlien, J. M., *et al.* Washington, D.C.: American Psychological Association.

MILLENSON, J. R. (1967). *Principles of Behavioral Analysis*. New York: Macmillan.

MOWRER, O. H. (1950). *Learning Theory and Personality Dynamics*. New York: Ronald.

PAUL, G. L. (1966) *Insight vs. Desensitization in Psychotherapy*. Stanford, Calif.: Stanford University Press.

SALZINGER, K. (1968). In *Research in Psychotherapy*, vol. 3, pp. 122–129, eds. Shlien, J. M., *et al.* Washington, D.C.: American Psychological Association.

SHLIEN, J. M., HUNT, H. F., MATARAZZO, J. D., and SAVAGE, C. (eds.) (1968). *Research in Psychotherapy*, vol. 3. Washington, D.C.: American Psychological Association.

SKINNER, B. F. (1938). *The Behavior of Organisms*. New York: Appleton-Century-Crofts.

SKINNER, B. F. (1953). *Science and Human Behavior*. New York: Macmillan.

ULRICH, R., STACHNIK, T., and MABRY, J. (eds.) (1966). *Control of Human Behavior*. Glanview, Ill.: Scott, Foresman.

WOLPE, J. (1958). *Psychotherapy by Reciprocal Inhibition*. Stanford, Calif.: Stanford University Press.

DISCUSSION

Jansson: The acceptance of behaviour therapy has been slow in the United States, and in some European countries, but the explanations for this delay differ in different countries. In Scandinavia the tradition of organic treatment for psychiatric illness is so strong that all kinds of psychotherapy, except perhaps supportive psychotherapy, are viewed with suspicion. Behaviour therapy will be more readily accepted than psychoanalytic therapy in Scandinavia, because it is nearer to our traditional way of thinking.

Frank: Professor Hunt, you included all psychological processes within the framework of behaviour therapy and conditioning, but this may be an oversimplification. If a patient who seems to be receiving only punishing treatment for a particular behaviour continues to execute this behaviour, we must conclude that the treatment means something other than punishment to him.

Hunt: Punishment is defined functionally, according to its effects on behaviour.

Frank: But if a punishing treatment does not produce the expected aversive effects, how can you define it as punishment?

Hunt: In common parlance punishment is defined as something that an *observer* considers to be aversive. Implicit in this definition is the inference made by the observer (not necessarily by the patient) that the "treatment" (an electric shock, for example) is punishing.

Frank: Then this concept involves internal symbolic processes, does it not?

Hunt: Not entirely. Data from animal experiments (for example, Church, R. M. [1963]. *Psychol. Rev.*, **70**, 369-402) showed that a shock which is aversive in some circumstances can become an appetitive discriminative stimulus, or even in some ways reinforcing, in others. In other words, a shock that one would expect to be punishing can facilitate rather than suppress behaviour in animals. The functional significance of a stimulus is determined by its implications for the recipient, not for the observer. A good illustration of this reverse effect occurred in a girl with a troublesome, compulsive behaviour pattern (making obscene sexual proposals to men); she was treated by a standard behaviour therapy technique in which she was punished for this behaviour by incarceration in a dark room. But the punishment only increased the girl's compulsive behaviour, because this was being maintained partly by attention, which was achieved when she was locked in the room. An additional secondary gain was that she could fight against being put in the room, and attract even more attention in this way.

Kaufman: How did you find this out?

Hunt: By trial and error. When we stopped paying attention to her obscene remarks she stopped making them. You might call this a primitive functional behavioural analysis of the case.

Miller: Then your definitions of reward and punishment are empiric.

Hunt: Yes.

Frank: I. Goldiamond and J. Dryud (1968. *Research in Psychotherapy*, vol. 3, eds. Shlien, J. M., *et al.* Washington, D.C.: American Psychological Association) suggest that the behaviour therapist first determines what the patient hopes to gain through his behaviour by analysing its consequences. Then the therapist uses behavioural techniques to help the patient develop more effective behaviour to gain these same ends. Would you comment on this view?

Hunt: Goldiamond's approach implies motivational constructs, and the role of motivation in behaviour theory is still an open problem. I avoided tackling it in my presentation. In behavioural analysis we try to find out what actually works in changing the patient's behaviour rather than what he says he wants. The things that patients say they want do often turn out to be effective incentives or reinforcers, but to suggest that a drive or motive underlies every reinforcement, or to take such motives for granted, is to risk becoming involved with value judgments and preconceptions about motivation. It may sometimes seem, in behavioural analyses, that we are studying the problem in terms of what the patient wants. It may be more economical and there might be less risk of error if we tried to emphasize the problem in terms of what the patient is getting that is maintaining his pathological behaviour. The correctness or otherwise of our analysis can be demonstrated by what happens to the unwanted behaviour. A patient is not necessarily looking for evil and violence when he seems often to be involved in them.

Bandura: We should, perhaps, distinguish between (a) the selection of treatment goals, which requires value judgments, and (b) empiric questions that relate to the selection of the best strategies for achieving the desired objectives. The patient should play a major role in determining the direction in which his behaviour is to be modified. If a client selects goals that the therapist does not wish to promote, the therapist may decide not to treat the patient or, if appropriate, refer him elsewhere. A more prevalent but largely ignored ethical issue is raised by the unilateral redefinition by therapists of the clients' goals. Clients may ask for help in modifying their interpersonal patterns of behaviour only to end up with the therapists' particular brand of insight.

Frank: Most therapists do not face these problems.

Bandura: Decisions about values are common to all forms of psychotherapy. Nevertheless, it is often assumed that traditional, analytic therapists are fervently on the side of humanism whereas behaviour therapists are either disinterested in the moral implications of their treatments or antagonistic towards humanistic values. But behaviour therapy is a system of principles and procedures, not of ethics. Any effective method of treatment can be used to threaten human freedom and dignity, or to enhance them.

Frank: For "good" behaviour (in the eyes of the observer) to occur, a behaviour therapist has to convince the patient that his values are wrong. In my view this is not behaviour therapy but instructional control.

Hunt: The issues are never as clear-cut as these comments suggest. Instructional control probably is an important part of behaviour therapy and we do have to deal with problems concerning values. Values change during therapy and we have to initiate or help the changes. It is a very important change if a patient's view of the world is altered so that he sees it as honest and responsive rather than as a hostile place where everyone is out for his blood; but it is difficult to discuss this sort of change within the language of behavioural analysis. I suggest that it is possible to use instructional control and ethical values as instructional discriminative stimuli.

Frank: When you introduce the symbolic world into your system, instructional control is inevitable.

Hunt: In one way or another we have to cope with the patient's symbolic world.

Kubie: This approach may dangerously oversimplify the problems of psychopathology. One of the natural and appropriate aims of the experimentalist is to reduce the number of variables in a situation: he has to oversimplify in order to conduct an experiment. The clinician, on the other hand, must remind the experimentalist of the complexity and subtlety of situations as they exist in nature. And we are ignoring this complexity at the moment. Social acceptability is a minor part of the problem of what to do about psychopathology. We are not seeking to create conformists. Our goal is to enable a patient to give up trying, consciously or unconsciously, to do what is inherently impossible. A human being who wants to be both sexes does not want to give up what he is, he wants to be that plus something else, although he may be completely unaware of this. This is the sort of psychopathological soil from which illness grows. The relief of a symptom may give much temporary comfort, and enable the therapist to understand the underlying psychopathology, but it is the latter that we must deal with if we are to help the patient.

Marks: A problem in connexion with values is whether we want to help a patient to realize his goals if these conflict with the social norm, or to help him to develop socially acceptable values. If a man can get prestige without working for it should we deter him? Similarly, if a particular transsexual patient tries to change his sex it may make him a happier person, even if the treatments he wants are incompatible with the values of society. These empiric questions can only be answered by helping such patients to make the appropriate changes to see if this does relieve their distress. These problems are currently being investigated (Green, R. [1968]. *Transsexualism and Sex Reassignment.* Baltimore, Maryland: Johns Hopkins Press; Hastings, D. W., and Blum, J. A. [1967]. *J.-Lancet,* **87**, 262-264). Whether a therapist accepts the values and goals of a patient surely depends on whether these goals can be realized and if their realization will make the patient happy.

Kubie: Many of these patients want to be both sexes simultaneously. No one can reconcile in a patient two incompatible and unattainable demands.

Hunt: The patient may not really want to be both sexes but rather to gain something that he believes will be available to him only if he is both male and female. For example, he may need some role or combination of roles for comfort. If we accede to the patient's demand as he sees it, and assess what he says and does at face value, we may be playing straight into his defensive structure. He may want to play aggressive and dependent roles simultaneously and visualize male and female sex roles as an easy way to implement this aim. But it is just because this strategy has not worked well that the patient seeks psychiatric help. And it is not possible to be both sexes at once. But we should try to devise some other means to help the patient to deal with his conflicting emotions (this is not a value judgment but a contingent prediction), and look for a way of producing the satisfaction and relief from anxiety that the patient needs without such a heavy cost in ostracism and unhappiness. Behaviour therapy and behavioural analysis thus represent an exciting challenge to the intelligence and ingenuity of the therapist.

Carstairs: Your argument implies that we can eventually discover what every patient wants. But patients may be ambivalent and oscillate between completely contradictory wants.

Hunt: This is a troublesome problem. The ambivalence may be superficial and easy to resolve but some problems are probably insoluble. The patient may have to accept his ambivalence and learn to oscillate. We live in a melioristic climate in which it is assumed that a solution to all problems exists. I doubt this.

Miller: Professor Hunt, the girl you have just described sounds as if she may want to be both sexes. How are you treating her?

Hunt: This girl presents a confusing problem. For her (and for many others) behavioural procedures may have to be aimed successively at different levels; we deal with one problem only to uncover another. We can only proceed step by step. This girl originally presented a compulsion to make obscene sexual proposals. When this behaviour disappeared she did not develop the anxiety and distress that would be expected to result from blocking a compulsion, but set fire to her night-dress. I expected suicide, and the burning may have been a substitute for this. What was the purpose of this very "resourceful" response? She told her therapist (a resident in the department) that the burning was intended to develop a specific relationship with him; I do not know if this is true. If the therapist is able to change his role-responses to the patient, and thinks it is wise to do so, we may find out. Then he would have to develop a strategy to deal with the new behaviour at this new level.

We should also note that a therapist is often trapped by the patient's behaviour. Behavioural control is a process that works in two directions, as illustrated by the tale of two rats talking in a Skinner box. One rat, with one paw on the lever, said to the other: "Boy, have I got this guy conditioned; every time I press the lever he puts some food down."!

Sandler: Was the act of burning the night-dress an adaptive or a maladaptive response?

Hunt: I do not know, but it must have been overdetermined. The previous behaviour was adaptive; the patient was using it instrumentally to get what she wanted—attention. She may later have derived other advantages from the dialogue that developed with her therapist when they discussed her previous behaviour, but these advantages may not have been sufficient to sustain her. The burning could have arisen out of the prolonged extinction (non-reinforcement) of her previous behaviour, depriving her of reinforcements she thought she could not live without. The new, self-destructive behaviour may have grown out of frustration, and been an expression of despair and desperation rather than an instrumental response.

Miller: Surely setting fire to herself was a very dramatic example of the replacement of her compulsion to make obscene proposals by a far more dangerous symptom or behaviour.

Hunt: Yes. These proposals, of course, had tremendous impact on the society in which she lived and on the analytically oriented residents in my department. Even I was trapped by it, to the extent of a brief speech block, although I was expecting it and had developed a strategy to deal with it. Eventually we all learned not to respond in the way she expected. This girl would also make disparaging remarks about Negroes—this was during the race riots of 1967—so we had to train our Negro aides, as well as ourselves, not to respond. These behaviours were fairly easy to abolish through selective inattention. We also looked for acceptable behaviour that this girl could enjoy, and found that she was a good cook and manager. We set up a situation for her in the ward such that she could take charge of domestic affairs (planning special dinners, parties and so on), thus giving her a reasonable method for getting attention. This worked so well that we were able to move her to an open ward where these special activities were no longer available to her. After a few weeks, she set fire to herself. So the burning may have been a response to the frustration caused by being deprived of her special activities. Or she may have been trying to get back to the locked ward, in which case the fire had the effect she wanted. This girl is very sophisticated about psychiatric ideology and how to play to it, which makes it very difficult to discover what is going on and to deal with it.

Lazarus: A difficult and recurrent problem in behavioural technology concerns the relative importance of antecedents and consequences. Emphasis has shifted from a pervasive interest in antecedents to attention to the factors that maintain aberrant behaviour. Although some behaviour technicians insist that it is more useful to find out what is maintaining a deviant behaviour, and to manipulate the consequences, than to determine how this behaviour arose, it is interesting to speculate on what happens if we completely ignore antecedents. H. Ginott (1965. *Between Parent and Child.* New York: Macmillan) provides an interesting illustration of what happens when the phantasy life of the patient is ignored and overt behaviour is given exclusive priority. A child who usually behaved very destructively in a confined area was unexpectedly quiet while travelling in the car with his parents and younger brother. His mother rewarded this unusual behaviour by telling him what a good boy he was—a typical operant strategy of social reinforcement for good behaviour. The boy immediately flew into a violent rage and attacked his parents and brother. When his mother spoke he had been deep in a phantasy, wondering how to get rid of his brother, and it was these murderous thoughts that his mother unwittingly rewarded. Behaviour is not just a function of its consequences; it is a product of antecedents and consequent interactions, both internal and external. Images and cognitions from past experience maintain many behaviours and have autonomic consequences in the present. The therapist must know how these various factors manifest themselves in each of his patients.

Hunt: I agree. The antecedents, particularly internal imaginings and phantasies, often determine the reinforcing properties (the significance) of contemporary stimuli.

Sifneos: Lack of motivation for psychotherapy is another difficult problem for the clinicians. Examples are the delinquent who is sent to the clinic by the courts; or the impotent man who is himself satisfied but whose wife is complaining; or the young student who burns his draft card because he does not want to go to Vietnam, and who is sent for therapy by the University authorities. Lack of motivation for treatment may often be connected with the patient's general ambivalence which, incidentally, is a very common phenomenon in almost all psychiatric problems. Professor Hunt how would you, as a behaviour therapist, deal with a young man who had burned his draft card?

Hunt: Young people are extremely clever at developing strategic systems of responses that are inaccessible to classical economic control and its consequences. The behaviour of the boys who burn their draft cards, and the hippies, very much in the Franciscan tradition, is itself a strategy. These boys are certainly motivated but it is difficult to see what for. I know of a boy who was brought up by loving parents in an enlightened environment. His father was familiar with behavioural techniques and supplied contingencies for most of the boy's actions: if he wanted money he had to earn it by mowing the lawn, and so on. The boy—a nice, cultured, middle-class, mildly rebellious adolescent—suddenly rebelled violently against his father by eschewing the need for all practical things. He now hangs round the house, plays a guitar, grows his hair long and does absolutely nothing. His family is in total despair. The boy is not unmotivated—he exercises powerful behavioural control over his parents. Such drop-out behaviour is an extremely effective disruptive response to power. The boys who are burning their draft cards feel impotent against the authority of the State. One of the few ways of influencing such a gigantic machine is to become unmotivated and unresponsive and thus escape from the system.

Sifneos: But the impotent man with the complaining wife presents a different problem: he is not motivated.

Hunt: I doubt that too.

Malan: The draft-card burners are not motivated towards changing their behaviour, but they are strongly motivated in many other directions. Do we want to persuade these boys to want to change and, if so, how can this be done?

Sifneos: Some draft-card burners come to us for help without the direction of the University authorities. They have a problem they cannot solve, namely, whether to go to Vietnam or not. But under the overt problem one may discover a quite different conflict.

Miller: If the draft-card burners have a real psychiatric problem, we must try to help them. Professor Hunt, as a behaviour technologist how would you set about motivating these boys to achieve their rebellion against authority in a less troublesome way ? For the moment let us ignore the issue of the morality of the war in Vietnam.

Hunt: My first response would be to remove as many contingencies as possible from this behaviour so as to make it unimportant.

Sandler: In other words, you would try to change the motivation.

Hunt: Yes. This behaviour is mainly sustained by the fuss it produces, and the best treatment for it is inattention.

Sandler: But isn't one motive in these boys to achieve a total drop-out from society ?

Hunt: That is one reinforcer of the behaviour. The escape from society, and the impact of this escape on society, are two sides of the same coin. The escape would be less rewarding if society objected to it less strenuously.

Kubie: Burning the draft card may be a normal act in one man; in others it may be the presenting symptom for many different psychopathological processes. Similarly, to drink a glass of water may be simply a social gesture, or a purification rite, or a means of quenching one's thirst. A young man can burn his draft card because he is sincerely opposed to the national policy in Vietnam, or because he is terrified that his latent homosexuality may become manifest in an army unit, or because of a deep feeling of impotence that is part of a hidden feminine identification, or a mixture of these and other determinants. We cannot talk of universal origins, or of a single line of treatment, for these boys; each case must be diagnosed on its merits.

Hunt: Nonetheless, burning the draft cards would not persist, whatever the reasons for it, unless it were effective. Until we stop maintaining the behaviour it is very difficult to unravel which of an almost limitless number of alternative antecedents it is reflecting. After my initial strategy of specific inattention, I would expect to find clues emerging about the underlying reasons for the behaviour. Then I would work out new strategies to deal with the deeper psychopathology. This is a rather superficial description of how I would treat these young men, but such a plan might work.

Carstairs: From the draft-card burners' point of view, of course, it is the authorities that are sick and unmotivated to change.

Sandler: Professor Hunt, there is a contradiction in your use of the word "effective" in connexion with behaviour. Effective must mean effective from the subject's point of view. The therapist will often see, as non-effective or maladaptive, behaviour which, to the patient, is highly effective. Our understanding of all these problems about behaviour—motivation, "what the patient really wants", and so on—depends on our awareness of the internal processes that lie behind a particular behaviour. We are avoiding discussion of these internal constructs, and may be rationalizing our avoidance by assuming that to talk about them is unscientific. We seem to be frightened of discussing parameters that cannot be defined in terms of measurement.

Hunt: I agree. We, as behaviouristic psychologists, will not be able to deal with the more complex symbolic reinforcers and discriminative stimuli until we can admit, organize and cope with our own as well as the patients' internal psychic processes.

Kaufman: One aspect of the problem is this: man is the only animal that has acquired the capacity to use symbols, and to manipulate them internally as representations of the external world. Symbolization is not something that happens in between pieces of behaviour, it *is* behaviour. Until we recognize this, no theoretical scheme will make sense for the human animal.

Miller: But the internal processes can only be observed *as behaviour*. We have no magic lens to allow us to see them directly as they really are. The psychoanalyst, more than any other type of psychotherapist, tries to externalize these internal processes.

Kaufman: I agree. And a phantasy is also a behaviour. The patient in analysis with a phantasy of tearing a building apart does not have to do it but to talk about it.

Miller: You are describing verbal behaviour. Ultimately, all internal processes are manifest as behaviour.

Krasner: It has been suggested that behaviour therapy involves more moral judgments than other form of therapy. I doubt this but, as Professor Hunt emphasized, behavioural techniques highlight the values of the therapist (the influencer of behaviour) and his responsibility in influencing the values of the patient. Behaviour therapy involves instruction and control. We may try to find out what the patient really wants, but eventually the changes in behaviour that we aim for depend on the therapist's view of good and bad. Behaviour therapists should be trained to realize the importance of their own values in the treatment of their patients. We have been evading these issues when discussing the treatment of the boys who burn their draft cards: the therapist's views about United States' policy in Vietnam will be highly relevant to the aims and results of treatment of these young men.

Kubie: If we really want to help a boy who tears up his draft card we must first determine whether he is mentally sick or not and why he is doing it. We also want to keep him out of the hands of the police if possible, or

nobody will be able to treat him. Similarly, we try to prevent a homosexual from promiscuous involvement with strangers because, if this
leads him into trouble with the police, we shall not be able to treat him at
all.

Krasner: The difference between these two approaches to the draft-card
burner may be that the analyst would ask the question: "Is the patient
sick?" and the behaviour therapist would try to unravel the consequences
of the behaviour.

Kubie: The internal consequences are the vital factors in determining
what happens.

Sackett: This symposium was mounted to study and try to define the
variables that underly the learning processes involved in the behavioural
changes that occur in the laboratory and in therapy. But we have been
side-tracked into discussing philosophical and moral issues concerning the
values that influence a therapist in influencing a draft-card burner. We
should be discussing the techniques available to the therapist, once he has
decided to try to change the behaviour of such a patient, and the underlying
variables in the patient on which the effectiveness of these techniques
depends.

Kaufman: Speculations about the effect of the values of the therapist on
those of the patient have little or nothing to do with the mechanisms by
which therapy occurs. But value systems have traditionally always been
included in discussions about therapy. The types of problems the therapist
is faced with vary widely and he should never have to decide if a behaviour
with which he is presented is proper or improper. But his values influence
the decision to start psychotherapy. Once this decision has been made
(usually partly because the patient has expressed a wish to change) the value
systems of the therapist should not influence the mechanisms through which
therapy operates.

Miller: I agree with Dr. Kubie that it is important for the therapist to try
to unravel the underlying motives of a draft-card burner as well as to change
his superficial behaviour. If this behaviour is a genuine protest against
government policy in Vietnam, therapy is quite unjustified brain-washing.
But if the draft-card burner is motivated by, say, unconscious irrational
rebellion against some frustration imposed by his parents in early childhood (that is, if the patient is mentally sick but is not aware of this), the
therapist's responsibility is to help the patient towards conscious understanding of the underlying motives. Once the patient understands what he
is doing the decision about starting therapy should be left to him.

Frank: My original intention in discussing the relevance of value systems in treatment was to show that even behaviour therapists become involved in symbol systems and internal constructs, and that these are important implicit features of behavioural techniques. But I agree with Dr. Sackett that we are now being distracted by philosophical issues.

Krasner: Value systems are not necessarily vague philosophical concepts; they can be objectively measured and included as one of the variables influencing therapy.

Miller: There is a continuum of activity in psychotherapy, from the relatively passive, non-directive, Rogerian therapy to the most instructional, active forms of behaviour therapy, with psychoanalysis somewhere in the middle. The more active the therapy, the more the therapist must be aware of the powerful effect of his views.

Hunt: The patient himself may propose a value confrontation in order to oppose the therapist. H. L. Cohen (personal communication) described this phenomenon as it occurred with a boy who threatened suicide during a psychotherapy session. The patient was a Roman Catholic and in his presence Cohen contacted the priest, but he was not available until three days later. The result was that the boy agreed to postpone his suicide until he had seen the priest and, in the event, the suicide was cancelled. Because Cohen could handle this situation in a matter of fact way, the problem was somehow redefined without judgment. Not all therapists can work like this; if one feels shock and horror at the notion of self-destruction this resonates to the patient, who realizes that the therapist cannot handle the confrontation.

Miller: But if the therapist is too casual and matter of fact, the patient may actually kill himself.

Sifneos: I would like to discuss a specific case of attempted suicide, with particular reference to motivation and the kind of therapy that was used. A patient who had made three serious suicidal attempts, was brought to the emergency ward after jumping in front of a truck which barely missed him. He was seen in psychiatric consultation but claimed that he was determined to try again. He was unmotivated (at least consciously) to stay alive. This situation was disturbing for the hospital staff—it seemed that we had either to certify the patient or let him kill himself. While one of the residents was talking to him, he noticed the man wince when another patient, bleeding profusely, was wheeled past. The resident encouraged the patient to talk about his fear of blood until he became so anxious that he begged for the conversation to be finished. The resident offered to help him get over his fear of blood, which was a painful subject, and did not mention the suicide, which was not. The patient agreed, and after a few interviews, he accepted the idea of receiving psychotherapy. Would you call the resident's technique with this patient a kind of behaviour therapy? Incidentally, this case may illustrate a way in which behaviourists and analysts can find common ground.

Hunt: I would call this technique "behaviour therapy" because the resident focused on one particular response and manipulated contingencies and symbols to produce a behavioural effect. But the label we use is not important; what matters is that, because of the clinical acumen of the resident, it was possible to redefine the patient's problem and to help him.

Sifneos: In psychoanalytic terms, we would describe this as breaking through a resistance.

Miller: Another way of describing what happened would be to say that the resident punished the talk of suicide by finding and using an aversive stimulus—blood.

Hunt: The behaviour was momentarily discouraged and this created an opening for therapy. This case report illustrates the power of aversive stimuli to arrest a behaviour pattern.

Lazarus: The notion of dyadic transactions has been implicit in many of our discussions. This concept should now be made explicit, because it broadens the therapeutic units which one can use and also fits well with operant-conditioning principles. When we shift our focus away from the individual to his significant interpersonal relationships and his role with significant others, new behaviours become available for inspection and modification. If we studied the impotent man (apparently unconcerned and therefore said to be unmotivated) described by Dr. Sifneos from the point of view of dyadic transactions, we might discover how his impotence is a direct consequence of aversive stimuli which his wife deliberately or inadvertently emits. The transactions and consequent positive and negative reinforcements within this dyad might yield a productive basis for treatment.

Hunt: This *is* behavioural analysis.

PSYCHOANALYTIC PSYCHOLOGY AND
LEARNING THEORY

JOSEPH SANDLER AND WALTER G. JOFFE

Academic Department of Psychiatry, Middlesex Hospital Medical School, and Index Project,
Hampstead Child-Therapy Clinic, London

SINCE the beginnings of psychoanalysis certain basic and stable concepts
have been the cornerstones of psychoanalytic theory. Such concepts
include, for example, the notions of unconscious mental functioning and of
instinctual drives and impulses. But psychoanalytic concepts have never
been fully organized into a coherent and integrated theoretical model, and
the various concepts in current use can only be fully understood if they are
considered from a frame of reference which includes a historical dimension.
This is largely because advances in psychoanalytic theory have tended to
take place along specific fronts, and the state of affairs has always existed in
which older concepts have existed alongside new ones. Perhaps the major
attempt to formulate an explicit and coherent model was the introduction
of the structural theory (Freud, 1923), but important revisions of psychoanalytic theory, such as that of the theory of anxiety (Freud, 1926), have left
us with further problems of conceptual integration which have not as yet
been faced.

This paper is an attempt to sketch an approach to psychoanalytic theory
which has evolved during the past ten years as an outcome of a specific
method of research into the conceptual problems of psychoanalysis. The
method used (Sandler, 1962a) has been one in which theoretical concepts
are tested against recorded clinical material in a systematic way. The
procedure has shown up many of the problems in regard to definitions in
psychoanalytic theory, and has led to the creation of altered and at times
new definitions within a revised theoretical framework. We have found
more and more that the findings and formulations of psychologists who
are not psychoanalysts have had to be brought into the psychoanalytic
model—for example the studies of Jean Piaget and other psychologists
working in the fields of cognition, perception, memory and the like. Thus,
for example, the conceptualization of an object relationship as the investment of a love-object with libido has altered to a concept in which the
notion of inner object representation (as opposed to the "real" external

object) is given prime importance (cf. Sandler, 1960b, 1962b; Sandler and Rosenblatt, 1962; Sandler, Holder and Meers, 1963; Joffe and Sandler, 1965). The idea of an investment of an object with energy has had to be replaced with the idea of feelings attached to the internal object representation (Joffe and Sandler, 1967). Indeed, the whole area of the development of the inner (or representational) world has come to play an increasingly important part in psychoanalytic theory, particularly in regard to children; and this not only from the emotional but also from the cognitive point of view.

There has been a general move in recent years to turn psychoanalysis into a theory which is not only a psychology of abnormal mental functioning, but which embraces a normal general psychology. This has been achieved partly by removing some of the links of psychoanalysis with treatment. The development of psychoanalytic theory has been strongly influenced in the past by its association with psychoanalytic therapy, and a model which is aimed primarily at meeting the needs of psychoanalytic practice may be substantially different from that created by the wish to construct a general psychology. The latter demands the building of conceptual bridges to other disciplines, and this presentation is addressed primarily to the possibilities of building a bridge between psychoanalysis and learning theory.

Many problems are involved in such an attempt. The levels of detail at which phenomena are being studied may vary; learning theories tend to emphasize external stimulus and overt response while psychoanalytic theory places stress on the inner, subjective world of the individual; and so on. But it is gratifying that certain learning theorists have shifted emphasis from external stimuli and observable behaviour, and have utilized concepts which are aimed at encompassing intra-personal phenomena. There is an increasing realization that the stimulus-response model is inadequate, and mediating concepts are now being used—for example, in relating studies of perception and problem-solving to learning theories. Such mediating concepts range from Hull's "habit strength" to such concepts as strategies, schemata and programmes.

Parallel changes are taking place in psychoanalytic theory. Influences from other fields include that of Piaget's work; computer models are being drawn upon; and experimental findings by psychoanalysts in the laboratory are having repercussions on basic psychoanalytic theory.

Some recent formulations will now be presented very briefly. We assume that our readers have a knowledge of the essentials of psychoanalytic theory—although it is unfortunate that what most people know of this theory may have been wholly derived from earlier formulations made at a time when psychoanalysis was investigating the derivatives of unconscious instinctual wishes as expressed in the material brought by patients in psychoanalytic sessions.

SOME RECENT ASPECTS OF PSYCHOANALYTIC THEORY

Psychoanalysis as a psychology of adaptation

By this we do not mean simply adaptation to the external world, but would emphasize that adaptation should be regarded as applying, on the one hand, to the external situation (as it is perceived by the individual) and, on the other, to inner promptings (wishes, needs, impulses and so on) which may arise spontaneously or may be triggered off by external situations. We should also include the concept of adaptation to those internal standards which have arisen during the course of development—standards which may be quite at odds with present-day reality, and which we subsume under the concept of the super-ego (Sandler, 1906b).

The psychoanalytic concept of the representational world

Apart from the conceptualization of the psychic apparatus into id, ego and super-ego, we have to formulate more clearly the psychoanalytic concept of the inner world. We have done this by putting forward the concept of the representational world (Sandler, 1962b; Sandler and Rosenblatt, 1962). This can be regarded as the whole complex of mental representations of inner wishes, feelings, memories, percepts and symbols. One specialized part of the representational world is that which contains the representations of what is external to the individual; another refers to the representation of the person himself (his self-representation); and other areas relate to images with various symbolic meanings. The representations of words and mathematical symbols are prime examples of this last, and form a substantial part of the representational content of normal thinking. Further, the *representation* of what is outside is never an exact reflection of what we assume to be *actually* outside the person concerned. His perceptions are structured and coloured by what has gone before and by his own (conscious or unconscious) wishes and desires.

Essential to the representational world are the many organized schemata which the individual constructs during the course of his development and which form the background frame of reference to all current processes of perception, imagining, remembering, feeling and thinking. The representational world in all the different aspects of its organization is constantly influenced by stimuli arising both from within and without the individual, and new schemata are constantly being created as new perceptual and conceptual solutions are being found. These schemata form the basis for future attempts at adaptation (in the sense in which we have used the term) and problem-solving, although they may in turn be modified by experience.

The fundamental distinction between structure and experience

We can now make a distinction which is implicit in the whole body of psychoanalytic theory, and which is a crucial basis for what follows: the distinction between *structure* and *experience*. The concept of structure refers not only to the basic inborn biological structures, but also to all the secondary psychological structures that are created during the course of development through interaction between the individual and the outside world. The concept of structure, as used here, is broad, including not only the schemata which relate to the person's inner world but also everything which is usually subsumed by the terms "mechanism", "apparatus", and so on. Thus perceptual structures will range from the biological, such as the sense organs, to the secondary psychological, which organize sensory input into formed percepts. Again, the structural aspects of memory include the so-called memory traces as well as the formal psychological organization of memories. The body schema can in this sense also be considered to be a structure—a frame of reference which informs us about our posture, provides the background frame of reference for purposive acts, and so on. In this context a "strategy" would also be a structure and, indeed, any learned link between sets of experiences or activities would imply the existence of some sort of structural connexion between them. Structures are essentially unknowable and exist outside consciousness. They can only become known to us indirectly through the formation of an ideational representation—in which case what we know is not the structure itself but its mental representation. In general a structure can be defined as a relatively permanent organization or an organization with a relatively slow rate of change.

Unfortunately the English term "experience" has more than one meaning. In this paper we do not refer to so-called life experience, that is, past training and learning, and the like, but rather to the content of purely subjective experience—the experiencing of the content of sensation, perception, memory and so on*. Thus a memory has both structural and experiential aspects, and the two should be sharply distinguished. Similarly, in regard

* In German there are different words for these two aspects of experience. In this paper we refer to *Erlebnis* rather then *Erfahrung*.

to the body image, we can distinguish between the subjective experience of our body at any one time, and the body schema which is the structural basis which lies behind, mediates, and gives form to the subjective experience.

If we learn to perform a particular voluntary intentional act (like reaching to pick up an object) we are not dealing with a simple and purely motor act. Motor activity and sensation are intimately connected. From the initiation of the action we experience a feedback of proprioceptive and other information which acts to guide the particular action. Similarly, motor activity accompanies such exercises as imagining oneself performing some activity, and this covert motor activity is related to the overt activity which would constitute the action if it were really performed. We all know how we change our posture when watching others move—a phenomenon that shows itself most dramatically when we watch ice-skating or a Western movie. The point which we wish to make here is that psychological structures have both a sensory and motor aspect, and that subjective experiences are highly correlated with particular forms of action, even though these actions may be restricted to covert trial actions. Thus one cannot speak of a mental image or experience without taking into account the actions or trial actions which accompany it and which are an intrinsic part of it.

It follows that when we speak of a wish we are not only speaking of the mental image of a desired state of affairs. A wish may carry with it a picture of what is desired, but also implies an impulse to act in a particular way, although this impulse may be inhibited before it reaches the threshold of overt activity. An exhibitionistic wish may, for example, be an impulse to expose oneself sexually—this action is usually restrained. One could say that in such a wish the ideomotor structures relating to self-representations and object representations, as well as those connected with the wish-fulfilling activities, are involved. A wish, therefore, implies a subjective representation of an action being propelled towards discharge and all that this involves. The force behind the wish can be conceptualized as the pressure or urgency which accompanies and propels the representation towards consciousness or motility. If the gratification of the wish provides a basic instinctual satisfaction (for example, of a sexual or aggressive sort) then we speak of an instinctual wish.

ESSENTIALS OF A BASIC PSYCHOANALYTIC MODEL

Fig. 1 shows the essentials of the basic model as it can now be formulated. Drive stimuli, arising from the inside, arouse instinctual wishes, the content of which is based on the experiences of situations and activities which have previously been associated with the reduction of instinctual tension and with the attainment of the appropriate gratification (see also below). External stimuli also arouse sensorimotor representations which are impelled towards discharge. It should be noted, however, that these so-called external stimuli are not truly external, as they create an effect through the arousal of internal impulses within the nervous system. Indeed, from a psychological point of view, all the stimuli which the psychologist locates outside the organism only *appear* to be the essential stimuli to which responses may be linked. All external stimuli act by arousing, in one way or another, internal signals which are the internal representations of the external world. If an external situation is to acquire meaning and significance, its internal perceptual representation must acquire that meaning.

Stimuli and information arising both as a result of changes in the external world and from the instinctual drives arouse associated sensorimotor representations (see left-hand side of Fig. 1) which are fragmentary and chaotic, being linked together only by processes of simple association (referred to by psychoanalysts as the primary process). Before being allowed to reach consciousness or motor discharge they are processed, modified, checked, organized and censored. There is an interesting parallel between the processes involved in organizing crude sensations and their associated memories into a final percept on the one hand, and the processes whereby the revival of infantile memories by drive stimuli are modified along their path to consciousness (as, for example, during dreaming).

Thus, from the point of view of psychoanalytic psychology, stimuli both from the external world and from the inner drives arouse internal signals which evoke sensorimotor representations. These representations are those that have previously been associated with the gaining of pleasure or with the avoidance of some form of unpleasure (for example subjective drive tension, anxiety, pain). The revival of these representations immediately presents a problem to the individual—are they to be allowed discharge, to flower into full action or into conscious experience, or not? And this applies as much to normal processes of perception as to the revival of past memories under the influence of the drives. "It seems that the central feature of the perceptual process is that it attempts to organize and structure the incoming data from the sense organs. In this way the ego deals with incoming stimulation in exactly the same way as it modifies latent dream thoughts and transforms them into manifest content. There is a 'perception work' corresponding to the 'dream work'. Indeed, this need not

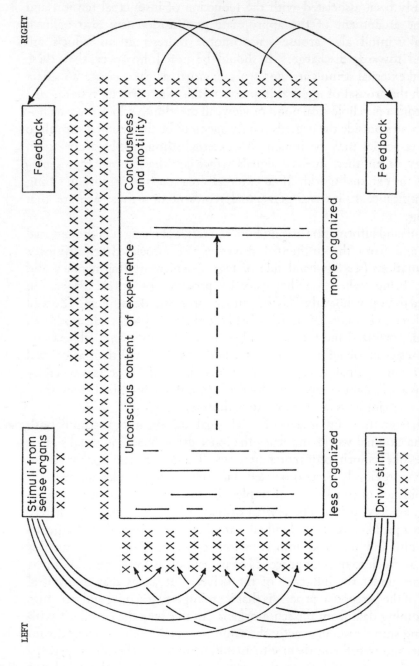

FIG. 1. Schematic representation of the proposed basic psychoanalytic model of the mental apparatus. X: structures in the general sense; they range from biological structures to psychological controlling and facilitating structures, and exist in all parts of the apparatus; vertical lines: unconscious and conscious ideomotor representations; it is only experiential content that can become conscious.

surprise us if we consider that the distinction between the various sources of excitation, between drive excitation and excitation from the real world, is only painstakingly built up in the infant over months and years." (Sandler, 1960a, p. 353).

Thus the distinction between the perception of reality and the hallucinatory revival of the memories of past experiences by the drives is a learned one; and this process of learning involves the development of psychological controlling structures based, of course, on appropriate inborn biological ones. The sum total of these controlling structures is what psychoanalysts usually refer to as the ego.

An essential part of this processing is the translation of input and primitive mental content into something which is reasonable or logical—which "makes sense". A primitive wish, or the content associated with it, may be fully inhibited (repressed) or may be absorbed into a thought or action which seems reasonable, logical and non-threatening, and which can then be allowed to proceed to discharge in consciousness or in action.

A distinction has been made between *structures* (which include the biological and psychological apparatuses, defence mechanisms, memory traces, schemata and so on) and *experiential content*, which embraces both ideational and "feeling" elements.*

There is thus a tendency to continuous movement from left to right in the schematic model shown in Fig. 1. On the left, primitive mental content is aroused as a response to inner stimuli (and outer stimuli must be treated as inner in this context). There will be a tendency for such primitive content to be propelled towards consciousness or action, that is, to move to the right in the diagram. During the course of this movement, the aroused content may be acted upon, turned back, deflected, modified, or processed in various ways.

Obviously the criteria upon which such processing is based—the ultimate motivations for it—are of crucial importance. Before discussing these it is relevant to make a further point which is vital to our model. No structure, once created, is ever lost (although it may be affected by normal processes of decay). Structures are continuously being modified on the basis of experience, but this modification comes about through the superimposition of further structures (which may retain substantial parts of the older ones). An essential component of these further structures is that they contain elements which are employed to inhibit the use of those structures which have been superseded.

* The term "feeling" is used here instead of affect, for the term "affect" often embraces both bodily and feeling aspects. The distinction between the two is important for the model discussed in this paper.

"By inhibition we refer here to some form of internal action which checks discharge along a particular pathway. This inhibition should not be considered as a static process—it has often been described, for example, in terms of the erection of dams which prevent discharge. We see it rather as a dynamic process, an internal checking action which follows a partial or trial discharge, a trial which may eventually come to be limited to a 'signal' discharge, or a 'sample' discharge. This is perfectly in accord with Freud's description of the role of inhibition in secondary process functioning given in *The Interpretation of Dreams* (1900, pp. 598–609). Although the trial action may be limited to a 'sample' action, it is nevertheless a covert internal action which is rapidly inhibited after it has been, in some way, evaluated by the unconscious ego. We can postulate that any overt discharge (whether in action, perception, imagination or thought) is preceded by processes of trial and inhibition. These may occur extremely quickly, and certainly outside conscious awareness, so that only the briefest moment of time may be involved. We shall ... put forward the argument that, even in this brief moment of time, trial forms of discharge are scanned and tentatively sampled by the ego. Unsatisfactory ones are normally rejected or inhibited, and suitable ones permitted some form of overt discharge in consciousness and motility." (Sandler and Joffe, 1967, pp. 263 and 264).

A hypothesis such as this is needed to account for aspects of regression and fixation. Progressive development involves the gradual inhibition of previous structured modes of activity and the substitution of revised ones. If we compare structures to computer machinery and programmes, then development and learning in general can be likened to the evolving of new computer programmes which also cut out (inhibit) aspects of previous ones. The older programmes remain, however, and may be utilized under special conditions. The later programmes may themselves become inhibited, and the past programmes re-utilized, which gives us a rather different view from the traditional one of the phenomenon of regression (cf. Sandler and Joffe, 1965).

THE SAFETY PRINCIPLE

It is clear today that Freud's pleasure principle is an amalgam of several different regulatory principles. It covers the seeking of sensual pleasure and the avoidance of unpleasure as well as being a principle of energic homoeostasis. Some ten years ago it was proposed that a further regulatory principle had to be invoked in order to account for certain forms of abnormal behaviour. This was referred to as the "safety principle" (Sandler, 1960a), and it also has direct relevance to theories of learning.

"We can speak of a successful act of sensory integration as one in which excitation (I speak now of stimulation from any source, from the id or the outer world) is smoothly and effectively dealt with by the ego. I want to suggest that such successful sensory integration is not only accompanied by anxiety-reduction, but also contributes to a background feeling . . . which can be referred to as one of safety or perhaps of security. I want to stress the positive character of this feeling (which need not, of course, be conscious) . . . . Genetically, this feeling must be a derivative of the earliest experiences of tension and satisfaction. It is a feeling of well-being, a sort of ego-tone. It is more than the mere absence of anxiety, and reflects, I believe, some fundamental quality of living matter which distinguishes it from the inanimate. It is a quality of feeling which we can oppose to the affect of anxiety, representing in a sense its polar opposite." (Sandler, 1960a, p. 353).

In the same paper some of the steps taken by the ego to deal with any reduction in the background tone of safety feeling were described, and the conclusion was drawn that there could be seen in all of this the workings of what might be called a safety principle. "This would simply reflect the fact that the ego makes every effort to maintain a minimum level of safety feelings . . . through the development and control of integrative processes within the ego, foremost among these being perception." (p. 355).

It was suggested that any experience of anxiety or disorganization lowers the level of safety feeling and that we may see the development of types of activity which at first seem to be inappropriate and unadaptive, but which are in fact adaptive in that they are aimed at restoring some minimum level of safety feeling. Included in this are, for example, some of the stereotyped and bizarre forms of behaviour shown by psychotics, who attempt in this way to control their activities in order to obtain a higher degree of perceptual security. They have to create a stable perceptual situation by hiding in a corner, clutching a doll or repeating a ritual, and must avoid activity which would lead to disorganized activity or the experience of loss of safety feeling.

The need to maintain a feeling state of safety (which is quite different from pleasure in direct instinctual gratification) is of enormous importance in learning and in development in general. The need to maintain safety gains dominance over the need to gain pleasure, and indeed the conflict between these different needs is probably the forerunner of neurotic conflict in general. An activity which leads to pleasure may be inhibited if it lowers the level of safety feeling. From the point of view of learning, it would seem that the maintenance of safety feeling is the most potent reinforcing agent, after a certain level of development has been reached.

Kohler (1964) and others have shown that it is "things of action" which are first organized in the child's perceptual world; we can take this further by suggesting that the whole of the representational world is created through the link between ideomotor representations and feeling states. Even the highest form of symbolic representation is only meaningful, and indeed is only created, through its direct or indirect link with feelings. In this sense there is no such thing as a purely cognitive process. A successful mathematical manipulation is associated with feelings of rightness, and these in turn have links with feelings of safety, of good feelings and of "function pleasure" (Bühler, 1927).

This view of adaptation (Joffe and Sandler, 1968) implies that the processes indicated towards the left in Fig. 1 are constant disruptors to the person's basic feeling state of safety and well-being, and that the aim, function or purpose of adaptation is to maintain a basic stability of the central feeling state. Of course the individual will allow his immediate impulses to proceed if these lead to pleasure, but only if at the same time they do not radically lower the safety level. If, as the impulse proceeds, there is a drop or threatened drop in his level of safety feeling, then he is motivated to apply the appropriate psychological structures in order to change the content of his representational world into a form which is safer, even if it means giving up direct instinctual gratifications. Thus, whatever he becomes conscious of, or what he finally actually does, is related to this regulatory criterion. The structures which he uses may be the ordinary perceptual or cognitive structures aimed at the avoidance of perceptual or cognitive dissonance, or they may be the employment of defence mechanisms in such degree that neurotic or even psychotic disturbances ensue (as in the massive use of projection in paranoid illnesses).

An important consideration will now be introduced. We have said that structures are intrinsically non-conscious. But the experiential content of the representational world is also largely unconscious. However, it can become conscious if attention is directed towards it provided it has not, for any reason, been made inaccessible to consciousness. All this implies a process of knowing, recognizing, thinking and feeling outside consciousness. Evidence is accumulating to substantiate this assumption, in spite of the philosophical objection which may be raised against such concepts as unconscious feelings.

THE BRIDGE BETWEEN PSYCHOANALYTIC AND LEARNING THEORY

What we have tried to do so far is to prepare the foundations on one side of the theoretical bridge between psychoanalysis and learning theory: we shall now attempt some of the bridge-building itself.

(1) Learning can be defined as progressive structural modification. If we take the view that no structure is ever lost, then unlearning, or extinction, would imply a process of inhibition. This allows us to explain both the reappearance of extinguished responses in experimental learning situations and the clinical phenomenon of regression.

(2) The elements which become linked in processes of learning are not stimulus and response but rather one ideomotor representation and another. Such learning can occur outside consciousness, but learning only takes place through (conscious or unconscious) changes in the experiential content of the individual's representational world.

(3) The reinforcing agents in the linking of one ideomotor representation with another are changes in feeling states. Gaining pleasure leads to reinforcement, as does the avoidance of pain or unpleasure, but dominant over this is the process of increasing or maintaining the safety feeling.*

(4) There is a process of scanning of the unconscious area of the representational world; in other words, of evaluating the ideomotor representations in terms of the feeling states or feeling signals associated with them. This occurs extremely rapidly, and a representation is normally only permitted discharge if the feeling state which accompanies it is not too disruptive of safety and well-being.

(5) Some structures may evolve in order to solve ongoing inner conflict. But they may persist and be utilized in order to maintain safety feeling even though the original impulses which entered into their formation are no longer operative in the same way. It is likely that the latter structures are those which are most amenable to change through behaviour therapy. Thus a neurotic symptom (and the structures which subserve it) may be directed towards solving, for example, an ongoing conflict between an instinctual wish and the internal (super-ego) standards of the individual. But it may equally function at a later date as a method of producing safety feeling, and if other methods of providing safety feeling are available then

---

* The relevance of this to masochistic behaviour is apparent. An activity which leads to correctly anticipated pain may be pursued if it leads to concealed sexual pleasure. But it may also be instituted if, in spite of the pain created by it, it leads to a heightening of the level of safety feeling (cf. Sandler, 1959).

10*

a different and more comfortable solution may be created and utilized, and the employment of the older symptom–structure inhibited.*

(6) Although the processes of adaptation described above have an immediate "here-and-now" quality, the capacity to manipulate trial actions in thought (as is evident in man) within or outside consciousness, and to assess the feeling signals associated with these trial ideomotor representations, leads to the function of anticipation and prediction through thought. This, in turn, provides a further dimension to the learning process.

CONCLUSIONS

We have been guilty of gross oversimplification in this presentation, but this is because we believe simplification to be an essential part of the ongoing construction of theory. The processes referred to are complex and continuous—every time one sees or does something new, a new structure is formed. We hope that our presentation may have contributed in some small part to those processes of structure formation which constitute development in our various fields.

ACKNOWLEDGEMENTS

We acknowledge with gratitude the contributions of our colleagues in the Hampstead Index Research Groups and in the Research Group on Motivation at the Instituut voor Kinderpsychotherapie, Leyden.

REFERENCES

BÜHLER, K. (1927). Die Krise der Psychologie. Jena: Fischer.

FREUD, S. (1900). In Die Traumdeutung. Leipzig: Franz Deuticke. (1953. The Interpretation of Dreams, in Standard Edition, vol. 5, pp. 598–609, ed. Strachey, J. London: Hogarth Press.)

FREUD, S. (1923). In Das Ich und das Es. Leipzig: Internationaler psychoanalytischer Verlag. (1961. The Ego and the Id, in Standard Edition, vol. 19, pp. 3–66. ed. Strachey, J. London: Hogarth Press.)

FREUD, S. (1926). Hemmung, Symptom und Angst. Leipzig: Internationaler psychoanalytischer Verlag. (1959. Inhibitions, Symptoms and Anxiety, in Standard Edition, vol. 20, pp. 77–175. ed. Strachey, J. London: Hogarth Press.)

JOFFE, W. G., and SANDLER, J. (1965). Psychoanal. Study Child, 20, 394–424.

JOFFE, W. G., and SANDLER, J. (1967). J. Child Psychother., 2, 56–66.

JOFFE, W. G., and SANDLER, J. (1968). Int. J. Psycho-Analysis, 49, in press.

KOHLER, I. (1964). The Formation and Transformation of the Perceptual World. Psychological Issues, Monograph 12. New York: International Universities Press.

SANDLER, J. (1959). In The Nature of Stress Disorder, pp. 187–195. London: Hutchinson.

SANDLER, J. (1960a). Int. J. Psycho-Analysis, 41, 352–356.

* All systems and techniques of psychotherapy (including behaviour therapy) abound with potential alternative safety-giving solutions which can be adopted by the patient. It would be instructive to examine such procedures as desensitization in this light.

SANDLER, J. (1960b). *Psychoanal. Study Child*, **15**, 128–162.
SANDLER, J. (1962a). *Int. J. Psycho-Analysis*, **43**, 287–291.
SANDLER, J. (1962b). *Br. J. med. Psychol.*, **35**, 91–100.
SANDLER, J., HOLDER, A., and MEERS, D. (1963). *Psychoanal. Study Child*, **18**, 139–158.
SANDLER, J., and JOFFE, W. G. (1965). *Psychoanal. Study Child*, **20**, 425–438.
SANDLER, J., and JOFFE, W. G. (1967). *Bull. Menninger Clin.*, **31**, 257–271.
SANDLER, J., and ROSENBLATT, B. (1962). *Psychoanal. Study Child*, **17**, 128–145.

DISCUSSION

Hinde: I expected to be a privileged bystander at a match between two teams, but I am amazed to find myself unable to determine which side the various protagonists are on. The scheme that you have presented, Dr. Sandler, closely resembles D. Hebb's scheme of the organization of behaviour (1949. *The Organization of Behavior*. New York: Wiley). You have added a few computer words and some material from the Held-Hein theory of visuomotor control (see, for example Held, R., and Hein, A. [1963]. *J. comp. physiol. Psychol.*, **56**, 872–876), but, to mention just one similarity between your model and Hebb's hypothesis, what Hebb called organized phase sequences seem to correspond exactly to what you call the basic feeling state.

Sandler: Hebb's work has undoubtedly influenced me and I am glad to acknowledge this. The essence of *feeling* as the consequence and reinforcer of phase sequence and organized behaviour is critical; the ultimate criterion of adaptive behaviour can be related to the feeling associated with the behaviour. The disorganized behaviour in schizophrenia, for example, cannot be understood unless we see the disorder not only as an expression of unconscious impulses breaking through, but as a desperate, sometimes frantic, attempt to maintain a feeling of safety. Man's adaptation to his external environment is a phylogenetic and ontogenetic consequence of his need to maintain basic elements in his feeling state. Disruption of this state is caused by changes in the external world interacting with internal psychic mechanisms. If we could achieve the basic feeling state of safety or well-being by any less painful means than the conflict between pleasure and safety, we would do so. Drug addiction is perhaps one way of finding safety because the instinctual drives, through an unknown mechanism, lose their intensity in drug addicts, even though the long-term consequences of addiction are ruinous. Similarly, for the autistic child who has to clutch a doll or beat himself, the self-infliction of pain may create safety even though pleasure is sacrificed thereby. This self-damaging behaviour, which seems completely inappropriate, is understandable when we realize that its very predictability maintains the feelings of safety.

Miller: Could you expand this conclusion, Dr. Sandler?

Sandler: My comments here exclude those types of masochistic behaviour in which the pain provokes concealed sexual gratification. Treatment of autistic children at the Hampstead Child-Therapy Clinic (unpublished) has shown that if we can create a controllable situation which, presumably, induces feelings of safety, the need for self-damaging behaviour may disappear. The pain seems to be the price these children pay for safety.

Miller: An analogous situation may arise when a rat has to cross a shock-producing grid to reach food. The food is analogous to the basic safety feeling; the rat tolerates the shock to get to the food, but does not actually *want* the shock. I had thought that a relatively small self-induced pain in autistic children could work as a signal that a more severe pain had been avoided, but I had not thought of the pain as the price of safety. We must infer this mechanism from your comment that a controllable situation abolishes self-damaging behaviour in children. If the autistic child abandons this behaviour when we satiate the need for safety by providing acceptable alternative security, then the motive behind the self-destructive behaviour must have been the need for safety. Is that right?

Sandler: Yes, but I differentiate between gaining pleasure during the process of satisfying instinctual needs, and the feeling of safety and security.

Hunt: J. Gibbon (1967. *J. exp. Analysis Behav.*, **10**, 451-460) studied rats under precise controlled conditions from this point of view. A rat could be trained to press a lever to abolish a signal stimulus which indicated that a shock was coming. The price for eliminating this warning stimulus was getting the shock when the lever was pressed. In effect, the rats learned to work for and take a shock to achieve a shock-free period in the apparatus.

Miller: I have also had similar results (Miller, N. E. [1951]. In *Handbook of Experimental Psychology*, p. 443, ed. Stevens, S. S. New York: Wiley). Rats were put in an experimental alley; at the start of the alley they received electric shocks and at the far end they escaped from them. The rats learned to run forward to escape the shocks. Then the shock-producing area was shifted to the middle of the alley so that when the rat ran forward he received the shock which he could escape by running still farther forward. The same act (running forward) led the rat into the shock and then was reinforced by allowing him to escape from it. In these circumstances, the rats continued to give themselves electric shocks. J. T. Gwinn (1949. *J. exp. Psychol.*, **39**, 260-269) and J. S. Brown (1968. In *Punishment*, in press, eds. Campbell, B. A., and Church, R. M. New York: Appleton-Century-Crofts) have studied in much more detail the conditions under which such a vicious circle can be maintained.

Sandler: With Dr. Joffe (Sandler, J., and Joffe, W. G. [1967]. *Bull. Menniger Clin.*, **31**, 257-271) I have studied these phenomena in connexion with regression, which has been explained traditionally in terms of a return to earlier types of instinctual drives. But regression often also seems to be a return to a situation in which the patient feels safe. In compulsive masturbation in adolescents or schizophrenics, for example, the sexual drive may be exhausted but masturbation continues because the person acts on the assumption that sexual stimulation will lead to a feeling of safety and satiation. In the search for safety, subjects often ignore or even put up with the unpleasant experiences associated with this search.

Miller: J. B. Watson and R. Rayner (1920. *J. exp. Psychol.*, **3**, 1-14), in the classical experiment in which they conditioned a child to fear a rabbit, noted that when they first struck the anvil behind the child's head, he put his thumb in his mouth. And as long as the child could keep his thumb in his mouth, he could not be frightened (he was a very stolid child). They had to prevent him from sucking his thumb in order to do the experiment on conditioning. It would be useful to determine experimentally if the mechanism by which fear is inhibited when the human baby puts its thumb in its mouth is innate or due to previous associations with feeding.

Similarly, L. A. Rosenblum and H. F. Harlow (1963. *Psychol. Rep.*, **12**, 83-85) have described how infant monkeys jump on the mother and hug it. If they are given aversive air-blasts whenever they do this, they cling all the tighter. As I have pointed out (Miller, N. E. 1963. *Psychol. Rep.*, **12**, 773-774), this behaviour, which Rosenblum and Harlow thought was paradoxical, becomes understandable in the light of evidence that the infant monkey has species-specific tendencies to cling when frightened, because its fear is reduced by the sensory feedback from the clinging. Are there any parallels to this sort of behaviour in other animals, Professor Hinde?

Hinde: There are parallels in many species.

Sandler: Clinging to the mother is associated with withdrawal of attention from the air-blast.

Hinde: It is not proven that clinging is associated with the withdrawal of attention from the frightening stimulus. The most conspicuous thing about baby monkeys who are subjected to such a stimulus and cling to their mothers is that they are able to look at the stimulus while they cling.

Sandler: Let me modify my previous statement: clinging to the mother provides enough safety feeling for the baby to tolerate looking at the frightening object. Behaviour therapy may give the patient a sort of thumb to put in his mouth, thus providing enough safety feeling for him to work towards solving his problems.

Foss: J. Bruner (1968, personal communication) claims that when a child sucks the nipple he stops looking, and when a visual stimulus distracts him he stops sucking. In other words, sucking and viewing in a baby are incompatible.

Hinde: But sucking is not the same as hanging on to the nipple. The nipple provides comfort as well as food.

Sandler: This is an essential distinction.

Miller: Further experimental investigation and clarification are needed in this area.

Hunt: W. Kesson and G. Mandler (1961. *Psychol. Rev.*, **68**, 396-404) have suggested that stimulation of the mouth has a specific inhibiting effect on the periodic upset of neonates. Since neonates have had only limited experience to learn from, this specific inhibition may be innate. Dr. Sandler, what part of the behaviours you have described as inducing safety feelings is learned and what proportion is innate?

Sandler: The basic patterns are innate but can be modified by learning.

Kubie: Although the number of events experienced by a neonate is quantitatively small, each single event is highly charged. The experience of changing from darkness to light, for example, is sudden and complete, and the rate and amplitude of this change are enormous (Homburger, E. [1937]. *Psychoanal. Q.*, **6**, 139-214).

Miller: How much behaviour is innate and how much is learned is not so important, provided both mechanisms are available. I have changed my earlier views (see Miller, N. E., and Dollard, J. [1941]. *Social Learning and Imitation*. New Haven: Yale University Press) that curiosity and various social motivations are entirely acquired as learned drives and learned reinforcements. I now think that these behaviours have an innate basis, analogous to that of hunger and thirst, and are not solely dependent on learning but only subject to channelling by it (Miller, N. E. [1959]. In *Psychology: A Study of a Science*, study 1, pp. 262-272, ed. Koch, S., New York: McGraw-Hill). My current opinion is that man probably has more numerous and complex innate components to his behaviour than other animals have, rather than less. The psychoanalysts have indicated the rich and organized instinctual tendencies in man and his strong genetic endowment for both selfish aggression and altruistic love.

My emphasis on the superiority of the innate perceptual and response mechanisms in man is not at all incompatible with a greater role for learning in his behaviour than in that of other animals. If an animal has only one innately organized form of locomotor response (for example, hopping in the kangaroo) it will be extremely difficult to modify this by learning. But an animal like the horse, with a considerable variety of innately organized locomotor responses (walking, trotting, galloping and so on) will be much easier to train because one type of gait can be rewarded preferentially to the others.

Sackett: Dr. Sandler, your model is admirable because it seems feasible to subject it to experimental investigation. You have implied that the conflict between safety and pleasure is the basic and essential condition for behavioural and psychosexual development. Is that right?

Sandler: This conflict is one of the necessary conditions but there are others.

Sackett: In principle, we would test this theory by rearing an animal so that its homoeostatic mechanisms are always at balance level. This animal is never hungry or thirsty, the food in its stomach is always at the optimum level, it is never too hot or too cold and never irritated by problems that need solving. In short, such an animal would be easily able to deal with the few stimuli in its environment. We could then test its development. Would you predict that such an animal would not mature psychologically?

Sandler: With such an undemanding external environment the animal certainly would not reach full psychological maturity. But in an experimental set-up you could not control the internal, developmentally determined disrupters of the feeling state. When the child is ready to walk, for example, innate drives to locomotion will inevitably disrupt his feeling. Every time a child, or a monkey, moves its head, say, changes occur in the internal sensory input. The child who has inner sources of safety can allow himself to explore solutions more readily than the child whose internal sources of safety are threatened. These internal sources of safety are therefore closely related to learning. Another similar area involves the first sexual experiences of the child. When a three- or four-year-old boy experiences his first erections he suddenly has to deal with sexual sensations.

Kaufman: Another reason that an animal cannot be reared in a completely predictable environment concerns the autonomic internal input—pulse rate, stomach movements and so on; in early life these sources of sensory input are continually changing the internal environment.

Sackett: But if the individual is protected from safety-pleasure conflicts during development will his intellectual growth be better or worse than if he is not?

Sandler: A child who is able to explore his environment freely and fairly aggressively, without diminishing his sources of basic safety feeling, may retain this freedom to explore (in activity or in thought) throughout his life because he has found appropriate techniques for doing this. If a child has a sufficient level of safety feeling, from external or internal sources, then safety-pleasure conflicts may be a profound stimulus to his development. In contrast, a child who has had to cope with too severe and extreme safety-pleasure conflicts in early life may restrict himself to stereotyped types of behaviour because he is frightened of his drives and exploratory impulses. He may thus develop as a restricted personality. Different combinations of internal processes and external environmental structure consequently influence development in quite different ways. So your question cannot have a simple "yes or no" answer. The best way to test these hypotheses is to set up experiments in which uncertainty (which reduces safety feeling) is the measurable variable. We need to find out how much pain animals reared under different conditions will put up with to avoid uncertainty. I cannot accept that you could rear an animal in whom the internal drive disrupters of the basic feeling state were controlled. An animal maintained in a state of unconsciousness from birth would be profoundly affected, but this is a different experiment.

Frank: There must be an optimum, but not maximal, degree of safety or people would not subject themselves to the risks connected with exploring, climbing mountains and so on.

Sackett: You have still not completely answered my question, Dr. Sandler. Are the causal variables that determine behavioural development innate, or acquired through safety-pleasure conflicts, and is there an optimum level for these conflicts? I would like to use this concept of safety-pleasure conflicts as a set of variables I can manipulate and measure, but I need some clear testable hypotheses about their effect before I set up my experiments. What would you predict about the psychological development of groups of monkeys whose sensory input in early life was completely predictable, completely unpredictable and of variable predictability?

Sandler: That the animals with variably predictable input would develop techniques aimed at increasing certainty and would show greater psychological development than animals in the other two groups. An example of "hyper-security" is seen in children who have been given a bottle of milk immediately, whenever they are hungry, from birth until the age of two or three years. Such a child may become "orally fixated". What has happened is that the mother (by supplying unlimited comfort) has warded off stresses that the child might normally develop mechanisms for dealing with. This is obviously harmful for normal development. The idea of an uninterrupted state of well-being, in life or in the laboratory, is an unobtainable goal, but if it could exist, one might expect that little or no psychological development would occur.

Sackett: But one can approximate to this goal.

Sandler: I agree that one might approach it by trying to vary the conditions of safety experimentally.

Miller: We should devise experiments in primates to test your model, Dr. Sandler, and use our results to reassess the problems of disturbed development in man.

Kubie: The answers to such questions should be looked for through study of psychiatric illness in man. We can observe the profound effect of emotional deprivation by neglectful parents on the development of, say, an autistic child. The problem is to translate such clinical observations into more precise, objective, qualitative and quantitative measures.

Kiernan: Dr. Sandler, could you comment on the relationship between your notion of safety and the concept of control? A situation in which an individual actively participates in controlling his environment is very different from one in which he is passively maintained in safety. One can be safe and bored or, to put it another way, one can be completely safe but unable to control the conditions under which one lives. In Dr. Sackett's proposed experiment, the monkeys in which the predictability of sensory input varies could be allowed to vary the input themselves, or simply have variable input imposed upon them. If techniques for developing increasing certainty are to be acquired by these monkeys then the former alternative would be necessary. The crucial variable may be the extent to which the individual can control his environment, and hence feel safe, rather than the state of what might be called "imposed safety".

Sandler: Successful control is an important source of safety, and this can be a stimulus not only to active mastery of the environment but, in extreme cases, to the compulsion to control others very rigorously indeed. Normal psychological development involves control as a central feature and this is very relevant to the creation and maintenance of safety feeling.

Kaufman: Safety could be defined as that momentary condition when a perfect match exists between inner psychic reality and external experience.

Sandler: I agree. Safety is experienced when we perceive something that we expect to perceive. To walk and to feel solid ground beneath our feet generates a constant feeling of safety.

VISCERAL LEARNING AND OTHER ADDITIONAL FACTS POTENTIALLY APPLICABLE TO PSYCHOTHERAPY

NEAL E. MILLER

Rockefeller University, New York

THE main additional fact of learning that I shall discuss is a recently discovered one, namely, that in spite of a strong traditional belief to the contrary, glandular and visceral responses are subject to instrumental learning. But first I would like to discuss one other possibility.

POSITIVE INDUCTION

A remarkable number of the laws of learning that Pavlov and his students formulated have been verified and found to be applicable to many types of behaviour. But one such principle, that of positive induction, has been almost completely neglected in the Western countries until very recently. According to Pavlov (1927, p. 188), the occurrence of the negative stimulus in a discrimination has the inductive effect of strengthening the excitability of the positive stimulus. Recently, Senf and I (Senf and Miller, 1967) have verified this principle in one classical conditioning and two instrumental learning situations, adding a number of controls which, as far as we could tell, were missing from the original experiments. Further, a phenomenon probably basically the same as positive induction has been noted in a number of experiments on operant conditioning, and given the title of "behavioral (behavioural) contrast" (Reynolds, 1963). Behavioural contrast shows itself in a more rapid rate of performance during a cue signalling a moderately favourable schedule when that schedule is presented in conjunction with a cue signalling a very unfavourable schedule than when it is presented in conjunction with a cue signalling a very favourable one.

Certain clinically significant phenomena seem to be analogous to positive induction and behavioural contrast. On several occasions I can remember being caught in a difficult situation climbing a mountain, and achieving considerable relief from fear by contrasting the current situation with previously still more difficult ones which I had survived. Similarly, it has often been noted that a person's neurotic fears disappear when he is confronted with strong enough realistic dangers in life.

Reactions to a cue that is negative in a Pavlovian discrimination, because responses to it are not reinforced, show considerable functional similarity to the reactions to a cue that is negative because of associations with punishment (Wagner, 1966). Are the responses to the latter type of negative cue subject to inductive or contrast effects? If so, it is conceivable that a subject who had learned, either during an earlier phase of life or as a result of chance association of a punishment with a negative cue, a discrimination between such a cue and one signalling positive reinforcement, might in certain circumstances have his resistance to the extinction of the currently unreinforced and unrealistic fear of the negative cue increased by induction from the reinforcement accurately predicted by the positive cue. Conversely, it seems possible that the extinction of the non-reinforced fears to the negative cue might be hastened by contrasting it with a negative cue to which fear was reinforced. This possibility could be tested out experimentally in animals, and indeed we need much more experimental research specifying the laws determining the most effective ways of eliminating fears (Miller, 1964).

Translated to the therapeutic situation, this possibility means that a therapist who warns a patient about realistic dangers may thereby be more reassuring about unrealistic ones, and that a punishment for socially inappropriate behaviour may not always generalize to produce fear of socially appropriate behaviour; such a punishment could even have the opposite positively-inducing contrast effect of helping the extinction of a maladaptive fear of socially appropriate behaviour. More work is needed to determine the conditions under which stimulus generalization is dominant and those under which positive induction, also called behavioural contrast, is dominant.

GLANDULAR AND VISCERAL LEARNING

I now come to the main subject of my paper, namely, the modification of glandular and visceral responses by instrumental training.

A strong traditional belief in our culture has been that reason and volition are superior while emotions and visceral responses are inferior. This belief goes back at least as far as Plato with his superior rational soul in the head above and inferior souls in the body below. Much later, the great French neuroanatomist Bichat (1800) made a distinction between the cerebrospinal nervous system of the brain and spinal cord, and the chain of ganglia which he referred to as "little brains", supposedly independent of the cerebrospinal system. He called this chain of ganglia the vegetative nervous system, indicating his opinion that it, and the emotional and visceral responses it controlled, were inferior.

Still later, students of learning distinguished between a lower form of learning called classical conditioning, in which the reinforcement is by an unconditioned stimulus that has to be able to elicit the specific response to be learned, and a superior form of learning, believed to be responsible for voluntary behaviour, in which the reinforcement has the property of strengthening any immediately preceding response. This superior type of learning has been called trial-and-error learning, operant conditioning or instrumental learning.

Finally, these three invidious distinctions have been coalesced in the strong traditional belief that the superior type of instrumental learning involved in the superior voluntary behaviour is possible only for skeletal responses mediated by the superior cerebrospinal nervous system; and, conversely, that the inferior classical conditioning is the only kind of learning possible for the inferior, presumably involuntary, visceral and emotional responses mediated by the inferior autonomic nervous system (Kimble, 1961; Konorski and Miller, 1937; Mowrer, 1947; Skinner, 1938).

A somewhat similar invidious distinction is found in psychiatry. Some, though not all, psychiatrists have made a sharp distinction between the hysterical and other symptoms that are mediated by the cerebrospinal nervous system, and the psychosomatic symptoms that are mediated by the autonomic nervous system. Psychosomatic symptoms are supposed to be direct, physiological consequences of the type and intensity of the patient's emotions and not subject to the higher type of symbolic control involved in other symptoms (cf. Alexander, 1950).

Theory and exploratory experiments

For many years my version of learning theory has assumed only one kind of learning, and therefore has logically demanded that instrumental training procedures should be able to produce the learning of any visceral responses that could be affected by classical conditioning procedures (Dollard and Miller, 1950; Miller, 1951; Miller and Dollard, 1941). But it was only about 10 years ago that I began experimental work on this problem. Since it seemed unlikely that the rigorous controls needed to rule out mediation through skeletal responses could be achieved with human subjects, I decided to work first with animals.

Since the preliminary, promising but inconclusive, results and the various difficulties encountered have been described elsewhere (Miller, 1966), I shall only list a few of the main difficulties. Perhaps the chief of these was the firm belief of my students and research assistants that such learning was impossible, so that they resisted working on the problem. Another difficulty was that the use of rewards with strong unconditioned effects obscured instrumental learning. Yet another difficulty was the assumption that such learning would be more difficult when the rat was paralysed by curare than when it was relatively free-moving, so that it would be better to demonstrate learning first in the latter type of preparation, leaving the former for a later, more rigorous test. Eventually we found that the training under curare was actually much easier. I mention these difficulties because, so often, published reports of research do not give students a realistic idea of how exploring the unknown may involve a long period of groping around in marshes and thickets before one finds the trail that leads to progress.

Salivation

In an experiment that finally yielded positive results, Alfredo Carmona and I started by using food to reward hungry dogs for either increasing or decreasing their rate of salivation (Miller and Carmona, 1967). But the food elicited so much salivation that it seemed extremely difficult (perhaps impossible) to use food to train dogs to decrease their rate of salivation. Therefore we eventually changed and used water as a reward for mildly thirsty dogs, after finding that the water had no appreciable unconditioned effect on the rate of salivation. Rewarding one group of dogs every time they showed a burst of salivation, and progressively requiring larger bursts to achieve the criterion, we were able to train them approximately to double their rate of salivation. Using the same method to reward another group of dogs for progressively longer pauses without salivation, we were able to train them to reduce their rate of salivation to approximately one-fifth of the initial rate. The training was slow, needing 40 days, but the highly reliable changes in opposite directions ruled out any simple explanation in terms of classical conditioning.

Although the dogs were not obviously cheating by panting or making chewing movements, those rewarded for increases in salivation seemed more aroused, while those rewarded for decreases seemed more drowsy. When we tried to rule out skeletal movements by paralysing them with curare, we found that this drug had two effects, both of which were peculiarly unfortunate for our experiment. Curare elicited such copious and constant salivation that there seemed to be no chance of further increasing the rate by rewarding increases and little likelihood of decreasing it by rewarding decreases. Further, the salivation was so viscous that it clogged up our recording apparatus.

Heart rate

At this time, Jay Trowill (1967) was showing great courage and resourcefulness in working with me on procedures for rewarding changes in a different response—heart rate—in rats with skeletal muscles paralysed by d-tubocurarine chloride and maintained on artificial respiration. Since there are not too many ways to reward such rats, he used direct electrical stimulation of the medial forebrain bundle at the level of the ventromedial nucleus. He secured statistically reliable changes in the correct direction in both the group rewarded for increases and the one rewarded for decreases, but the differences were small, only approximately 5 per cent. To secure larger changes, DiCara and I (Miller and DiCara, 1967) modified the procedure slightly by immediately rewarding first very small changes and then progressively larger ones. In this way, we secured changes averaging 20 per cent in each of the rewarded directions during 90 minutes of training. Further, we found that, at the end of 45 additional minutes of training, the changes in the required direction were larger during the time-in stimulus, which indicated that a heart rate reaching the criterion would be rewarded, than they were during the time-out stimulus, which indicated that no reward would be delivered.

In the experiments on heart rate, the changes in opposite directions ruled out any interpretation in terms of classical conditioning, while the paralysis by curare ruled out any mediation by feedback from the overt performance of skeletal responses. There remained, however, the possibility that the changes were by-products of shifts in some general factor, such as the level of activation. The next step, therefore, was to determine the specificity of visceral learning, an interesting question in its own right and one whose answer would throw light on the possibility of mediation through such a general factor.

Intestinal contractions versus heart rate

After first determining that either increases or decreases in intestinal contractions could be secured by rewarding appropriate changes, Ali Banuazizi and I performed an experiment in which both heart rate and intestinal contractions were recorded but only one of these two responses was rewarded (Miller and Banuazizi, 1968). The results (see Figs. 1 and 2) indicate that the group rewarded for increased intestinal contraction learned an increase, the group rewarded for decreased contraction learned a decrease, but neither group showed appreciable changes in heart rate. Conversely, the group rewarded for increases in heart rate showed an increase, the group rewarded for decreases showed a decrease, but neither group showed changes in intestinal contraction.

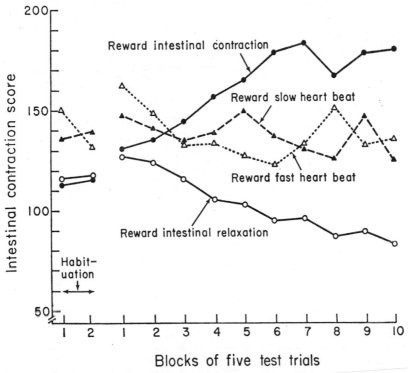

FIG. I. When increases or decreases, respectively, in spontaneous intestinal contraction are rewarded, changes in the appropriate direction are produced; when a different response—heart rate—is rewarded, intestinal contractions are unaffected. (Fig. reproduced from Miller and Banuazizi, 1968 [Fig. 3, p. 5], by kind permission of the editors, *J. comp. physiol. Psychol.*, and the American Psychological Association).

All twelve of the rats in the experiment showed reliable changes in the rewarded direction, most of this learning was highly specific, and a statistically reliable negative correlation showed that the better the rewarded visceral response had been learned, the less was the change that occurred during learning in the different, non-rewarded response. Such results clearly rule out any mediation by such general factors as the level of activation.

To make sure that the visceral learning of rats paralysed by curare was not peculiarly limited to reward by electrical stimulation of the brain, we next performed experiments showing that the escape from and/or avoidance of mild electric shocks could be used to reinforce increases or decreases, respectively, in either heart rate (DiCara and Miller, 1968*a*) or intestinal contractions (Banuazizi, 1968). Another experiment showed that learned changes in heart rate could be retained for at least three months (DiCara and Miller, 1968*b*).

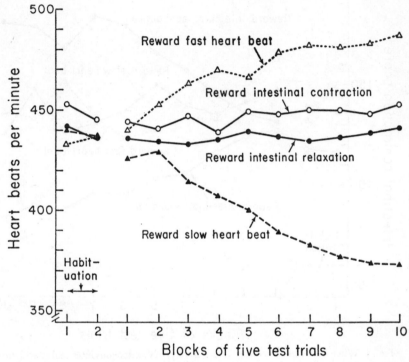

FIG. 2. When increases or decreases, respectively, in heart rate are rewarded, the rate changes in the appropriate direction; when a different response—intestinal contraction —is rewarded, no changes in heart rate are produced. (Fig. reproduced from Miller and Banuazizi, 1968 [Fig. 4, p. 5], by kind permission of the editors, *J. comp. physiol. Psychol.*, and the American Psychological Association).

Responses by the kidney

Encouraged by these successes, we decided to see whether the rate of formation of urine by the kidney could be changed in the curarized, water-loaded rat, with a chronic catheter eliminating the bladder, and changes rewarded by electrical stimulation of the brain (Miller and DiCara, 1968). After the results on the first few rats had clearly shown that such changes could be produced, we decided to add to the experiment in order to track down the mechanism of the change.

As Fig. 3 shows, changes in the rate of urine formation were not related to changes in blood pressure but were related to whether increases or decreases had been rewarded. Similar results ruled out the effects of heart rate.

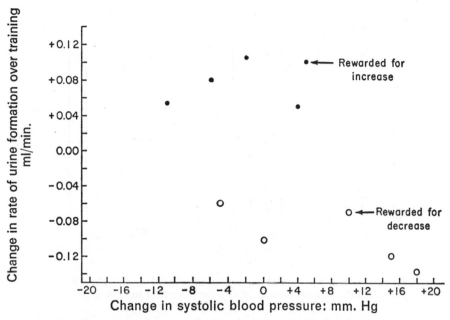

FIG. 3. Rate of urine formation as a function of reward for increase or decrease (of urine formation) rather than for changes in blood pressure. (From data by Miller and DiCara, 1968.)

As the first set of bars in Fig. 4 shows, the rate of filtration, measured by [14C]-inulin, increased when increases in urine formation were rewarded and decreased when decreases were rewarded; we have already seen that the changes in the rate of filtration were not produced by changes in blood pressure or heart rate. The second set of bars (Fig. 4) shows that they were achieved by changes in the rate of renal blood flow as measured by [3H]*p*-aminohippuric acid. When increases in urine formation were rewarded, the blood flow through the kidney increased; when decreases were rewarded, the blood flow through the kidney decreased. Since this change in blood flow was not accompanied by changes in blood pressure or heart rate, it must have been achieved by vasodilatation and vasoconstriction, respectively, of the renal arteries. That this vasomotor change was at least somewhat specific is shown by the fact that there was no difference between the two groups in the vasomotor responses in the tail.

The final set of bars in Fig. 4 shows that when decreases in urine formation were rewarded a more concentrated urine with higher osmolarity was formed. Since the slower passage of urine through the renal tubules would afford more opportunity for reabsorption of water, this does not necessarily

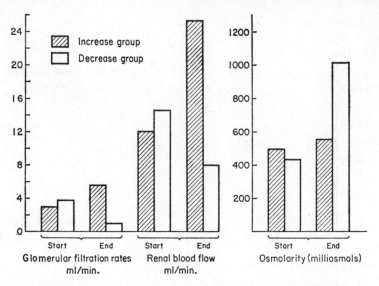

Fig. 4. Effect of instrumental training on filtration rate, renal blood flow, and osmolarity of urine formed. (From data by Miller and DiCara, 1968.)

mean an increased secretion of antidiuretic hormone. When an increased rate of urine formation was rewarded, the urine was not more dilute (this would have been indicated by decreased osmolarity); therefore, the increase in formation cannot be accounted for in this experiment by an inhibition in the secretion of antidiuretic hormone. Since the rats were water-loaded in order to secure a rapid enough flow of urine for small changes in rate to be detected promptly, and rewarded, it is possible that antidiuretic hormone was already maximally inhibited in this experiment.

Vasomotor responses

Having shown that the blood supply to an internal organ—the kidney—can be modified by instrumental learning, we next studied peripheral blood flow. In the first experiment, the blood flow through the curarized rat's tail was measured by a photo-electric plethysmograph, and the changes were rewarded by electrical stimulation of the brain (DiCara and

Miller, 1968c). Four out of the four rats rewarded for vasoconstriction showed vasoconstriction, and at the same time their average core temperature measured rectally decreased from 98·9 to 97·9° F. Four out of the four rats rewarded for vasodilatation showed vasodilatation, and at the same time their average core temperature increased from 99·2 to 101° F. It is interesting that the direction of change in temperature was opposite to that which would be expected from the conservation of or loss of heat caused by peripheral vasoconstriction or vasodilatation respectively. The changes are in the direction that would be expected if our training were altering the rate of heat production, and the vasomotor changes were an attempt to compensate for the consequent changes in temperature.

Specificity of sympathetic control

The next experiment was designed to find out if instrumental learning could produce an extremely specific peripheral vasomotor response. With perhaps foolhardy over-confidence, DiCara and I (1968d) put photocell

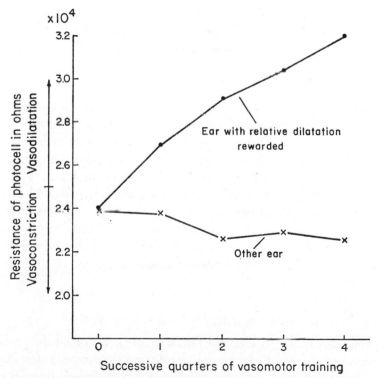

FIG. 5. Specificity of vasomotor response produced by rewarding difference between the two ears. (From data by DiCara and Miller, 1968d.)

devices on both ears of the curarized rat and connected them to a bridge circuit, so that only differences in the vasomotor responses of the two ears were rewarded by electrical stimulation of the brain. To our surprise and delight, the experiment worked. Each of the six rats rewarded for relative dilatation of the left ear showed such dilatation, while each of the six rats rewarded for relative dilatation of the right ear showed this. The average results are shown in Fig. 5: one ear changed while the other ear did not change, or else changed slightly in the opposite direction. Recordings from the right and left forepaws showed little or no change.

It is clear that these results could not be by-products of changes in either heart rate or blood pressure. Since the innervation of the blood vessels of the ears of the rat is primarily or exclusively sympathetic, these results show that the sympathetic nervous system is capable of a great deal more specificity of response than is usually attributed to it. The fact that it functions as a single unit in an extreme situation of general emergency, as when a cat is confronted by a barking dog, does not mean that the sympathetic nervous system is incapable of learning more specifically differentiated responses. Such specific changes in blood flow could account, of course, for specific psychosomatic symptoms, especially if the changes in the blood supplies to different internal organs can be as specific as blood supply to the ears.

Blood pressure

Although changes in blood pressure were not induced as by-products of rewarding changes of urine formation, another experiment on curarized rats, using escape from and/or avoidance of mild electric shock as a reward, showed that seven out of seven rats rewarded for increased blood pressure, recorded by a chronic catheter in the aorta, showed increases, while seven out of seven rats rewarded for decreases showed decreases. The average initial level of the blood pressure was 140 mm. Hg, which happens to be roughly comparable to the blood pressure of an adult man, with the increase reaching 170 mm. Hg (on the borderline of abnormally high blood pressure for man) and the decrease reaching 113 mm. Hg (DiCara and Miller, 1968e).

Transfer to the non-curarized state: implications for mediation

In an earlier article (Miller and DiCara, 1967), we raised the possibility that the animals might be learning to send from the motor cortex impulses to struggle or to relax, and that these impulses to skeletal muscles might elicit conditioned or unconditioned changes in heart rate through central connexions. If this were so, paralysing the motor end plates would not rule out the possibility that the visceral changes were not directly instrumentally learned, but instead were mediated indirectly by instrumental learning of the cerebrospinal nervous system. If the learned changes in heart rate were indeed mediated *via* impulses to paralysed skeletal muscles, and if such learning did transfer from the curarized to the non-curarized state, we should expect to see these responses in the latter state.

Therefore, DiCara and I (1968*f*) performed an experiment on such a transfer. We found that both increases and decreases, producing a total difference of approximately 20 per cent, did transfer from the curarized to the non-curarized state. But we did not find that such increases or decreases in heart rate were accompanied by the type of differential changes in skeletal motor activity (recorded by a sensitive stabilimeter) or in breathing (recorded by a thermistor in the nostril) that could be used as an explanation of the changes in heart rate. In view of the paper by Ehrlich and Malmo (1967), summarizing studies on the amount of motor activity necessary to produce appreciable changes in heart rate, it seems unlikely that the required amount of motor activity could have escaped detection. Further, it is difficult to conceive how all the different types of visceral learning we have demonstrated, and the specificity of much of this learning, could be accounted for as by-products of motor impulses to specific types of movements, or even of specific emotional thoughts.

These experiments have demonstrated that glandular and visceral learning can occur in the curarized rat. Exploratory work currently in progress makes it clear that such learning can also occur, at least for heart rate and blood pressure, in the non-curarized rat, and for salivation in the non-curarized dog. But it is also clear that visceral learning is considerably more difficult in the non-curarized than in the curarized state. This difficulty may be caused by the confusing effects of visceral changes mediated by skeletal movement and of changes in the stimulus situation induced by such movements.

Instrumental learning of changes in electroencephalogram (EEG)

In an experiment dealing with a slightly different type of response, A. Carmona, working in my laboratory, has shown that when cats are rewarded for high-voltage EEG waves from the brain, they learn to show high-voltage, low-frequency waves and also to sit sphinx-like, staring into space. Conversely, when they are rewarded for the absence of high-voltage activity, they learn to show low-voltage, high-frequency brain waves and are unusually alert and active. That the differences are not merely the by-product of feedback from overt muscular activity is shown by the fact that curarized rats rewarded for high-voltage activity learn to show more of this, and those rewarded for the absence of such activity learn to show less (Carmona, 1967) (see Fig. 6).

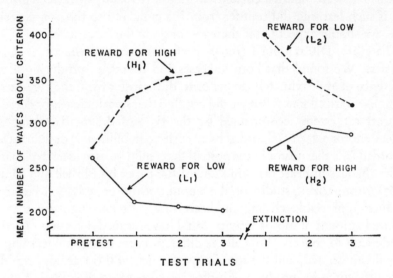

FIG. 6. Instrumental learning by curarized rats rewarded for high-voltage or low-voltage waves recorded from the cerebral cortex. H_1, H_2: high-voltage waves rewarded first and second respectively; L_1, L_2: low-voltage waves rewarded first and second respectively. (From Carmona, 1967.)

Learning of visceral responses in man

Our assumption is that people can learn anything that rats can. Recent experiments on visceral learning by people, summarized by Katkin and Murray (1968) and by Kimmel (1967), strongly suggest that this is the case although, as the former authors point out, most of these studies in man are subject to a number of criticisms, and hence fall somewhat short of conclusive proof. Incidental observations (originally called to my attention by Professor George Mahl at Yale University) on the secretion of tears by children also tend to support our assumption. A small boy who receives a severe bump in rough-and-tumble play will tend to learn to inhibit the secretion of tears while he is with his peers, who would ridicule him for crying, but may burst into tears later in the presence of his mother, who does not reinforce the inhibition of crying and may even reward tears with sympathy.

Implications for aetiology

As I have already pointed out (Miller, 1966, 1968), the foregoing experiments have obvious implications for the aetiology and therapy of psychosomatic symptoms. We have shown that the reinforcement of changes in glandular and visceral responses is not limited to those unconditioned stimuli that elicit the specific change to be learned as an unconditioned response. Instead, it is highly probable that visceral responses can be modified by any one of the great variety of rewards and punishments that are known to be capable of producing the learning of skeletal responses. Psychiatrists commonly refer to such rewards as secondary gains.

The foregoing experiments show that it is theoretically possible for previous learning to produce the tendency, experimentally demonstrated by Lacey and Lacey (1958, 1962), for certain individuals to respond to a stress primarily with one visceral system while other individuals respond to it primarily with another. It is also theoretically possible that such learning can be carried far enough to create a psychosomatic symptom. The possibility of such learning does not, of course, rule out the possibility of innate differences in the susceptibility of different visceral systems. Indeed, it seems probable that, in circumstances that will reward any psychosomatic symptom with a secondary gain, the subject will be most likely to learn that symptom to which he is innately most prone. In a different set of circumstances that will reward one symptom but not another, it seems possible for learning to override the tendency to respond with an innately preferred type of symptom. The degree to which a given society actually provides the conditions for effectively rewarding the theoretically possible psychosomatic learning remains to be determined by clinical research.

Implications for therapy

From the point of view of research in psychotherapy, it would be highly desirable to select patients who, because of their innate predisposition and/or past experience, respond to a stress such as fear with some clear-cut, easily measurable, psychosomatic symptom, such as a rapid heart rate. In such cases, the measurement of the symptom will give both the therapist and the patient an objective record of the progress of the therapy.

If the symptom is medically undesirable, it may not make much practical difference whether its amelioration is produced by the learning of direct visceral control, or by learning which has an indirect effect through removing muscular tensions or fear. To the extent that the symptom is itself a source of tension and fear, which in turn maintains the symptom, a break into any part of the vicious circle may be equally effective. In other circumstances, there may be differences between the effects of concentrating on the symptom and on the emotional responses that mediate it (*vide infra*). In research on the dynamics of treatment, the objective recording of a highly significant symptom should be of value.

The fact that curarization greatly facilitates visceral learning, which then transfers efficiently to the normal state, suggests that similar effects might be achieved by hypnotism, which could be used to relax all skeletal muscles, stabilize breathing, and direct the patient's attention away from other and toward visceral sensations.

Even when the symptom is organic in its origin, there may be some possibility of modifying it by learned control, and such modification may be highly desirable provided the symptom is clearly medically disadvantageous to the patient rather than a necessary homoeostatic compensation, as increased blood pressure is for kidney damage.

As an illustration of what may be achieved, Engel and Melmon (1968) have recently secured results strongly suggesting that organic cardiac arrhythmias may be ameliorated by suitable regimes of instrumental learning. In collaboration with Drs. Clark T. Randt and Julius Korein, Dr. Alfredo Carmona and I have shown that patients with abnormal EEG activity, either spontaneous or induced by photic stimulation, can learn to control this if paroxysmal spikes activate a tone and they are instructed to keep the tone from sounding. While the work has not yet progressed far enough to permit an adequate evaluation of the therapeutic value of such procedures, it is clear that they are worth a thorough trial. By objectively recording harmful symptoms and then immediately rewarding, first, small changes in the desired direction and then larger ones, we may be able to give patients a unique opportunity for therapeutic learning.

ACKNOWLEDGEMENTS

The studies described from the author's laboratory were supported by US Public Health Service Grant MH-13189 from the National Institute of Mental Health.

REFERENCES

ALEXANDER, F. (1950). *Psychosomatic Medicine: its Principles and Applications*, pp. 40–41. New York: Norton.
BANUAZIZI, A. (1968). Unpublished Ph.D. thesis, Yale University.
BICHAT, X. (1800). *Recherches Physiologiques sur la Vie et la Mort*. Paris: Brosson, Gabon.
CARMONA, A. (1967). *Trial-and-Error Learning of the Voltage of the Cortical EEG Activity*. Unpublished Ph.D. thesis, Yale University.
DiCARA, L. V., and MILLER, N. E. (1968a). *J. comp. physiol. Psychol.*, **65**, 8–12.
DiCARA, L. V., and MILLER, N. E. (1968b). Submitted manuscript.

DiCARA, L. V., and MILLER, N. E. (1968c). *Commun. behav. Biol.*, **1**, 209–212.
DiCARA, L. V., and MILLER, N. E. (1968d). *Science*, **159**, 1485–1486.
DiCARA, L. V., and MILLER, N. E. (1968e). *Psychosom. Med.*, in press.
DiCARA, L. V., and MILLER, N. E. (1968f). Unpublished observations.
DOLLARD, J., and MILLER, N. E. (1950). *Personality and Psychotherapy*. New York: McGraw-Hill.
EHRLICH, D. J., and MALMO, R. (1967). *Neuropsychologia*, **5**, 219–235.
ENGEL, B. T., and MELMON, K. L. (1968). *Modification of Cardiac Arrhythmias through Voluntary Control*. (Mimeographed manuscript.)
KATKIN, E. S., and MURRAY, E. N. (1968). *Psychol. Bull.*, **70**, 52–68.
KIMBLE, G. A. (1961). *Hilgard and Marquis' Conditioning and Learning*. New York: Appleton-Century-Crofts.
KIMMEL, H. D. (1967). *Psychol. Bull.*, **67**, 337–345.
KONORSKI, J., and MILLER, S. (1937). *J. gen. Psychol.*, **17**, 405–407.
LACEY, J. I., and LACEY, B. C. (1958). *Am. J. Psychol.*, **71**, 50–73.
LACEY, J. I., and LACEY, B. C. (1962). *Ann. N. Y. Acad. Sci.*, **98**, 1257–1290.
MILLER, N. E. (1951). *Psychol. Rev.*, **58**, 375–381.
MILLER, N. E. (1964). In *Personality Change*, pp. 149–175, eds. Byrne, D., and Worchel, P. New York: Wiley.
MILLER, N. E. (1966). In *Proc. XVIII Int. Congr. Psychol.* (Moscow, 1966). Printed report at Congress, awaiting publication.
MILLER, N. E. (1968). *Ann. N. Y. Acad. Sci.*, in press.
MILLER, N. E., and BANUAZIZI, A. (1968). *J. comp. physiol. Psychol.*, **65**, 1–7.
MILLER, N. E., and CARMONA, A. (1967). *J. comp. physiol. Psychol.*, **63**, 1–6.
MILLER, N. E., and DiCARA, L. V. (1967). *J. comp. physiol. Psychol.*, **63**, 12–19.
MILLER, N. E., and DiCARA, L. V. (1968). *Am. J. Physiol.*, in press.
MILLER, N. E., and DOLLARD, J. (1941). *Social Learning and Imitation*. New Haven: Yale University Press.
MOWRER, O. H. (1947). *Harvard Educ. Rev.*, **17**, 102–148.
PAVLOV, I. P. (1927). *Conditioned Reflexes*, ed. and trans. Anrep, G.V. London: Oxford University Press. (1960, Reprinted New York: Dover Publications.)
REYNOLDS, G. S. (1963). *J. exp. Analysis Behav.*, **6**, 131–139.
SENF, G. M., and MILLER, N. E. (1967). *J. comp. physiol. Psychol.*, **64**, 121–127.
SKINNER, B. F. (1938). *The Behavior of Organisms*. New York: Appleton-Century-Crofts.
TROWILL, J. A. (1967). *J. comp. physiol. Psychol.*, **63**, 7–11.
WAGNER, A. R. (1966). In *Current Research in Motivation*, pp. 229–239, ed. Haber, R. N. New York: Holt, Rinehart and Winston.

DISCUSSION

Kiernan: The early literature on instrumental control of autonomic responses puzzles me. In the first successful experiment recorded (Lisina, M. I., quoted in Razran, G. [1961]. *Psychol. Rev.*, **68**, 81-148), changes in vasomotor control did not occur until the subjects were shown a record of their vasomotor activity. Results consistent with this finding have been reproduced by several investigators (for example, Hnatiow, M., and Lang, P. J. [1965]. *Psychophysiology*, **1**, 330-336; Brener, J., and Hothersall, D. [1966]. *Psychophysiology*, **3**, 23-28). These observations, in direct contrast to your own and to those of B. T. Engel and S. P. Hansen (1966. *Psychophysiology*, **3**, 176-187) and T. W. Frazier (1966. *Psychophysiology*, **3**, 188-202) suggest that learning an instrumental response can only occur under conditions of augmented feedback. Can you explain this contradiction?

Miller: First, now that a more complete English translation of Lisina's article on the role of orientation in the transformation of involuntary reactions into voluntary ones is available (1965. In *Orienting Reflex and Exploratory Behaviour*, pp. 450-456, eds. Voronin, L. G., Leontiev, A. N., Luria, A. R., Sokolov, E. N., and Vinogradova, O. S. Washington, D. C.: American Institute of Biological Science), it is clear that Lisina's subjects did not learn a direct instrumental control of the vasomotor responses; instead, they learned to perform various skeletal responses, such as tensing their muscles or changing their breathing, which in turn elicited vasomotor changes. Apparently it was much easier for them to learn to "cheat" in this way when they had some continuous feedback from the vasomotor response than when they were merely rewarded for making a large enough response to meet a criterion.

Second, we must distinguish between continuous (step-by-step) and discontinuous (all-or-nothing) feedback. Every reward for a specific response is a feedback indicating that the correct response has occurred. In my experiments, the rewarding electrical stimulation of the brain (or the termination of the warning signal and punishing shocks to the tail) were very perspicuous forms of feedback, indicating that a sufficiently large change in the correct direction had occurred. This was a discontinuous feedback, however, and hence supplied less detailed information than might have been provided by a continuous feedback.

A possible advantage of continuous feedback is that a slight change in the correct direction ("you're getting warmer") may acquire secondary reinforcing value and thus help to shape the response by rewarding a change too small to meet the criterion for primary reward. I have discussed the dynamics of such learning in more detail in my analysis of copying (Miller, N. E., and Dollard, J. [1941]. In *Social Learning and Imitation*, pp. 153-164. New Haven: Yale University Press). If only large changes in response are rewarded, the difference between continuous and discontinuous feedback is large. But if smaller changes are rewarded, as in the procedure for "shaping" behaviour, the difference is reduced. In our experiments we rewarded changes that were small enough to occur very frequently, several times per minute. Thus our conditions approximated to continuous feedback. Lisina's criterion for reward may have required a larger change occurring considerably less frequently. This would account for the importance, in her experiments, of supplementing the discontinuous feed-back supplied by the reward with some form of continuous feedback.

Kiernan: Another contradiction is that Engel and Hansen (1966, *loc. cit.*) conditioned the heart rate in man and found that learning was superior in subjects who were not aware of the reinforcement contingency.

Miller: Engel (personal communication) noted that his patients were so aware of their heart rate anyway that they responded very easily to changes in it. Further work is needed in this area, but it is fairly well-established now that continuous feedback is not a *sine qua non* for instrumental learning. J. Konorski used to believe this, but experiments by his students have caused him to change his mind.

Kiernan: I doubt if it is valid to extrapolate the data from animals to man. Although the basic fact (that instrumental learning of autonomic responses can occur) is established, evidence on the most effective methods of inducing such learning needs clarification before these methods can be used thera-peutically in man.

Sifneos: Professor Miller, which are the rewarding areas in the brain of the rat?

Miller: M. E. Olds and J. Olds (1963. *J. comp. Neurol.*, **120**, 259-295) have mapped out these areas for the rat. In our experiments we used the medial forebrain bundle of the hypothalamus at the level of the ventromedial nucleus—an area that consistently produces rewarding effects when stimulated. Incidentally, the electrode we use in the rat is large in relation to the size of its brain, so we could not detect subtle differences in effects in slightly different sites.

Kiernan: Does curare eliminate the orientation reaction (Lynn, R. [1966]. *Attention, Arousal and the Orientation Reaction.* Oxford: Pergamon) in the rat and, if so, would this be relevant to human autonomic conditioning where curare cannot be used?

Miller: I do not know. We purposely used responses such as the rate of urine formation, vasoconstriction, blood pressure and heart rate because the orientation response is subject to so many variables. We started by trying to condition the heart rate in curarized rats on the basis of previous studies on the conditioning of autonomic responses in curarized animals (Black, A. H., Carlson, N. J., and Solomon, R. L. [1962]. *Psychol. Monogr.*, **76**, No. 29). These workers had shown that classical conditioning of the heart rate can occur under curare in dogs. Thus any negative results we obtained would be convincing proof that instrumental learning was not effective.

Bandura: The antecedent stimulus control of autonomic responses is emphasized in two-factor theories of learning (Skinner, B. F. [1961]. *Cumulative Record*. New York: Appleton-Century-Crofts; Rescorla, R. A., and Solomon, R. L. [1967]. *Psychol. Rev.*, **74**, 151-182). An interesting experiment would be to use the eliciting stimulus to activate the autonomic response, and then pit consequent reinforcement control against the eliciting stimulus to see if the latter can be overridden in this way.

Miller: The eliciting stimulus can be partly overridden. We found a slight decrease in urine formation as an unconditioned response to electrical stimulation of the brain, and we were able to use this stimulus to reinforce either increases or decreases in urine formation. Similarly, the unconditioned effect of a mild electric shock was to increase the heart rate, but we could nevertheless use escape from shock to train rats to decrease their heart rates. I hope these experiments will be relevant to the treatment of psychosomatic illness in man.

Hunt: I once used hypnosis to treat a patient with a psychosomatic disease—ulcerative colitis—and she responded surprisingly well to this approach. As an intercurrent complaint she developed attacks of hay fever in mid-winter. I first brought on and then completely reversed an attack of hay fever by suggestion under hypnosis in this patient. During this procedure the objective changes inside her nose were observed appearing and then disappearing, by a medical colleague using a nasal speculum. The woman had no amnesia, so after the trance I asked her what she remembered about it and if she now believed that words and ideas could bring on hay fever. She replied that she knew that what I had suggested was working because the man who was looking up her nose stopped breathing! We had no more complaints of hay fever from her that winter (Hunt, H. F. [1948]. *J. consult. Psychol.*, **12**, 68-75).

GROUP DISCUSSION

Frank: We have not yet discussed one possible difference between the psychoanalytic and behaviour therapy approaches. Behaviour therapy deals with a highly structured situation in which the patient is constantly rewarded and the next step is always clear to him, whereas analytic therapy creates an exactly opposite situation—as unstructured as it can be. In psychoanalytic therapy the therapist does not respond preferentially to any particular activity of the patient, so he presumably runs through his whole neurotic repertory and only when this is exhausted can the therapist start showing the patient what adaptive behaviour is. Is this a real difference between the two forms of therapy, or has the analyst now abandoned this completely non-structured technique?

Sandler: The analytic situation itself is highly structured in that it contains certain explicit or implicit rules (notably the rule of free association). But what the patient brings to the session is not structured in this way. Today's analyst does not wait for the patient to run through his entire neurotic repertory before he responds, but may start active intervention, by interpretation, on the material the patient brings to the first therapeutic session. So guiding does occur, not by suggesting that the patient discuss one subject rather than another, but by interventions which influence the material the patient brings up next. There is a continuous interaction between patient and therapist. Does this answer your question?

Frank: Yes, but this is not what Karl Menninger (1958. *Theory of Psychoanalytic Technique.* New York: Basic Books) described as psychoanalysis.

Miller: Free association has not been abandoned in psychoanalysis. It is an important instruction which elicits an unusual type of verbal and other behaviours.

Frank: I agree that the rule of free association involves setting up a programme of instructional control, but this is not a structured situation in the same way as rewarding each step in behaviour therapy is.

Malan: Many analytic techniques today contain a great deal of differential rewarding; mine certainly does.

Kubie: The one neurotic symptom that has never been cured in analysis is compulsive talking. Why should anyone give up something he has been consistently rewarded for?

Miller: Interpretations may be extremely punishing if, for example, they draw the patient's attention to something he is trying to avoid. And "Aha" can be quite rewarding as an indication that the therapist believes a statement to be important.

Frank: Then has the original theory of non-intervention by the analyst been abandoned?

Malan: Most analysts are much freer than they used to be in their responses to the patient. I doubt if the classical Freudian technique of saying nothing until the transference becomes resistant is ever taught or practised today.

Sandler: I agree with this. Freud's orginal idea was to explain everything to the patient; later he found out more about the transference and resistances and included the interpretation of these in his technique. Every intervention and interpretation made by the analyst affects the patient's value systems. If the analyst tells the patient that he feels aggressive towards him (the analyst), the message implicit in this interpretation is that the aggressive impulse is acceptable as a wish or thought. This applies even if the analyst says only that the patient does not think it is safe to feel aggressive. Similarly, the analyst's grunts, as Professor Miller has said, may be rewarding for the patient.

Marks: Reward is often described as one of the prime movers of change in the psychotherapeutic situation. Another important instigator of change is the provision of cognitive feedback, in other words, the provision of a label for actions of whose meaning the patient is not aware. When he can see that what he is doing is maladaptive, there is at least a possibility for him to change his behaviour. Evidence now exists that the provision of external feedback can help the patient to achieve new controls. Petrinovich's work (Hardyck, C. D., Petrinovich, L. F., and Ellsworth, D. W. [1966]. *Science,* **154,** 1467-1468) on subvocalizing during reading has shown that "semi-silent reading" can be rapidly eliminated by feeding it into an auditory feedback system. A similar mechanism, which we tend to ignore, may be important in psychotherapy.

Bandura: As well as differences in the techniques of analytic and behaviour therapy, there are basic differences in the locus of treatment, its content, and the selection of agents of therapy in these two approaches. In traditional psychoanalytic therapy, professional psychotherapists attempt to modify behaviour in office settings mainly through work with verbal symbols. By contrast, behaviour therapists characteristically apply the treatment procedures to the problems themselves rather than to their symbolic equivalents; the treatment is often carried out in the social settings in which the problems arise; and the treatment programme is generally implemented under close professional supervision by the persons who have the most intense contact with the patient and can therefore serve as powerful therapeutic agents. The potential influence of such persons derives from the fact that they are in such close contact with the patient and exercise considerable control over the very conditions that govern his deviant behaviour. These conditions are probably the best available for producing enduring and generalized changes in social response patterns.

Freeman: Behaviour therapists are so concerned with items of behaviour (such as the withdrawal of the schizophrenic, or the suicidal attempt of the depressive) that they pay too little attention to clinical syndromes. A piece of behaviour may be just one, or a set, of a constellation of phenomena which make up a clinical entity with a known natural history. A suicidal attempt may represent a real suicidal intent in a depressive patient, or it may be a manifestation of something quite different in, say, a hysterical patient. We can diagnose the underlying syndrome by the associated clinical features and, in the two examples just cited, the patient would be treated quite differently.

Gelder: I agree about the importance of the clinical entity. There is an unfortunate tendency to try to deal with too much when using behavioural techniques and learning theories. A phobic disorder, for example, does not always need behaviour therapy: it may be the presenting symptom of a depression, in which case we need to treat the underlying depressive illness. We have shown (Gelder, M. G., Marks, I. M., and Wolff, H. H. [1967]. *Br. J. Psychiat.*, **113**, 53-73) that the outcome in phobias can be partly predicted in terms of the symptomatology. The prognosis for patients with many obsessional symptoms or much free-floating anxiety is poorer than for patients without these features. An initial psychiatric assessment of phobic patients is essential, because it differentiates the patients with more isolated phobias, who will do well with behaviour therapy, from those with free-floating anxiety, underlying depression and so on, who will not. The psychiatric assessment must be combined with a psychodynamic assessment to determine the place of the symptom in the patient's mental economy. We are in danger of losing sight of the value of behavioural techniques by trying to apply them where they are not appropriate.

Jansson: Too much emphasis may be given to separate symptoms while the overall form of the clinical entity is neglected.

Krasner: This difference in emphasis is one of the important differences between analytic and behavioural techniques. Behaviourally oriented therapists may not make enough use of the notion of the disease entity, but there are also dangers in its overemphasis. Once a patient is labelled with a diagnosis one tends to react to him as if he had all the associated characteristics. The most satisfactory approach is behavioural analysis, which pays attention to each individual and his particular deviant behaviour without resort to labelling him. There is a risk that if one gives a patient a diagnostic label we may treat the label rather than the individual.

Marks: The same piece of behaviour may have different significance in different situations. It may be unassociated with other clinical phenomena or it may be part of some complex psychopathology. In the former situation behaviour therapy, and in the latter psychodynamic therapy, is appropriate. If we overextrapolate by taking everything to the extreme we may lose the value of any new technique by applying it to all patients, for some of whom it is completely inappropriate.

Jansson: A clinical syndrome should not be a rigid compartment excluding all other compartments. We should think in terms of syndromes that can be combined in various ways rather than in terms of isolated items of behaviour.

Gelder: Disease entities and the behavioural characteristics of an individual are not mutually exclusive. There is virtue in picking out the features that one patient has in common with others, and what is peculiar to himself.

Krasner: It is what is particular to an individual that is important in therapy, rather than characteristics attached to him by means of a label.

Gelder: But one must take into account the features that a number of individuals have in common. One cannot analyse and treat every patient as if one had never seen another. The features which group patients together have gradually been worked out during the evolution of psychiatry and are especially important because shared symptoms often imply common treatment.

Miller: A large backlog of experience shows that when a patient with a severe depression starts to recover, the risk of suicide increases. This information, the product of psychiatric experience, must be known and used by any therapist who is treating such a patient. I would feel safer if any relative of mine with a psychiatric illness were treated by a therapist (whether behavioural or analytic) with considerable experience in general clinical psychiatry, including experience in working in a mental hospital.

Foss: The model used by behaviour therapists may be much too simple. It deals with isolated items of behaviour; but these items are usually part of a complicated whole. The acquisition of skills is an example of how complicated behaviour can be. The original workers in this field (Bryan, W. L., and Harter, N. [1899]. *Psychol. Rev.*, **6**, 345-375) described skilled behaviour as a hierarchy of habits. The acquisition of the skill of playing tennis is an illustration of what I mean. At an early stage one learns how to grip the racket and is constantly and acutely aware of doing this. Later, through practice, grip becomes automatic and drops out of consciousness. When one progresses to a more important and complex goal or skill and concentrates on something new one ceases to be aware of the lower-order habits involved. It is as though the learner has a limited amount of attention and has to over-learn a lower-order habit so that it no longer occupies his attention before he can progress. But curious things can happen to these apparently forgotten habits. If one runs down the stairs and suddenly brings one of the lower-order habits into consciousness (say you start to think about where you are putting your feet) the whole skill deteriorates and you fall over. Stress is another situation in which things may go wrong and a lower-order habit may claim attention again. I view personality as a hierarchy of lower-order habits, but the important thing is that these habits may have been acquired in different ways. For relearning in the therapeutic situation or during remedial education the subject may have to regress so that an early maladaptive habit returns to consciousness before adaptive relearning can take place. Once the relearning of this particular part of the hierarchy has occurred, it may be built up again, and the new habit must now work automatically (unconsciously) for the skill as a whole (that is, the personality) to function smoothly. These notions fit well with Dr. Sandler's comment that insight gained by children in a previous analysis is lost from consciousness in later analyses (this volume, p. 132).

Several kinds of learning are probably necessary in the various hierarchical systems, at the molar if not at the molecular level. Some of these processes will be simply the inhibition of earlier learned responses, and others will involve interpersonal interactions. For successful treatment of a particular maladaptive behaviour the paradigm for unlearning and re-education may have to be the same as that of the original learning process for that behaviour. Thus, transference will be important in treating a maladaptive habit learned through interpersonal relationships; reconditioning will be appropriate if conditioning was originally involved; and modelling or copying is important in a habit originally learned by copying. In Professor Bandura's patients the snake phobia had been acquired through social learning. The subjects had not been bitten by snakes but had copied a reaction to snakes in other individuals. I would therefore expect modelling to be effective in patients with snake (or spider) phobias, but not in agoraphobic patients. To put it another way, behaviour therapy will be effective if the item to be treated is not an important part of the hierarchy of learned skills or behaviours.

Kiernan: As a non-clinical experimental psychologist, I can see an impediment to progress in research arising from the clash between the development of a therapeutic procedure and the need to cure the patient. The danger is that the procedures will not be developed to their fullest extent. From the clinical point of view it is probably right not to use a form of therapy beyond the point where the therapist can see that it is useful. Thus Drs. Marks and Gelder will not use simple behavioural techniques in, say, extremely severe agoraphobia. But the danger for research in this approach is that it blocks further development of the procedure. Unfortunately we do not have a reasonable theory underpinning any of this research. The quasi-Hullian model (Wolpe, J. [1958]. *Psychotherapy by Reciprocal Inhibition.* Stanford: Stanford University Press) which underlay the early research in behaviour therapy seems naïve and is now rejected by behavioural analysts. But the operant conditioning approach does not have a sufficiently well-developed theory of reinforcement to specify what is to be a reinforcer (see Premack, D. [1965]. In *Nebraska Symposium on Motivation*, vol. 13, pp. 123-180, ed. Levine, D. Lincoln: University of Nebraska Press, for a possible approach to reinforcement). Clinicians can thus use whatever therapy they fancy—psychoanalysis, general psychiatry, behaviour therapy, drugs and so on. Paradoxically, as more patients recover, the possibility of achieving what should be our main long-term goal—the development of a theory to underpin the research—recedes.

Hunt: I agree with *my* interpretation of what you have said! The operant-conditioning approach was deliberately made to be "empty", that is, to contain no theory. It posits simple notions about the underlying organism and formulates simple rules that can be tested through a simple set of procedures. These are powerful procedures, when applied with sensitivity and sophistication, and can produce significant behavioural changes. But many behaviour therapists handle these procedures carelessly or ignorantly. Behavioural technologists may be poorly informed but more often they are proudly ignorant about all other theories of personality. Without these, and without common sense, one cannot make good guesses about what is going on in mentally sick patients. To understand this militant narrowness one must realize that operant conditioning is not only a procedure but in some quarters has become a movement, taking on the characteristics of a beleaguered minority beset by hostile critics. Such defensiveness has retarded progress; an orthodoxy undisturbed by new ideas stays where it is. Our procedures must be added to by information from other schools of psychology, particularly at this time when so much is waiting to be discovered and created.

Kiernan: What worries me is that the information that the operant conditioner has to turn to is a combination of observation and personal interpretation. Distortion of the facts is inevitable unless the operant conditioner makes a thorough experimental analysis of his own postulates and those of others.

Kubie: One aim of multidisciplinary conferences such as this is to break down some of the ignorance of the protagonists of one discipline for the theories and practice of another. But such conferences can be very frustrating, in spite of goodwill among the participants.

The most useful impact of such a conference is to challenge our confidence in our respective techniques and theoretical positions. If we emerge from the conference unshaken, we have (mis)used it merely to entrench ourselves in the biased positions in which we arrived. But if we are shaken, this promotes a conflict between doubt and confidence and we become defensive. If an interdisciplinary symposium is to be effective it must be a psychotherapeutic experience in the sense that it will evoke some degree of change as an essential part of the learning process, whatever the mechanism (operant conditioning or analysis) through which this change occurs. Intrapsychic changes depend upon an unstable balance between humility and defensiveness, and even when this balance is altered favourably during a conference how can we be sure that the change will persist?

Every psychotherapeutic process of learning demands dedication of time, effort, intellect and heart, indeed of the complete self. This deep commitment to and affiliation with what one has been doing must be linked to a willingness to change. Multidisciplinary symposia may have to be differently organized in future, and the participants differently prepared, in order to achieve these goals.

Lack of time for communication is one of the problems of multidisciplinary symposia. Lack of time is also a problem for psychotherapists. No one can experience all the different facets of psychotherapy in one lifetime. Of course behaviourists should undergo psychoanalysis and, equally, analysts should experience behavioural techniques; clinicians should apply experimental methods to their material just as experimentalists should know the challenge and frustrations of clinical practice. But we do not have time to implement this ideal. One way of approximating to it, however, is through the intensive study of Videotape recordings, both of clinical procedures and of experiments. By studying these recordings over and over, both alone and with colleagues from different disciplines, we might emerge with more courage to want to change and a lessened tendency to retreat to our old and well-defended convictions.

Miller: A continuing case conference on patients in active therapy would be most valuable. Ideally Videotape recordings of one patient currently in behaviour therapy and one in analysis should be discussed by analysts and by behaviour therapists. In this way we would be forced to make predictions, to wait and see what happened, and thus really to learn in detail what occurs in these two types of psychotherapy.

Lazarus: Psychoanalysts and behaviour therapists are working together in our department in the way you suggest. Herbert Freed, a psychoanalyst, (1968, personal communication) has defined the differences between the two approaches as follows: "Psychoanalysis endeavours to see through people and behaviour therapy endeavours to see people through."

Miller: Dr. Kubie, will you now present a case that you have treated by psychoanalysis? Then Professor Lazarus will submit this same case to behavioural analysis and we can all discuss it.

Kubie: I am not completely happy about any such verbal presentation, with its inevitable fallacies and misrepresentations. I will be as honest as I can, but I would far prefer to be studying with you some sample tapes of the sessions which this account attempts to summarize.

CASE PRESENTATION: A PATIENT WITH A HEIGHT PHOBIA*

Kubie: The patient had repressed and forgotten the moment at which his phobia arose, and the reason for it. He was a man in his early thirties who had been an able student and athlete. When he first consulted me he was a successful engineer, married and with children. Some months before starting treatment he had been standing on the balcony of a mountain chalet belonging to relatives of his wife. Suddenly he was overcome by a terror of the height. (Something preceded this moment which came to light two years later in his treatment, *vide infra.*) From that moment his whole life changed. He could not do anything which involved heights—riding, going over a bridge or up a ladder, climbing a mountain, or even going to the upper floors of a building. Thus he could not go to a client's office, or dine at the home of a friend, or eat in a restaurant if these places were situated on an upper floor. He was even afraid to drive his car over a bridge to take his children to see their grandparents. Not only did his life become constricted: he also felt humiliated and depressed. At first he forced himself to perform these terrifying acts but, when they became no easier, he gradually wavered in his determination and started to make excuses and to tell lies in order to avoid heights. He broke appointments, began to drink heavily and to hide from people because he felt that they knew something terrible about him. He developed an almost paranoid distrust and fear of what people were thinking about him.

In early childhood this man had been shamefully mishandled by an aggressive mother who hated all men—his father, his older brother and himself—and drove his older brother into permanent illness. The mother was passionately attached to the patient's older sister, a beautiful girl, a fine student and a fine athlete. The patient was attached to her too, but also afraid of her. He could never use his own abilities until he left home and went away to school. He finally tried to conquer his ambivalent attachment to his sister by marrying her best friend. He functioned happily and well after this until his sister died suddenly. He then found himself in a marriage

* See also p. 245.

whose purpose (the relationship with his sister) no longer existed. He had in this sense married the wrong woman.

A little time after his sister's death, in the chalet of his wife's family, the moment of terror struck. What he had repressed until he was far along in his analysis was the terrifying thought that he wanted to pitch his wife over the parapet. At that precise moment his own terror of heights started. Would it have helped this man to relieve him of his terror of heights by some operant-conditioning technique? He had only had one experience with a woman (his sister's friend) and his analysis exposed a whole area of emotional illness, namely his distorted attitude to all women. He was full of buried envy, jealousy and hate carried over from mother and sister. I doubt if simply eliminating his height phobia would have helped him. On a deeper level, a close identification with his weak, submissive father was slowly uncovered. This identification involved the patient in secret terrors about possible homosexuality.

The resolution of his illness started with some lessening of his terror of heights, so that he could live again and stop lying to his family, friends and associates. The method by which this is achieved is unimportant provided that when the presenting symptom is relieved the patient does not escape into pseudo-health and leave therapy—a natural reaction to the easing of his pain. The second phase for this man (who did stick to his analysis) was to re-orient himself to the problem of his marriage to the un-loved substitute for his sister. He had to sort out his basic relationship to women and to the underlying and unreal terror that he might be predominantly homosexual. This was a slow, painful, step-by-step process. No one can face such terrors without pain; and in such a voyage through pain your hand must be held by someone both in love and hate. The patient finally recovered.

This example of the process of psychoanalytic therapy focuses on the differences between behavioural therapies, and analysis which tries to deal with the problems which underlie the symptoms.

Lazarus: I shall discuss Dr. Kubie's case as a behavioural clinician rather than as as a behaviour therapist. I depart radically from the Wolpean and the Skinnerian systems of therapy, both of which, although extremely useful in specific cases, are basically simplistic, narrow and limited. Psycho-therapy (and life) is extremely complex; it is not just a system of operant principles and counterconditioning. To plunge ahead with a programme of desensitization, or to assume that an entire problem is purely a consequence of various rewards and reinforcements which are open to direct manipulation, is painfully superficial.

This patient's presenting complaint is acrophobia—he is so afraid of heights that he cannot do his work properly and is incapacitated and crippled by his problem. I would first search for interpersonal factors, because I believe that most emotional problems are maintained by current interpersonal events, while also having important connexions with previous interpersonal relationships. The behavioural analyst would take a detailed life history. The patient would probably also receive a battery of personality inventories and other psychological tests. Careful questioning might soon indicate that despite the vague origins of the problem there is a definite relationship between his fears and the death of his sister. It would then be necessary to discover more about the patient's relationship with his sister. By focusing on the temporal sequence of events, many otherwise obscure links might be discerned. It should be easy to find out that the patient had married his sister's best friend, which, in turn, would lead straight to questions regarding the basis of his marriage. I would hope to get this far in about six 50-minute sessions. Throughout these sessions I would look for non-verbal cues—blocks and hesitations, and changes in breathing, posture and facial expression—and also note any facile replies and contradictions. It should be possible to infer that the patient married his wife as a substitute for his sister, and might feel great hostility towards his wife. He would almost certainly be unaware that this hostility was connected with his phobia. We know from Dr. Kubie's analysis that hostile impulses were most crucial, but it is not necessary for the patient to recognize this in order to progress. As long as the therapist grasps the critical elements he can systematically alter his patient's behaviour. Skilful questioning about the patient's early background would soon reveal that his home life was a breeding-ground for deviant responses. Features such as his unassertiveness and hypersensitivities might be expected to emerge. From Dr. Kubie's description I would expect to find that the patient was intimidated by his mother, and was consequently unassertive to women in general and especially compliant to his wife. Verbal testing might reveal undue sensitivities to such words as passive, cowardly, effeminate, weak, clumsy and homosexual. This might give no hint of the possible existence of latent homosexuality, but it is not too far-fetched to suggest that the therapist would at least unearth the presence, and perhaps suspect the significance, of the patient's identification with his weak, submissive father.

Malan; Sifneos: (simultaneously) But your procedure so far is indistinguishable from the technique I use in assessing a patient for brief dynamic psychotherapy.

Sandler: This lucid case history describes exactly the psychoanalysts' approach except that it would take the analyst several years, not six sessions, to elicit all this information. Analysis is a lengthy process precisely because of the patient's defences against the painful and threatening discoveries of the real origins of his illness. I cannot believe that these rather simple leading questions would unearth the material so quickly and efficiently. An illustration of this problem concerns a child who was severely traumatized by seeing his mother murdered by his father. It took several years to discover that the really traumatic experience for the child was not seeing the murder, but that, when the mother was dying after she had been assaulted, she said, "Get out, get out." Such a terrible repressed memory can never become conscious in response to direct questioning, but can normally only be found, and the child helped to tolerate it, by working with the distorted derivatives of the original experience in the material brought up by the child and with the associated defences. Your approach, Professor Lazarus, which has not taken into account the barrier between what is conscious and what is unconscious, must be a gross oversimplification in such a complicated case.

Malan: I do not completely agree. A psychodynamic interview enables the *therapist,* not necessarily the *patient,* to become conscious of the antecedents. The therapist's knowledge is irrelevant to the patient's resistance, because the latter does not know that the therapist is making these deductions about his painful feelings.

Lazarus: Of course the patient need not be conscious of the origins of his illness at this stage; he may never become fully aware of the antecedents. But direct and insistent questions about numerous possible stimulus-response connexions can elicit an astonishing amount of information in a remarkably short time. A well-conducted "stimulus analysis" can cut through many of the patient's defences. Psychoanalysts who have observed these behavioural inquiries have commented that a mass of relevant material emerges which it would take years of psychoanalysis to uncover. As soon as seemingly relevant problems or dimensions are identified, behaviourally oriented clinicians deal directly with the deviant responses. I would immediately start to train this patient in assertive responses on the grounds that assertive-expressive behaviour, especially towards women, would be one of the ways in which he could acquire a sense of masculine adequacy. By teaching him open and honest patterns of expression and communication I would hope to enable him to cultivate more satisfying interpersonal relationships. It would not be enough to rely on words or insight alone for the full development of the anticipated changes. The patient would be taught various new forms of behaviour and would be provided with the opportunity to rehearse these new responses within therapy before applying them in his daily interactions.

I would endeavour to establish a warm, non-judging, open and empathic relationship which would in itself have anxiety-reducing properties, but the main line of treatment would be to direct attention to specific hypersensitivities. I would deal with the cowardly, effeminate, weak, clumsy, homosexual spectrum of anxiety by direct desensitization, modelling, behaviour rehearsal, or any other method that seemed appropriate.

I would also try to bring the wife into therapy, because of the importance of the dyadic interactions. By dealing with the relationship between husband and wife, not only would the current situation between them be expected to improve, but the wife might provide otherwise inaccessible information which would open up even more productive therapeutic areas. I would expect the patient to learn reasonably assertive behaviour and to show decreased anxieties about homosexuality, and a new ability to relate more confidently to his wife in particular and to women in general, in about ten to twenty sessions. He might also, in this time, appreciate some of the operant consequences and secondary gains of his phobia (for example avoiding hard work and not having to visit his parents-in-law). But he might still be afraid of heights. We would therefore start specific desensitization to heights at this stage. Previous clinical and experimental findings (Lazarus, A. A. [1961]. *J. abnorm. soc. Psychol.*, **63**, 505-510) lead me to anticipate that he would lose his fear of high places after not more than ten of these sessions. He might never remember wanting to throw his wife off the balcony (recalling this repressed memory seemed to be a decisive factor in his recovery in psychoanalysis), but with desensitization therapy this would not matter.

Kubie: Improvement did not occur immediately this man remembered his impulse to throw his wife off the balcony. But the recall of this impulse shocked him into asking himself many questions which he had always avoided. This started a gradual recall of much of the buried information about his early life. Psychoanalysts and behaviour therapists may never agree on how rapidly it is safe to gather information about the conflicts that underlie a patient's illness. Our experiences teach us that gathering this information can itself be dangerous. Only after we have acquired the information can we decide how, and at what rate, to communicate it to the patient, and how to prepare him for these communications.

Miller: This is a real difference in the two approaches. Dr. Kubie would communicate this information to the patient; Professor Lazarus would not, but would deal directly with the patient's behaviour. Would you discuss the patient's fears of homosexuality with him, Professor Lazarus?

Lazarus: I have no hard and fast rules about making an interpretation of this sort. But many patients, as their behaviour changes, acquire spontaneous insights, and a discussion about the man's fears of homosexuality might ensue as he developed more adaptive behaviour.

In summary, the behaviour therapist rapidly gains insight into his patients and uses *his* insight to change the *patient's* behaviour. The patient, in turn, may or may not gain much insight about himself but fundamental changes in his behaviour will persist and spread.

Kubie: Another feature that was brought out only after some months in analysis was that the patient wanted to bring his wife into the treatment. As one might have anticipated, the wife was a thin, boyish *gamin,* an unfeminine young woman with her own needs for treatment which, after discussion, she started with a female analyst. When analysis released my patient from bondage to his sister through this surrogate figure, he went through a period in which he experienced overwhelming impulses to become sexually involved with every woman he met. These promiscuous impulses distressed him, and caught him up in a fresh series of previously unconscious conflicts. It was only after working through these that he was able to try to create a new and real relationship with his wife.

I cannot see how this treatment could have been done in a hurry. It involved the resolution of level after level of conflict, each level with its own destructive consequences, and each resolution leading to a burst of new destructive involvements which had to be resolved. The process of analysis is like growing-up. I know no way of hastening either. There must be some limits to the extent to which behavioural analysis can speed up these processes.

Miller: We could only solve this problem by following recordings of therapy sessions, making predictions about what will happen and how long it will take, and seeing to what extent the predictions turn out to be correct.

Marks: We may be making false assumptions about causality. Are we entitled to assume that the fear of heights and the general problems (with women, interpersonal relationships and so on) are related in this patient simply because he remembers that when he first noticed his phobia he also wanted to throw his wife over the parapet? He may have had many other hostile impulses against his wife in other situations to which he developed no phobias. The phobia itself may have released the pre-existing hostility at that moment. When emotional problems are discovered in a phobic patient, the temptation to link the phobia causally with the problems is difficult to resist, but can be misleading. In this patient, and many others, two independent problems may coexist, each needing different treatments. Data in similar cases (Gelder, M. G., Marks, I. M., and Wolff, H. H. [1967]. *Br. J. Psychiat.*, **113**, 53-73) suggest that the phobic part of an illness can be resolved with desensitization independently from the interpersonal problems which need more general psychotherapy; on the other hand, interpersonal difficulties can be modified by traditional psychotherapy without any effect on the phobia. We should not jump to too many conclusions about the relationships between different psychopathologies in the same patient. We must at least submit our assumptions to the test by seeing what happens to one part of the psychopathology when we treat another.

Sandler: Confusion may arise because we are grouping together all analytic psychotherapeutic methods and contrasting them with the behavioural methods. Short-term, dynamic psychotherapy (Malan, D. H. [1963]. *A Study of Brief Psychotherapy*. London: Tavistock) and Professor Lazarus' behavioural analysis have much in common. Both methods are based on the assessment of the main problems, followed by direction based on predictions of outcome. One major difference between these two approaches and classical psychoanalysis is that making a diagnosis and treating the patient often proceed concurrently in psychoanalytic treatment. I can only admire Professor Lazarus for his skill in amassing all these data in such a short time. In my experience this is exceedingly difficult in all but the most straightforward cases unless one imposes one's own preconceptions about psychopathology on the patient.

Lazarus: Dr. Kubie and Dr. Sandler have shown me that in discussing this hypothetical case I must have sounded glib and facile. Let me re-emphasize that I do not view behaviour therapy as a panacea and that many seemingly simple and straightforward cases are totally unresponsive to behavioural tactics. Nevertheless, so many patients have responded so rapidly and so well to this active, integrative approach, that I feel justified in asking all my colleagues, whatever their own theoretical orientations, seriously to consider using behavioural techniques.

Krasner: There are genuine, crucial differences between psychoanalytic and behaviour therapies. The goal of this symposium, to try to form bridges between the two schools, may be a mistake. Behaviourally oriented therapists are more reluctant than analysts to work for this goal. This problem is also relevant to the training of psychotherapists: should they be exposed to psychodynamic formulations before getting experience in behavioural techniques or *vice versa*? I foresee that in about ten years' time clear differences, not only between analytic and behaviour therapies, but between different sorts of behaviour therapies, will have emerged. I doubt if any of the current attempts to integrate the various therapies have any value.

Sifneos: I profoundly disagree. If we use the analogy of peeling the onion, the difference in the two approaches lies mainly in the number of layers one needs to remove. Behaviourists may peel off one layer and Dr. Sandler may wish to reach the core. In short-term dynamic psychotherapy (Malan, D. H. 1963, *loc. cit;* Sifneos, P. E. [1967]. *Am. J. Psychiat.,* **123**, 1069-1075; Sifneos, P. E. [1965]. *Seven Years' Experience with Short-term Psychotherapy: Selected Lectures,* pp. 127-135. Basel: S. Karger), one first finds out from the patient at what level his emotional difficulties are to be found. We may have to peel one or two skins or to go much deeper. It was necessary to remove many layers in Dr. Kubie's patient, but in other cases our treatment would be more superficial. My technique and Professor Lazarus' would be somewhat different; I would work with the transference, which he would not, but we would probably both reach the same outcome by the use of a different route. The bridges between the different types of therapy are here if we want to cross them.

Gelder: The more time one spends with a patient, the better one understands him, but this cannot be an indefinite process; only a small proportion of patients seeking psychiatric help can be investigated in full analytic detail. As practitioners we have to be content with limited but realistic aims, even though as scientists we might wish to pursue the problem until we understand it completely. The practical question that can be investigated empirically, is this: how much do we need to understand about a patient in order to help him?

Sandler: A therapist needs a great deal of training before he can fully recognize his own limitations in assessing the patient. Dr. Gelder has raised the crucial issue of how much we *want* to know about our patients.

Kubie: In general medicine, we learn how to treat patients in large numbers by first studying the individual patient in minute detail. We did not learn about the process of typhoid fever by studying thousands of patients with typhoid. Assembly-line techniques came later. The same principle applies to psychotherapy. When efforts to spread psychotherapeutic novelties are made prematurely and without enough basic investigation, there is danger that more harm will be done than good.

I share the yearning for techniques that could shorten the psychotherapeutic process, and have engaged in many different kinds of research to this end. Yet the effort to cut short the processes of therapy arouses in me an uneasy doubt. This is because of my conviction that the neurotic process is one of the great unsolved problems of human culture, that it makes of the task of being a human being at all a most difficult assignment, that we have been at this for many centuries without success but are just beginning to realize and acknowledge this, and to study it, and that it is out of these difficulties that the neurotic process and its destructive consequences arise and grow. These are the underlying problems which must be solved in an approach to the techniques of education, maturation and psychotherapy, which are all three inseparably intertwined. Psychiatry, psychophysiology, psychopharmacology, psychotherapies and experimental psychology will thus contribute jointly not merely to the transitory relief of symptoms, but to the study and solution of the basic problems of our human culture.

CHAIRMAN'S CLOSING REMARKS

N. E. MILLER

THE magnitude of the problem of mental illness is clearly shown by the fact that approximately one-half of the hospital beds in the United States are occupied by mental patients. Further, careful studies of the non-hospitalized population show that a startling proportion is handicapped to a greater or lesser degree by psychiatric symptoms. One representative study (Srole, L., et al. [1962]. *Mental Health in the Metropolis.* New York: McGraw-Hill) found only 19 per cent of the population studied to be symptom-free, while 36 per cent had mild symptoms and 23 per cent had symptoms which impaired their functioning in adult life. I used to think that these figures for psychiatric difficulties were ridiculously high but, as I have had the opportunity to observe more people for a longer time, I am forced to apologize for my previous scepticism. Apparently normal, happy people are often wearing masks which conceal considerable psychiatric burdens.

Our present resources for psychotherapy are vastly inadequate to meet the problem. Further, with present techniques, it is a sobering thought that those patients who are most likely to benefit from any one of the various forms of treatment are those with the best prospects for spontaneous remission.

As has already been suggested in our discussions, the type of patient selected is an important factor in evaluating the effectiveness of any therapeutic technique. It seems reasonable to assume that patients who are willing to pay from $20 to $50 per hour for psychotherapy will tend to be those with severe problems which they have tried hard, but unsuccessfully, to solve by other means. By contrast, patients who either volunteer or answer an advertisement, even though they may describe their problems as bothersome, will tend to be those with less severe problems which they have not tried as hard to solve. The expected length of treatment may also exert a similar influence, with only patients with the most severe problems being willing to start protracted treatment, and with such treatment being more likely to attract patients who feel a special need for a continuing supportive relationship.

We have seen that one of the main differences between behaviour therapists and psychoanalysts is whether they concentrate on treating the patient's symptoms or on giving him insight into the unconscious motivations causing these symptoms. To state the issue in its sharpest form, the analysts claim that merely removing a symptom without getting at the underlying cause does not solve the problem, so that the patient is likely merely to learn a new and possibly worse symptom. The behaviour therapists challenge this by saying that symptom substitution does not necessarily occur, and that giving the patient insight does not automatically lead to improved behaviour. They claim that the patient needs specific training in more adaptive types of behaviour.

In practice, however, we have seen that the issue has become somewhat less clear; Freud and his pupils soon found that insight must be emotional as well as intellectual, and that a considerable amount of working-through in a variety of life situations is usually needed for a successful analysis. Further, it is sometimes necessary to deal with a specific symptom before therapy can proceed. As the behaviour therapists are acquiring more experience and tackling more difficult cases, they are finding that it is essential to treat the "real (underlying) phobia" or else the patient may indeed only learn another symptom. When the behaviour therapists describe discovering the underlying phobia as analagous to peeling the layers off an onion, and the psychoanalysts say that the patient must become well in real life, the differences between them are reduced. If this trend is continued these two approaches may converge toward some improved version of an early description of psychotherapy as learning (discussed by Dollard, J., and Miller, N. E. [1950]. *Personality and Psychotherapy*. New York: McGraw-Hill; Miller, N. E. [1964]. In *Personality Change*, pp. 149–175, eds. Byrne, D., and Worchel, P. New York: Wiley).

The classical cases of symptom substitution were initially observed when the subject was simply forbidden to exhibit his symptom by an authoritative command, frequently made still more forceful by the use of hypnosis. We should notice that this kind of treatment is different from trying to eliminate, by counterconditioning or desensitization, the fear underlying the symptom, or from trying to strengthen by reward an alternative, more socially acceptable, form of behaviour. When the practitioners of behavioural analysis treat diffuse, strong feelings of hostility and alienation by training the patient to be more active in a number of social relationships, they are still further away from the type of symptomatic treatment that Freud tried and abandoned on his way to evolving the psychoanalytic technique.

We must also note that not all symptoms are functionally similar. Examples at one extreme are certain cases of enuresis in older children;

enuresis, as well as its possible deep psychodynamic origins, may also be partly caused by faulty learning. Whatever the cause, the syndrome becomes extremely troublesome to an older child, producing additional conflict with his parents, feelings of shame and inferiority, and eliminating the opportunities to attend camps and visit friends overnight. Thus, it is not surprising that B. Baker (1968. *J. abnorm. Psychol.*, in press) found that when this symptom was eliminated by the superior training technique of using an electronic device that sounded a warning buzzer to wake the child immediately after the first drop of moisture, he found not symptom substitution but the opposite. Thus teachers who did not know that the child was undergoing treatment, as well as parents, reported that other symptoms disappeared and that social and emotional adjustment was generally improved. This is not surprising since the training had removed a serious problem for the child.

At the other extreme we might consider the classical case of a wife with intolerable fear of sexual intercourse, so that the elimination of a hysterical symptom that was enabling her to avoid intercourse is likely to be followed by the substitution of some other symptom that achieves the same goal. In such a case the behaviour therapist would say that the symptom substitution was the result of not treating the real phobia.

I believe that these two situations represent the extremes on a continuum and that we need more empiric information on the degree to which, and the conditions under which, symptom substitution occurs. I deplore any use of a dogma that symptomatic treatment is evil if it prevents us from getting such empiric data. I particularly deplore the kind of opposition that Baker encountered when a number of physicians who had failed to cure children of enuresis used the full sanction of their medical prestige to bring pressure to bear on the parents to withdraw their children from Baker's study. Fortunately for the children, most of these parents were desperate enough to resist such pressure from the physicians who had failed to help them.

We have seen that the facts of nature have forced the behaviour therapists to discriminate between the patient's reported phobias or other problems, and his "real" phobias or other problems. This puts a premium on taking a good history and on using that history as the basis for a sound diagnosis. We have seen that when, in contrast to psychoanalysis, the main goal is to give insight to the therapist, rather than to the patient, the history may be collected in a different and more active way; and that this method may not differ much from the procedure of certain psychoanalytically trained therapists conducting brief treatments. The efficient taking of a thorough history requires specially skilled training and clinical insight.

This aspect of psychotherapy deserves further theoretical analysis and empiric evaluation.

After the diagnosis is made, the behaviour therapist differs sharply from the psychoanalyst in that he tries to attack the patient's problems directly, believing that the patient's insight may or may not follow improved behaviour, and that such insight is relatively unimportant. He also believes that it is important only to locate the current "real" problem and not to go into its historical antecedents.

It is my impression that, whereas Freud in his earlier days seemed almost exclusively interested in uncovering the childhood origin of the patient's difficulties, present-day analysts are at least supplementing this emphasis with more attention to the patient's current problems. Nevertheless, they still differ markedly from the behaviour therapists in their emphasis on the necessity of allowing the patient to achieve insights into unconscious motivations and the childhood origins of such motivations. Theoretically, one question at issue is whether or not teaching the patient to discriminate between the childhood conditions under which certain motivational tendencies, such as a crippling unrealistic anxiety, were acquired, and the real conditions of adult life is the most efficient way of changing the motivation, for example eliminating the unrealistic anxiety. A related question is the degree to which insights lead to wider generalizations of therapeutic gains. It should be possible to answer these empiric questions from our data.

I believe that there is considerable value in learning the techniques of acquiring insight (through free association) and having them available for use in self-analysis. In this way a situation which seems unrealistically threatening can be handled in a calm and fairly effective manner. Psychoanalysis is one way of learning the techniques for emotional adjustment discovered by analysts. There may be other techniques that could be learned by studying especially well-adjusted people and contrasting them with neurotic patients. We can probably discover still better ways of actively teaching generally applicable techniques for achieving social and emotional adjustment.

Because the need for psychotherapy so far exceeds the supply, and because our present techniques are so far from ideally successful in all cases, we need to continue to innovate. We need to explore all the possibilities of preventive training for mental health, for new combinations of individual and group therapy, for therapeutic communities, clubs or associations, for re-education, and for combining the use of therapeutic drugs with other techniques.

One of the extremely encouraging features of this conference is the courageous spirit of innovation coupled with a critical attempt to secure data for evaluating the effects of innovations. As long as we combine innovation with evaluation and encourage two-way communication between the laboratory and the clinic, we are likely to continue to find better solutions to the urgent problems of mental ill health.

INDEX OF AUTHORS*

Numbers in bold type indicate a contribution in the form of a paper; numbers in plain type refer to contributions to the discussions.

* Indexes compiled by Mr. William Hill.

INDEX OF SUBJECTS

Printed by Spottiswoode, Ballantyne & Co. Ltd., London and Colchester